G E R M A N Y

● Salzburg

Feldkirch ● ● Innsbruck   A U S T R I A

Langen   **BRENNER**   ● Bockstein

ARLBERG   ● S...   ● ...allnitz

S...

A

Y U G O S L A V I A

● ...rieste

...C

NAT
KIEL

80   100

TUNNELS

St. Barbara, patron saint of miners.

(Wood sculpture made in Lubeck in 1480, now in the State Historical Museum, Stockholm.)

TUNNELS

GÖSTA E. SANDSTRÖM

HOLT, RINEHART AND WINSTON

NEW YORK   CHICAGO   SAN FRANCISCO

87704-0113
Printed in the United States of America

CONTENTS

		page
	Preface	ix
Chapter		
1	Going Underground	1
2	The Quest for Metals	20
3	The Quest for Water	52
4	Early Railway Tunnels	84
5	Methods of Tunnelling	102
6	The First Alpine Tunnel	132
7	The St. Gotthard Tunnel	161
8	The Arlberg Rehearsal for Simplon	180
9	The Simplon Tunnel	184
10	Subaqueous Tunnelling	208
11	Tunnel Surveying	245
12	The Strange Story of Explosives	271
13	Rock-drilling Machines	286
14	Tools for a New Age	304
15	Underground Power	316
16	Trouble in Lötschberg	330
17	The Channel Comedy	340
18	Geographical Surgery	359
19	The Knights of Mt. Blanc	382
	Glossary	411
	Bibliography	415
	Index	419

ACKNOWLEDGMENTS

IN the preparation of this book I have had recourse to numerous printed sources, books and technical periodicals. Of the books, H. S. Drinker's encyclopaedic *Tunneling* (John Wiley, New York, 1878) has been used to a considerable extent for factual information and illustrations on tunnels and the machines employed up to about 1875. The chapter on ancient mining draws on classical authors and Agricola's *De Re Metallica*, as translated by Herbert Hoover, while old-time conduction of water in tunnels and canals relies heavily on *A History of Technology* (Oxford U Press, 1954) and to some extent also on R. Payne's *The Canal Builders* (Macmillan, New York, 1959). C. Noble's *The Brunels* (Cobden-Sanderson, 1938) has lent some interesting details bearing on the Thames and Box tunnels. Some of the factual information on the English Channel Tunnel derives from two recently published books, viz., D. Abel's *Channel Underground* (Pall Mall, 1961) and H. Slater and C. Barnett's *The Channel Tunnel* (Allan Wingate, 1958). Frequent references have also been made to *A Manual on Rock Excavation* (Atlas Copco-Sandvik Steel), as well as to *Rock Drill Data* (Ingersoll-Rand).

However, the bulk of the technical information derives from official reports and technical papers published during the course of eighty years by *Engineering* and *Schweizerische Bauzeitung*, while a number of old engravings illustrating the chapters on Alpine tunnelling are from *L'Illustration*. Information of historical and anecdotal interest has also been gathered from old volumes of the *Compressed Air Review*. These and other sources have been listed with thanks in the Bibliography.

As for the rest, I have relied on the records of the Swedish Power Board and on the recollections of old-time tunnellers and miners collected by the Nordic Museum in Stockholm as well as personal interviews with tunnellers and manufacturers in many European countries during the last fifteen years.

I am indebted to these numerous sources for much valuable information. In particular my thanks are due Messrs. G. Widegren and G. Lai of Atlas Copco Italia for their aid and hospitality whereby I have been able to visit tunnelling sites in the Alps and Apennines. Beyond all, my greatest debt is to my wife for her great forebearance and active participation in the lengthy preparation of this book.

The illustrations have been drawn from the following sources which I acknowledge with gratitude:

Agricola, Georgius: *De Re Metallica*: Figures 16–18, 108

Annales des Mines, 1898: Figure 14

Ardaillon, E.: *Les Mines du Laurion*: Figure 12

Atlas Copco for the photographs in Figures 150, 151

Buschenfelt: unpublished travel notes, Uppsala University Library: Figure 116

Cancrinus, F. L.: *Erste Gründe der Berg- und Saltzwerkskunde*: Figure 117

Compressed Air Review, 1938: Figures 105, 123

Dolezalek, C.: *Der Eisenbahntunnel*, Urban & Schwartzenberg: Figure 97

Drinker, H. S.: *Tunneling*, John Wiley: Figures 1, 19, 20, 24, 26–60, 70, 72, 76–80, 85, 86, 98, 102, 103, 106, 112, 118–122, 126–8

Engineering, 1871: Figure 110; 1876: Figure 82

Falu Mine Museum: Figure 115

Hammond, Rolt: *Tunnel Engineering*, Macmillan: Figure 91

Historical Museum, Stockholm: Frontispiece

Ingersoll-Rand for the photograph in Figure 144

L'Illustration, 1871: Figures 61–64, 73, 74, 81; 1872: Figure 5; 1882: Figures 83, 84, 87–89; 1905: Figure 95

Ministero dei Lavori: *Il Traforo del Monte Bianco*, 1960–2: Figures 139–143, 145, 146, 149

Natkiel, R.: *Tunnels of the Alps*: Endpapers, Figures 25, 75, 104

Noble, C.: *The Brunels*, Cobden-Sanderson: Figures 99–101

Persson, Arne, for the photographs in Figures 147, 148, 152

Ranie, Hans: Archives of Bergslaget, Falun: Figures 3, 4

Rössler, B.: *Hellpolierter Bergbauspiegel*, 1700: Figure 114

Schweizerische Bauzeitung, 1902: Figures 90, 92, 93, 113

Singer, C. et al.: *A History of Technology*, Oxford University Press: Figures 10, 15, 21, 23.

Figure 6 adapted from J. G. D. Clark: *Prehistoric Europe*, Methuen. Figure 7 after J. Andree: 'Bergbau in der Vorzeit', in

H. Hahne, _Vorzeit_, 1922. Figure 8 after G. L. Armstrong: _Proc. Prehist. Soc._, 1927, Cambridge Prehistoric Society. Figure 9 after original photograph by courtesy of the _Institut Royal des Sciences Naturelles de Belgique_, Brussels. Figure 11 after P. Brandt: _Schaffende Arbeit und Bildende Kunst im Altertum und Mittelalter_. Figure 13 after H. Sandars: 'The Use of the Deer-horn Pick in the Mining Operations of the Ancients', _Archaeologia_, vol. LXII (1911), Society of Antiquaries, London. Figure 22 after W. Gesenius: _Hebrew Grammar_ ed. E. Kautsch, Oxford U. Press. Figure 107 after C. Bailey (ed.): _The Legacy of Rome_, Oxford U. Press. Figure 109 after J. Ball: _Egypt in the Classical Geographers_ by courtesy of Survey Dept. Ministry of Finance, Egypt.

Swedish Power Board, 1948: Figures 129–131; 1959: Figures 133–138

Traforo delle Alpi, 1863: Figures 65–69, 71, 111

Wreszinsky, W.: _Atlas zur Altägypt._ Kulturgesch. J. C. Hinrichs: Figure 2

GÖSTA E. SANDSTRÖM

PREFACE

THE underground world, the life and work going on in mines and subterranean construction, is a *terra incognita* that one only hears about when something goes amiss, when the newspapers blare out the news of catastrophe and death, of miners buried under collapsing rock, of tunnellers blown to bits in premature explosions. This is hardly surprising, because today there is no one who has an over-all view of the immense activities going on in the bowels of the earth. It was different a century ago; then there were men, most of them professors of civil engineering, who kept records of underground developments the world over. Today those concerned with underground construction are specialists who leave it to others to worry about what goes on elsewhere, outside their own restricted area of professional interest.

Yet this troglodyte world is of vital importance because it has a direct bearing on the daily life of all surface dwellers, past and present. The backbreaking labour of the coal-miners produced the impetus for the industrial revolution. Without metals neolithic husbandmen would never have been able to break out of their dreary cycle of brief feast followed by long famine. For thousands of years men have slaved in the bowels of the earth to gather the wealth required for the development of urban civilization, but their life and labour have always been ignored by philosophers and writers whose very existence depended on the metallic wealth brought forth in distant mines. It never occurred to the Greek philosophers gathered in the shade of a stoa[1] to utter a word of appreciation for the silver brought up from the Attic mines, which was voted by the Athenian assembly to build the fleet that defeated the Persians at

[1] Greek portico.

Salamis and thus saved their lives. The references to mining by classical authors can be recorded in a couple of pages; only one geographer took the trouble to visit a mine, and was shocked at what he saw.

This book, however, is concerned with mining only to the extent that it bears on underground construction. Urban communities were a direct outcome of access to and insight into the use of metals, but no settlement could continue to grow without recourse to underground structures. For one thing, it needed water, and since water evaporates under the hot sun it had to be conducted in underground conduits, by tunnels leading from a source in the foothills to the place of consumption in the plains or, more probably, to the walled city nestling around an acropolis.

After water has been obtained, it must be disposed of. Water supply and drainage are two facets of the same problem. A water tunnel sooner or later leads to the building of sewers, frequently placed underground. Eventually traffic congestion within the confines of a metropolis, or along the highway connecting such centres, will also require underground structures, or tunnels, to alleviate it. The development of underground structures follows this simple pattern, which is repeated again and again throughout history.

Some such conclusions become inescapable upon a study, however brief, of the development of tunnelling through the ages. This particular study began some years ago with the idle thought, while waiting for the blasting of a round in an underground power-house development in distant Lapland, that, surely, this had been done many times before, but without the help of electrical power, modern explosives and mechanized facilities. There are railway tunnels through the Alps, tunnels under rivers, aqueducts linking cities with remote water sources, not to mention innumerable honeycomb mines, all completed long ago. How were they made, by whom and when?

A technical reporter has no reason to dwell on what has been accomplished, his business is with the present and preferably the future, to report on technical trends and experiments which may become routine practice tomorrow. The blasting operation mentioned above, whose dull thud released thousands of cubic yards of granite in uniform fragments suitable for rapid loading, was such an occasion. Yet, confronted with this heap of rock, the triumphal outcome of the modern science of rock blasting, the author's thoughts strayed to the past, to the railway age and beyond.

Thus began a search that is by no means ended and may, indeed, go on indefinitely. It has been a meandering journey through time and space, through dusty tomes that have not been opened for the last eighty years, hidden in the storerooms of technical or specialized libraries, through hundreds of volumes of technical journals extending to the early half of the last century, old newspaper files, obscure provincial publications celebrating local centenaries, personal recollections of old-time railway workers and tunnellers gathered by folklore investigators, engineering text-books discarded since their content has lost its interest for working engineers—and so on. Indeed, a person curious to know how things were done in the past, if only as far back as the turn of the century, has to forage for information over a wide field. Literary research has its rewards but also its dangers. One of the best-known encyclopaedic reference works in the English-speaking world kills off a prominent continental tunneller of the nineteenth century by a falling rock—which seems a reasonable end for a tunnelling man: that the man actually died of a stroke (German *Schlaganfall*), in the manner of all outstanding tunnel engineers and contractors of the last century, has to be dug out from an obituary in a contemporary Swiss journal. Similarly, it is a fascinating experience to follow the increasing distortion of facts the further one gets from the source, by condensation, translation error, conversion from metric measures into English, and vice versa.

A personal visit to the sites may help to eliminate errors with reference to the terrain, place names, and other factors. But place names have a tendency to change, particularly in border regions: they become Italianized, Frenchified, Germanized, depending on the outcome of wars. If one is lucky one can find the semicircular scars left by drill steels in the contour of an early railway tunnel, the gad and pick marks left in the drifts of ancient workings, traces of soot and smoke in medieval mines worked by fire. The shape and general condition of the underground structure also speak for the skill, or lack of it, of the miners who worked it. When fortune smiles one may stumble on the tools and machines actually used, in some out-of-the-way museum.

But such quasi-archaeological field studies, although valuable as a complement, are not very rewarding. What one likes to know in technological history, and this, after all, is what this modest study amounts to, is the logistics of old-time underground workings, the number of men, horses and machines employed, the type of tools used, the routine methods, the production or rate of advance, the time consumed, the unit and total costs, the nature of the portal installations, the hygienic and sanitary conditions, and as a corollary thereto the attrition of the work force by disease and accidents. It is infuriating to be confronted with the imposing archaeological remains of ancient civilizations and have to listen to harpings on the doings of gods and heroes, the behaviour of captains in silly little tribal wars, or the death of an apostle, while the basic questions bearing on the economy and real life of the ancient cities, the *raison d'être* of their existence, is shrugged off as the concern of slaves.

There is still sufficient material available from the railway era— although, as previously stated, it is not very readily accessible—to throw full light on the construction of the *grands souterrains*, as the French called them, perhaps the most magnificent work ever per-formed, considering the difficulties involved. It is still possible to dis-tinguish also the details of the human drama and, upon occasion, the comedy played out beneath the shadow of the conspicuous technical stage. But probably not for long. Within another generation or so the mighty deeds of nineteenth-century tunnellers will sink still deeper into the limbo where dwell the builders of the Greek temples and Roman aqueducts, to be ignored as the doings of just another bunch of slaves.

TUNNELS

Chapter 1

GOING UNDERGROUND

*'As for the earth, out of it
cometh bread.'*

THERE comes a time in the life of all peoples and nations when they must go underground to survive, to seek shelter, to get water, acquire metals, to overcome obstacles above ground, to rid themselves of the detritus of their urban civilization. Whatever the reason, going underground is a significant step. It means, for one thing, that a civilization has become sufficiently complex, relatively and absolutely, and that some pressing issues cannot find a satisfactory solution above ground. The surface deposits of flints and elementary metals have been consumed, water holes and wells are no longer adequate for the growing needs of the community, additional land for the increasing population has to be found by the draining of lakes and waterlogged land.

In the ancient hydraulic civilizations, a tunnel was frequently the only practical solution for overcoming topographical obstacles to the gravity conduction of water. The Romans occasionally resorted to tunnels when building roads through rugged mountainous country, such as the famous tunnel on Via Flaminia built by the Emperor Vespasian, and the Pausilippo tunnel between Naples and Pozzuoli built by Cocceius in 36 B.C. The latter tunnel appears to have been the largest driven in ancient times. It was 25 ft. wide and 30 ft. high and ran for a distance of 1,000 paces.[1]

[1] Equivalent to 4,833 ft.

A tunnel, then, can be regarded as a measure of the state of the prevailing culture, of the technical and economic development of the society producing it. The mere existence of a tunnel, at any time and place, is evidence that the problems created by a flourishing economy have reached such magnitude that they cannot be solved by conventional means. At the same time, it proves that the people possess unusual funds of energy, knowledge, hardihood, tools, and specialized skills to cope with the hazards met underground. Piling stone upon stone in the manner of the builders of surface structures is one thing, advancing a tunnel through the bowels of the earth calls for courage and skill of the highest order. A hundred years ago a tunnel was regarded as the most difficult and hazardous branch of construction. In spite of the scientific advances recorded since then, reflected in current machines and methods, tunnelling is still an enterprise calling for rugged virtues, skill and judgment if it is not to end in tragedy.

Ancient Rock Temples

Although in the ancient civilizations tunnels were driven chiefly for economic ends, tunnellers have been busy also in the service of priests. The tombs, royal and otherwise, in Egypt were excavated in rock and connected with the surface by tunnels, some of them angled and interrupted by shafts to confound grave-robbers. In Nubia, the temples were excavated in rock; the two at Abu Simbel have been in the headlines in recent years owing to international action to save them from being permanently submerged by the backed-up waters of the High Aswan Dam.

These particular rock temples, adorned with colossi some 70 ft. high sculptured in the rock, were built by Rameses II in 1250 B.C. A thousand years later, a similar craze for building rock temples began in India, where Brahmins and Buddhists vied with each other in carving out temples and monasteries until in the end there were about a thousand such rock structures throughout India, most of them in the trappe formations in the state of Bombay. The caves of Ellora, excavated between A.D. 200 and 600, contain six miles of underground structures cut by chisel.

The provision of burial space has been another reason for vast excavations in many lands. The ancient peoples around the Mediterranean—Hebrews, Scythians, Greeks, Romans, Carthaginians and others—interred their dead in rock tombs which as the centuries passed grew into a complex network of catacombs. Early Christians followed the same practice, as evidenced by the catacombs of Rome, Palermo, Naples and other places. It seems likely that this burial

custom will be revived in the metropolitan areas of western Europe
and America, because eventually there will be no room for the

Fig 1. An Indian **rock** temple—the Cave at Bhaja—chiselled
out of solid rock.

present type of surface cemeteries. Allowing costly land to lie fallow
in the heart of a major city cannot be tolerated indefinitely.

Tunnelling for Military Ends

It goes without saying that the tunnelling art was also employed
from earliest times for military ends; it began to be used as soon as
people started taking refuge in walled cities. Instead of inviting
casualties by a direct scaling attack or attempting to breach defences

with siege engines, intelligent commanders resorted to tunnelling to
subdue an enemy seemingly secure behind his battlemented walls.
Joshua caused the walls of Jericho to crumble from trumpet blasts; a
more strenuous and less musical way of accomplishing the same end
would have been to drive a tunnel under one of the towers and undermine it by excavation. The sappers would underpin the foundations
of the tower with timbering while the work was in progress. Having
completed the excavation, they would put fire to the timbers and
cause the structure to collapse, while horns sounded an attack
through the breach, or a sham attack at some other point to divert
attention from the sappers' work.

But many a walled town was captured simply by tunnelling under
the wall and sending in storm troops to take the defenders by surprise
from the rear. This tactic seems to have been quite common according to the Roman architect Vitruvius, who in his famous book *On
Architecture*, written before 27 B.C., discusses defensive measures
against tunnelling enemies. He quotes the case of the siege of
Appolonia in Illyria in 214 B.C., when the enemy sappers drove a
number of tunnels under the walls, and the inhabitants became
panic-stricken since they did not know what counter-measures they
could take. Vitruvius, always anxious to prove the resourcefulness
and skill of colleagues, tells how in their despair the Appolonians
entrusted the defence of their city to the architect Trypho of Alexandria. He instructed the defenders to dig a deep trench parallel to and
within bowshot of the walls. Along this trench he hung a number of
bronze vessels. When the vessels reverberated to the blows of the
sappers' tools, he knew the location and direction of the tunnels they
were driving. From the sound of the vibrating vases he calculated
where the sappers would break through, and at these points he hung
large vessels filled with boiling water and pitch, and for good measure
'human dung and sand roasted to a fiery heat'. In the night he
rapidly sank holes over the headings and dumped the unpleasant
contents of the vessels on the enemy sappers.

Vitruvius reports a similar feat during the siege of Marseilles in
49 B.C. Here the besiegers drove thirty tunnels under the walls, but
as these tunnels were being advanced, the resourceful defenders
matched the progress by digging a deep trench inside the walls and
across the tunnel advance. They filled the trench with water and
then sat down to await further developments. When the besiegers
broke through to the trench they were met by a flood of roaring
waters which filled the tunnels and drowned the attackers.[3]

[3] Vitruvius: *On Architecture*, Book X, trans. by Frank Granger (Heinemann, London, 1931).

While on the subject of the military applications of tunnelling, mention should also be made of the tunnel that put an end to the Etruscans as a political entity. The Etruscan towns had been invaded and subdued one by one and put under Roman domination, but Veii, the leading Etruscan town and stronghold, still held firm against the relentless Roman pressure. A Roman army laid siege to Veii in 406 B.C., but was unable to subdue it for ten years. The capital was situated on a hill and surrounded by a wall; water and food were supplied by a secret system of tunnels. In 396 B.C., the Roman commander Marcus Furius Camillus followed the Etruscan example and drove a tunnel through the tuffe formation on which the acropolis was built, in the south-eastern part of the town. While a sham attack was mounted against the walls, a picked band of Romans went through the tunnel and took the Etruscans in the rear.

Livy dresses up this Roman feat of arms with one of his usual apocryphal anecdotes. It seems that while the advance guard of the tunnel attackers waited under the floor slab of the temple, they overheard an Etruscan horospex, about to read the auguries, say that victory would go to the one who should open up the entrails of the sacrificial animal.

Upon hearing this the Romans broke through the floor, snatched the sacred carcass from the stupefied horospex and sent it to Camillus, who thus became the recipient of the favour of the gods. No doubt the Etruscan priests found some other interpretation of this tunnel stratagem which closed the ten years' siege of Veii and put an end to the Etruscan power.

Mining of Metals

After these sacerdotal and martial footnotes to the history of tunnelling, let us return to the main stem of underground development, to the excavations and tunnelling required to extract metal from the ground. The development of any civilization, in the broadest sense of the word, requires metal tools, and since the supply of elementary metals and their easily processed oxides has always been limited, there arises an early need to follow the ore outcrops into the ground.

The miner, then, becomes the first tunneller when forced into the ground by the depletion of open-cast workings. At any time and any place, the overwhelming majority of subterranean excavations has been made for the purpose of ore extraction. As the consumption of metal grows, there arises a need for other types of underground structures: for the purpose of draining the mines, for conducting water to dress the ores mined, and for supplying urban settlements that have arisen principally on account of the accelerated economic pace brought about by the increase in the supply of metals.

This is how it has always been, this is the case today. It may take many centuries, while distant ore-bearing regions are being honey-combed with drifts and stopes, before the need arises for any other kind of underground structure. This applies of course to regions and countries where the mineral wealth is not being used locally, where it is being shipped abroad, to aid in the development of the economy of distant lands or cities. Not only are the mineral resources being drained, but the region from which they derive remains in a state of social, ethical and moral backwardness. Such was the case in Egypt and other ancient lands, and in Scandinavia until quite recently. It still holds true in many mining countries beyond the seas.

Mining is an extraction industry; therein lies the explanation of its peculiarities and contradictions. Prince and peasant alike dream of riches easily gained. With gold and silver all material human needs can be satisfied, and status and power bought as in no other way. Anywhere, at any time—in Athens, Carthage, Rome, London or New York—there have never been any difficulties in raising share capital to work a Golconda, real or existing only in the promoter's imagination. But apart from the ubiquitous lust for gold and dreams of easy gain, metals are the only means of breaking the dreary circle of a primitive agrarian economy, with complete dependence on the vagaries of nature and the annual cycle of a brief feast followed by a long famine.

With access to metals all this changes. Metals start a spiralling movement that keeps accelerating as more and better tools become available. With metal implements farmers can raise harvests yielding a surplus for feeding craftsmen, priests, merchants, princes and soldiers. With better weapons a metal-working people can subdue and enslave its neighbours and keep poets to record the lethal prowess of their masters. In the end, such a people can even afford an occasional philosopher or prophet and permit him to harp on the error of their ways. In short, metals generate power and contribute to the development of the gentler arts. This elementary truth has been grasped from the beginning of mining. Rulers have always encour-aged the search for and extraction of metals.

One would have thought that the men directly concerned with the collection of this wealth from the bowels of the earth would become if not a pampered, at any rate a privileged people. It would not be unreasonable to assume that the direct beneficiaries of the metallic wealth, the rulers and financiers of a mining enterprise, would see to it, in their own interests, that the men working the mineral deposits should be well maintained so as to keep them healthy and in good working order, and should be provided with the best tools and engines available. Nothing, however, could be further from the truth. With a few illustrious exceptions, the history of mining is an unbroken sequence of man's beastliness to his own kind, of unscrupulous disdain for elementary decencies, of ruthless killings and maimings.

Agricola, the most scholarly and erudite of the early writers on mining and metallurgy, was aware of the dubious aspects of the industry, and tried in the first book of his opus magnum *De re metallica* to convince himself and his readers that mining was indeed a creditable way of making a living, and that the benefits brought to humanity compensated for the sordid practices associated with extracting the ore from the ground. It should perhaps be noted in this context that Agricola wrote against the background of a well-regulated, humanized and technically well-developed mining industry, lacking the horrors of the ancient slave workings and the brutality of contemporary northern mining. Had he written 300 years later, he would no doubt have accepted the opinion of ancient writers, Greek as well as Roman, who condemned metals and their mining on moral grounds. Had he written 400 years later, Agricola would have had less occasion to modify his positive views on the industry.

Many of the Greek writers abused gold and silver as 'deadly and nefarious pests of the human race because those who possess them are in the greatest peril, for those who have none lay snares for the possessors of wealth, and thus again and again metals have been the cause of destruction and ruin'. Phocylides[4] elaborates on this theme: 'Gold and silver are injurious to mortals; gold is the source of crime, the plague of life, and the ruin of all things ... Because of it arise robberies, murder, war, brothers are set against brothers, and children against parents.'

The Spartan view was different and more materialistic. Aristodemus put the modern view succinctly: 'Money makes the man; no one who is poor is either good or honoured.' Agricola himself contributes the 'old saying' that: 'Every rich man is either wicked himself, or is the heir of wickedness.'

Classical philosophers were less concerned with the methods employed in getting the corrupting wealth out of the ground. Their lack of sensitivity was probably due less to the fact that slave labour was

---

[4] A Greek poet known for his axioms.

used in the mines than to their ignorance of the realities of mining.
Had they been aware of contemporary conditions in mines, their
strictures would no doubt have been vehement.

The earliest detailed account of ancient mining is given by the
Greek geographer Agatharchides[5] who visited some Egyptian gold-
mines in the second century B.C. and was deeply shocked by what he
saw. He wrote as follows:

'In the confines of Egypt . . . there is a place full of rich gold
mines, out of which with much cost and pains of many labourers gold
is dug. The soil here is naturally black, but in the body of the earth
run many white veins, shining like white marble. . . . Out of these
laborious mines, those appointed overseers cause the gold to be dug
up by the labour of a vast multitude of people. For the Kings of
Egypt condemn to these mines notorious criminals, captives taken in
war, persons sometimes falsely accused, or against whom the King is
incensed; and not only they themselves, but sometimes all their
kindred and relations together with them, are sent to work here, both
to punish them, and by their labour to advance the profit and gain
of the Kings.

'There are infinite numbers upon these accounts thrust down into
these mines, all bound in fetters, where they work continually, without being admitted any rest night or day, and so strictly guarded that
there is no possibility or way left to make an escape. For they set over
them barbarians, soldiers of various and strange languages, so that
it is not possible to corrupt any of the guard by discoursing one with
another, or by the gaining insinuations of familiar converse.

'The earth which is hardest and full of gold they soften by putting
fire under it, and then work it out with their hands. The rocks thus
softened and made more pliant and yielding, several thousands of
profligate wretches break in pieces with hammers and pickaxes.

'There is one artist that is the overseer of the whole work, and who
marks out the stone, and shows the labourers the way and manner
how he would have it done. Those that are the strongest amongst
them that are appointed to this slavery, provided with sharp iron
pickaxes, cleave the marble-shining rock by mere force and strength,
and not by arts of sleight-of-hand. They undermine not the rock in
a direct line, but follow the bright shining vein of the mine. They
carry lamps fastened to their foreheads to give them light, being
otherwise in perfect darkness in the various windings and turnings

[5] Agatharchides' work is lost but the passage was quoted by Diodorus
Siculus a century later. The abstract given here is taken from Booth's translation of Diodorus (London, 1700) slightly amended by Herbert Hoover
(1912).

wrought in the mine; and having their bodies appearing sometimes of one colour and sometimes of another, they throw the lumps and pieces of the stone cut out of the rock upon the floor.

'And thus they are employed continually without intermission, at the very nod of the overseer, who lashes them severely besides. And there are little boys who penetrate through the galleries into the cavities and with great labour and toil gather up the lumps and pieces hewed out of the rock as they are cast upon the ground, and carry them forth and lay them on the bank.

Fig 2. Captives of war doomed to slavery in the Egyptian gold mines, from rock engravings in Egyptian tombs. They have been recognized as Libyans, Hamites, Semites and other neighbouring peoples.

'Those that are over thirty years of age take a piece of the rock of such a certain quantity, and pound it in a stone mortar with iron pestles till it be as small as a vetch. Then those little stones so pounded are taken from them by women and older men, who cast them into mills that stand together near at hand in a long row, and two or three of them being employed at one mill they grind a certain measure given them at a time, until it is as small as fine meal.

'No care at all is taken of the bodies of these poor creatures, so that they have not a rag so much as to cover their nakedness, and no man who sees them can choose but commiserate their sad and deplorable condition. For though they are sick, maimed, or lame, no rest nor intermission in the least is allowed them; neither the weakness of old age, nor women's infirmities are any plea to excuse them; but all are driven to their work with blows and cudgelling, till at length, over-borne with the intolerable weight of their misery, they drop down dead in the midst of their insufferable labours; so that these miserable creatures always expect the future to be more terrible than even the present, and therefore long for death as far more desirable than life.

'Therefore, I cannot but conclude', ends Agatharchides, 'that nature itself teaches us, that as gold is got with labour and toil, so it is kept with difficulty. It creates everywhere the greatest cares; and the use of it is mixed both with pleasure and sorrow.'

This catalogue of horrors and the cruelties and indignities imposed by man on his fellow-men refers, as has been stated, to Egyptian mining and could no doubt be extended to all phases of work conducted by the monopolistic and monolithic Egyptian state. In the mines of the Caucasus, which seem to have been worked by free men, and later in the Greek and Roman mines, although worked by slave labour, conditions were not quite so sub-human. In the second century A.D., the Emperor Hadrianus ordered baths to be established at all Roman mines, which definitely suggests a concern for the physical welfare of the miners. At the peak of Saxon mining, at the time of Agricola, working miners were members of an honoured and privileged trade, despite occasional complaints of exploitation and swindles by mining promoters and their managers. But in Scandinavia, and particularly in Sweden, at that time one of the major sources of mineral wealth and fuel in Europe, there was nothing honourable about mining. Had Agatharchides visited any of the Swedish silver and copper mines during the sixteenth and seventeenth centuries he would have found conditions similar to those prevailing in the Egyptian mines seventeen centuries earlier.

'Beat their heads in,' wrote Charles IX in 1608 to his bailiff at the Sala mine, 'stick a spear in their sides, if you should kill one it does not greatly matter.' This was the only solution the king could think of for solving the production problems of his greatest single source of wealth. He had sent Polish prisoners of war to work the mine, which was in a miserable condition, with collapsing stopes, earth slides and falling rock killing the miners. After the king's soldiers had prodded the prisoners underground the regular miners were naturally loath to follow. Without overseers the prisoners stopped working and production ceased. With no silver forthcoming for the royal treasury, the

Fig 3. A rock fall in a Swedish seventeenth-century mine, as
sketched by a contemporary artist.

Fig 4. A Swedish mine churl called 'Fats Mats' killed in the Falu copper mine in 1677. His body, fully preserved by copper salts, was recovered in 1719. From a contemporary drawing.

king's rage poured out in daily orders and directives on how to proceed against the stubborn Poles. 'Hang them up in gallows, and two should hang the third, and the first to refuse working you should hang up and let the others do the hanging.' The orders ended with the threat that if the bailiff did not do the hanging he was liable to be hanged himself.

Northern mining history, indeed any mining history, is a long and dreary tour through a man-made hell. This is not a particularly original observation. The naturalist Carolus Linnaeus summed up his impressions after visiting the Falu copper mine in 1734 in the following manner: 'The mine is more terrifying than the Hades as described by classical writers and Hell as painted in the sermons of our clergy.'

'The sulphurous smoke', continues Linnaeus, 'poisons the air and kills everything growing, and fills the cavities of the mine with evil fumes, dust and heat. Here 1,200 men labour shut off from the light of the sun, slaves under the metal, less men than beasts, surrounded by soot and darkness. Fear of being crushed under falling rock never leaves them for a moment. These damnati work naked to the waist and have before their mouths a woollen cloth to prevent them from breathing too much smoke and dust. They cannot take a breath of pure air, sweat streams from their bodies as water out of a bag. But the horrors and dangers notwithstanding there is no lack of workmen. Such is the hunger in these parts that men clamour for work in these mines in order to get their daily bread.'

Indeed, the strictures of the Greek philosophers against the pursuit of metals and the human degradation pursuant thereon were without a doubt well founded, perhaps even better than they realized. To mining has clung tenaciously through the centuries the curse of an angry tribal Bronze Age god: 'Cursed is the ground for thy sake. In sorrow shall thou eate of it all the dayes of thy life.'

Tunnelling

Tunnelling for water and subsequently also for other ends, although related to mining and employing similar methods and tools, has been carried out in an entirely different psychological climate. From the outset, with the driving of the early *qanaats* or underground aqueducts in the Fertile Crescent[6] and elsewhere, tunnellers

[6] So called because of the crescent-like shape on a map of the continuous belt of fertile land running northwards from the cataracts of the Nile, through the coastlands of Palestine and bending eastwards to the south of the Taurus range and then southwards to the Persian Gulf.

appear to have been free men and members of a respected, even privileged trade. Even today a two-man team of *qanaat* builders working in the ancient manner is looked upon with respect in Iran and worthy of introduction to foreign visitors. Perhaps the reason for this difference in outlook is due to the end product of the underground work. Basically, water is more valuable than metal. The early tunnels were driven to supply urban developments with sorely needed water, and the realization by kings and commoners alike of the vital importance of the *qanaat* builders' work would presumably inhibit the stupid brutalities associated with mining. Moreover, tunnelling of this nature is a highly skilled work mastered by relatively few men, whom a tyrant would hesitate to put to death. Whatever the reason, tunnelling has always been different from mining. Primitive Europe had no need for tunnels for more than 1,200 years after the fall of Rome, and when the first European tunnel was built on the Languedoc Canal the cultural climate of France permitted the work to be conducted under acceptable conditions.

With the canal tunnels and, a few decades later, the railway tunnels in Britain, tunnelling entered its heroic age. The nineteenth century saw more economic and technical progress than any previous one. It was a century when optimism ran at high flood. The entrepreneurs and engineers changed the face of western Europe and tied its constituent parts together with a network of steel. They had many obstacles to overcome, and tunnels were used to master the worst. For this reason tunnelling came to be in the van of technical progress. A tunnelling project of some size was such a difficult, costly and hazardous venture that to undertake it with any hope of success required the mobilization of the best engineering brains and technical facilities available at the time. In fact, such major triumphs as the Alpine tunnels had to be deferred several decades for new inventions to mature.

The debate raging about the feasibility of the grand tunnelling schemes, by leading scientists and engineers, not to mention newspapers, made them into public issues which the literate public followed with unabated interest. To newspaper readers a tunnel was an exciting adventure; to the engineering profession, with its newly acquired status, it was a fascinating exercise in applying fresh insight into the workings of nature to overcome nature's obstacles to economic progress. To the entrepreneurs, finally, a grand tunnel was a tempting venture, a great gamble promising profits and honours.

The railway tunnelling era offers a fascinating study of the working of the nineteenth-century mind, freed from feudalistic restraints and mercantile bondage. Anything could be done, there was no limit to what could be achieved. Early in the century a plan for tunnelling under the English Channel was presented by a French engineer to Napoleon, who had the good sense to turn it down. But time and again new plans for a Channel tunnel were brought forth and seriously discussed in scientific academies and engineering societies. That the schemes were sheer nonsense was seldom, if ever, acknowledged.

Nothing, fortunately, came of these schemes; they were pigeon-holed by the military authorities for strategic reasons. But many less grandiose tunnelling plans were carried out, and the European economy benefited by the tremendous sacrifices of men and money involved in the advance of the long railway tunnels. It can now be questioned whether such tunnels as the Gotthard, Hoosac and others, should have been built at all at the time, because the sacrifice in human lives and money was too high. There was insufficient insight into the problems involved in such large-scale tunnelling. Nobody—no geologist, engineer, or medical authority—knew enough about how to advance a long tunnel through rock or under water, and ignorance had to be paid for.

On the other hand, it can equally well be argued that the inadequate knowledge could not have been improved upon without accepting the challenges and coming to grips with the unknown difficulties. Furthermore, the numerous geology professors who stated categorically that the geothermal gradient—the temperature increase with increasing rock cover—would prevent any tunnelling under high mountains were also proved wrong. According to their theory, the temperature in the bowels of the mountain would reach such heights that the blood of the miners would boil. Medical authorities were also certain that it was impossible to supply air to the miners beyond a modest distance from the portals.

By ignoring these forebodings, the engineers responsible for the Fréjus, the first long Alpine tunnel, proved a century ago that all such talk was old men's tales. But a decade later, in St. Gotthard, the scientific soothsayers were found right: lack of air, high temperature, and water killed off practically everyone who had anything to do with the tunnel—miners, engineers, the contractor himself and, because of the stress induced by the long series of disasters, the better part of the railway management also. Who is to say? Perhaps the road through Gotthard had to be pursued in order to learn from bitter experience. The reasons for the Gotthard disasters, it became clear in the subsequent technical inquests, were lack of power and elementary hygiene. The lessons were not lost, and when Simplon was built at the turn of the century the Swiss authorities, prodded by the *Bundesversammlung*, saw to it that the horrors of Gotthard were not repeated. However, in spite of all precautions, Simplon too came close to ending in failure. The technical resources were strained to the breaking-point.

When looking back over the era of railway tunnelling, it appears quite evident that out of the three-cornered partnership involved in building the railways and tunnels—the entrepreneurs, the engineers and the labourers—the latter can take most of the credit for carrying through this gigantic construction feat. This is not arguing that nothing could have been accomplished without them, but rather that labour was called upon to make up for the inadequacies of the entrepreneurs and engineers.

As noted in passing, the nineteenth-century engineers saw no limits to their own capabilities. There was no problem too difficult for them, no difficulty that science could not resolve. As a consequence, they grossly underestimated both the difficulties involved and the money needed to overcome those difficulties. We are not here concerned with the crooks, those who swindled away the capital entrusted to their care, nor with the speculators, but with honest promoters, who were seldom able to supply sufficient capital for the projects envisaged.

That in spite of these inadequacies the railways and tunnels were in most cases actually built was due to the men, the host of illiterate rural labourers that poured forth from the hovels of Europe: from Ireland in the west to Austria in the east, from Sweden in the north to Italy in the south. Ill-paid, cheated on contract work when such applied, badly housed and fed, callously exploited in innumerable ways, the railway gangs were indeed called upon to do more than their share. When the capital was inadequate for the hiring of horses they had to push, shovel and carry the loads excavated; for lack of machines they hacked their way through rock, for lack of pumps they bailed by hand, for lack of the most elementary camp hygiene they died like flies, of cholera, typhus, smallpox.

It was the same everywhere. Entire regiments and brigades of men were mobilized and put to work in the long tunnels. During the second half of the century, when rock-drilling machines became available, their number dropped by half, but even then several thousand men were crowded together in camp and underground workings. Providing them with even the barest necessities of life was frequently beyond the resources of a contractor seeing his profits and capital draining away in flooded workings.

Nevertheless, in spite of the deplorable conditions a tunnel advance was vastly preferable to mining. The pay, such as it was, was better, the work was conducted with great vigour in order to carry it out within the stipulated contract time and, it should be added, to reduce the hazards as much as possible. There was always pride of achievement, the competitive aspects were, and still are, a prominent feature of the work. Tunnelling was also democratic in a basic sense; if men were killed under collapsing roofs so also were contractors and their engineers; when typhus scourged a camp it was not a respecter of

Fig 5. Alpine tunnellers at the middle
of the nineteenth century.

status. If tunnelling labour was called to work under hazardous and sub-human conditions, so also were the contractors. The stresses put on an old-time tunnelling contractor were frequently too much for human flesh to bear. None of the great tunnellers of the last century reached sixty years of age. Not one of the contractors of the three Alpine tunnels, Fréjus, Gotthard, Simplon, lived to see the result of his gigantic efforts. All three dropped dead on the job.

The superhuman difficulties frequently met with in railway tunnelling were of course fundamentally due to one source, lack of power. Once it became possible to obtain electric power on the site, whether from a neighbouring power main or generated by internal combustion engines, the worst aspects of tunnelling were eliminated. But by then, except for some long mountain tunnels in the American West and some supplementary work in the Alps, there was no longer a need for railway tunnelling in the western world.

In these introductory notes accent has been put on the social and human aspects of mining and tunnelling, with the aim of presenting a rounded picture of underground work. Economic and technological history—like most histories—is strangely barren of human content, so that one easily forgets that the great events, the seemingly abstract forces of the market place, the methods and techniques employed, are shaped and influenced by anonymous men wielding tools, with muscles and sinews directed and co-ordinated by disciplined and reflecting minds, and possessing the same passions and dreams as the personages recorded in conventional histories. Just what did it mean to them to be grasped by the steel gauntlet of technology and flung underground to burrow through mountains in the wilderness or through the silt of river beds with inadequate equipment and meagre technical insight?

Making a living in the primitive phases of an emerging industrial economy, be it a steel mill, a textile plant, in a stokehold, or behind a bookkeeper's pulpit, was not exactly a pleasure. But the rural pro-letarians put to work on the railways had to bear the.brunt of the brassy machine civilization bearing down on them with the full force generated by the single-minded aim of getting rich quick. In Europe they were able to take it, there was no need to import coolies or similar slave labour to do the job. The railway labour was strong and tough, their literacy on a par with their bosses', but to them working on the railroad for cash wages was vastly preferable to their former life in bondage to a mean farmer or landlord. By alternating hard work with hard drinking they managed to give themselves a good time while it lasted, until their backs broke, a rock hit them on the head or a round blew up in their faces.

All this belongs to the past. Safety legislation did away with the worst abuses long ago. Labour unions gathering strength gradually succeeded in improving conditions not covered by statute. Neverthe-less, the old sins were slow in dying. In some countries the old mean attitudes, no doubt stemming originally from inadequate capital resources, which found such ridiculous expressions as charging the men for the metal worn off their tools, prevailed on the sites until the depression following the First World War.

Now all, or nearly all of them have gone down the drain of economic history. Post-war tunnelling gives no cause for social in-dignation. It is a mechanized, high-productive industry founded on scientific gains in many fields. The heavy work is performed better, faster and more economically by machines organized in working cycles timed to the minute. But the dangers are still there. Tunnellers are still being killed and maimed despite all precautions. Now as ever underground work is a hazardous way of making a living.

Chapter 2

THE QUEST FOR METALS

'Surely there is a veine for the silver, and a place for gold where they fine it.'

FROM earliest times men in their daily foraging for food must have stumbled upon ores on the ground. When leaning over to drink from clear streams they saw native gold glimmering in the gravel. They must have picked up chunks of native silver and copper, scooped up the black sand constituting native tin. Some hunters would have come across runs of silver glittering on a mountain slope, melted from an outcrop by the heat of a forest fire.

Metals were all around them, the shiny ones attracted attention and were picked up, and used as amulets, but beyond that they were worthless from a practical point of view. They could not be shaped into tools or weapons and when subsequently the art of smelting was mastered, the early metal implements were inferior to the traditional ones made of wood, bone and stone.

Early mining was conducted not with the aim of extracting metals from the ground but to gain access to much more desirable material, flint nodules from which a multitude of efficient weapons and tools could be made: axes, arrow-heads, lance-heads, knives, burins, scrapers, saws and numerous special-purpose tools. So comprehensive a catalogue of flint artifacts does not suggest the haphazard making of tools by just any member of a foraging tribe. For one thing, the intricate skill required to work flint in the technically advanced phases of the late Palaeolithic Age called for specialists; for another, there is nothing haphazard about the flint-working stations where the flint chips, the tailings from tool-making, form heaps still measuring several feet in height. Such workings would require a large and enduring supply of flint somewhere in the neighbourhood. There is no particular mystery about the development of an early flint deposit. The stone was originally found on the ground from which it had been picked up intermittently and shaped into rough hand-axes for perhaps a hundred thousand years or even longer. But ultimately the surface supply gave out and the workers began to follow the flint outcrop into the ground, first in pits, later by means of shafts from which galleries were driven into the deposits.

Just when did this happen? It must have been at any time during the post-glacial Holocene Age, which began something like 15,000 years ago. Some day in a not too distant future it will be possible to obtain an accurate carbon-14 dating from the bones, antlers and other organic tools left by the flint miners.

There is a great deal of evidence to choose from. At several locations in Europe—in England, Belgium, France, Portugal and Sicily

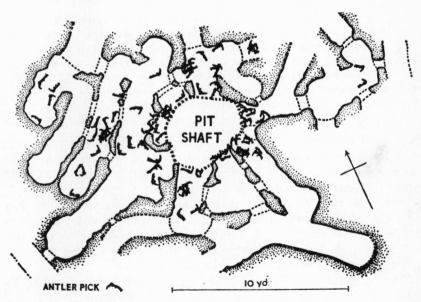

ANTLER PICK   10 yd.

Fig 6. Stone Age flint mines at Grimes Graves, in East Anglia. The pit descends 30 ft. below the ground level and from its bottom have been driven irregular galleries extending 33 ft. in length. The chalk was worked with picks made of deer antlers.

—flint was mined underground in the early post-glacial period. At Grimes Graves, on the Norfolk-Suffolk border, flint nodules were extracted from an outcrop in shallow pits. Later, deep shafts were sunk to the lower flint beds and when the 30-ft. level was reached, lateral galleries were driven to a length of 33 ft. to mine the bed. At Spiennes, in Belgium, similar mines cover an area of about five acres. The outcrop was first mined in open workings at the bottom of a hill, but later shafts were sunk from the top of the hill to the pitching flint deposit. At the bottom of a shaft a bell-shaped chamber 6 to 10 ft. in diameter was excavated and galleries were driven radially.

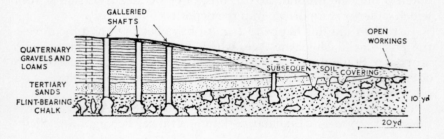

Fig 7. Layout of Stone Age mines at Spiennes in Belgium which suggests that the principles of mining were well understood. The deposits of flint nodules were first worked in open pits at the bottom of the small hill to the right. When the open workings gave out the miners sank shafts from the top of the hill to the pitching flint deposit. From the bottom of the shafts galleries were driven into the deposit.

Some galleries even connect with neighbouring shafts, which suggests that these early miners possessed a well-developed mining skill. In some French flint mines the workings were drained by sump holes at the bottom of the shafts.

The tools used by the flint miners included picks made from deer antlers, flint axes and hammers, and shovels made from the shoulder-blades of oxen and horses. The splitting action of the wedge was mastered and the chalk was split by hammering wedges made of horses' bones and horn tines into the soft rock.

The Metal Age, according to the conventions used by archaeologists and historians, is defined as a period when metal tools and weapons began to predominate over those made from wood, bone and stone. It is an elementary observation that a new material and the artifacts made therefrom are seldom decisively better than the conventional materials employed up to the time of their appearance.

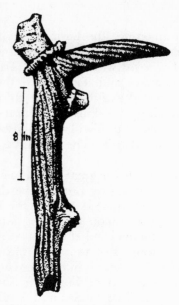

Fig 8. Pick made of deer antler was
the principal tool used by the Stone
Age miners.

The stone tools were superior in all respects to any tool made of
native copper, and more economical in use than the early bronze
tools, just as the latter were infinitely better than the early iron tools.
For many purposes in mining and quarrying, stone tools continued
to be used for thousands of years after bronze and iron tools were in
adequate supply.

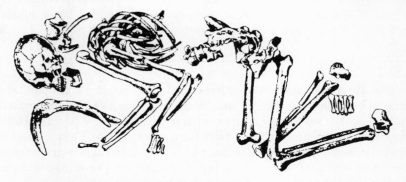

Fig 9. Stone Age miner killed under the collapsed roof of a
gallery in the Belgian flint mine at Obourg.

Bronze Age Mining

The knowledge of smelting, the basic metallurgical technology, seems to have been developed in Central Asia and diffused into the western world and India by way of Persia. The mountains from which spring the Euphrates and Tigris, and the Caucasus-Ararat region, are usually regarded as intermediate diffusion centres from which mining and metallurgical skills spread into Europe by way of Anatolia, Cyprus, Greece and Tyrol, later also to Italy, western Europe, Scandinavia and Russia. The extensive Egyptian industry also derives from the East.

While native copper, never in great abundance, must have been found and used haphazard at any time in the distant past, copper reduced from oxide ores was used by the Sumerians as early as 3800 B.C. It had become common 500 years later. This Sumerian copper derived from Armenia, and that centre remained for 2,000 years one of the major sources of supply to the successive states in the Mediterranean area. The Ararat mines were of major importance for the southbound trade in copper, but other Caucasian mines supplied the tribes north of the Caspian Sea and the Danube valley.

Obviously, the early copper ores mined in the Caucasus were outcroppings, that is to say, eroded blocks or parts of lodes extending above ground. In certain spots the working of an outcrop continued into open pits which were abandoned owing to landslides and water. But at an early date, say about 3500 B.C., the deposits began to be mined by means of sloping shafts and tunnels entering from an adit on a mountain slope. Tunnelling, in its true technological sense, may therefore be said to have been developed before 3000 B.C. This method of mining an ore body continued in common use for 4,500 years and, although not much used in modern mining, it is the only economical way of excavating a power-house or any large subterranean structure necessitating the removal of millions of tons of rock.

The Sinai Mines

The Egyptian state, the other major consumer of copper, also carried on extensive mining operations during which, it is estimated, more than 10,000 tons of copper were produced in 1,500 years. However, little of this tonnage derived from mines inside Egypt; most of it was mined on the Sinai peninsula. The mines there were worked for turquoise and pottery-glazing materials in pre-dynastic times (before 3000 B.C.) but later mainly for copper ores.

The Sinai deposits were worked by sloping shafts and level tunnels driven 130 to 160 ft. into the rock. Stone tools were used and wooden wedges driven into the rock and moistened with water. When the wet wedges expanded, blocks of ore were loosened from the rock. The ore was smelted on the spot, but subsequent refining of the metallic copper was done in Egypt.

Another important copper centre originally mined by the Egyptians was the Arabah, between the Dead Sea and the Gulf of Aqaba. Later, the mines were worked by the Edomites (1800–1300 B.C.) and subsequently by Solomon and other kings of Israel. The mining was conducted by the pillar-and-stall method, and pillars which remain still show veins of ore. This mine is also of interest for having inspired a magnificent Biblical poem (Job XXVIII). Although the poem is dated about 400 B.C. it could equally well apply to metal mining a couple of thousand years earlier. Some of the verses have been used as chapter headings in this book and there is no need to repeat them in this context, except for the fifth verse which reads as follows:

> 'As for the earth, out of it cometh bread: and under it
> is turned up as it were fire.'

If the last line is read 'And underneath it is turned up by fire' we have an excellent poetic synthesis of fire-setting, perhaps the earliest reference in literature to the ancient practice of breaking hard rock by heating it with log pyres.

The Egyptian Mining Monopoly

By 1200 B.C. Egypt had become dependent on Cyprus and Armenia for its supply of copper, but gold-mining was carried on at an undiminished rate. The Egyptian state mining monopoly extracted gold ore from some hundred mines, most of them situated in the Nubian Desert. The annual yield of these mines has been estimated at 66 lb. which, modest as it may seem today, was considerably more than that derived from other gold-bearing regions.

The Egyptian mines consisted of deep underground workings connected by vertical shafts. The work was performed by criminals condemned to hard labour and by prisoners of war. Hittites and Philistines captured in military operations appear to have supplied the mining know-how. In order to conduct these extensive mining operations in the desert it was necessary to dig and maintain wells certain distances apart so as to keep communications open and enable men and animals to be supplied in these remote areas. An officer of the Eleventh Dynasty (c. 2000 B.C.) in charge of an expedition which passed through the gold-mining centre at Wadi Hammamat (of which a map, the earliest mining survey known, is still in existence) reports having dug fifteen wells, 20 to 30 cubits deep, along his route in the desert east of the Nile. 'I proceeded', he reports, 'with a force of 3,000 men ... I gave them a leather bottle and a carrying pole and two jars of water and twenty loaves daily.'

The mines in the Wadi Allaqi in Nubia, south of the Tropic of Cancer, presented ugly problems of logistics. 'If a few of the gold-washers went thither,' writes a chronicler of Rameses II (1298–1232 B.C.), 'only half arrived, for the rest died of thirst on the road, together with their asses. There could not be found for them their necessary supply of drink in going up or coming down the Wadi, from water in their water skins.' This echo from the distant past has a familiar ring to placer miners and prospectors in the American desert where not so long ago similar difficulties prevailed.

From these Egyptian gold workings in the desert has survived a detailed account which bears every sign of accurate reporting. Agatharchides' description of the horrors of Egyptian mining has been quoted in Chapter 1 and there is no need to repeat this catalogue of cruelties and indignities inflicted by man on man. In the mines of the Caucasus and, later, in the Greek and Roman mines, although they were largely worked by slaves conditions were less atrocious. On the other hand, some comfort may be derived from the fact that stupid brutalities do not pay: the untold thousands worked to death in the Egyptian mines, the thousands of soldiers and overseers who guarded them, the tremendous cost of operating the mining monopoly, resulted in the production of a few hundred pounds of metallic gold.[1]

Before leaving this phase of Bronze Age mining, interesting because of its strong influence on all subsequent underground workings, some space should be devoted to tin. To make hard tool and weapon material, copper must be alloyed with at least 15 per cent of tin. Ancient bronzes containing 3 per cent or less of tin may be regarded

[1] The output of the three main gold mining regions (Coptos, Wawat and Kush situated in the Eastern Desert extending roughly from the north of the First Cataract towards the Fifth) naturally varied according to the intensity with which the ranges were worked. The output appears to have culminated in the New Kingdom, during the reign of Tuthmosis III (1504–1450 B.C.). For three years of the reign of this Pharaoh the output of two of these ranges is known, viz.:

Year of reign	Wawat Range		Kush Mines	
34	2,554 deben	(512·4 lb.)	300 deben	(60·6 lb.)
38	2,884 ,,	(570·7 lb.)	100 ,,	(20·1 lb.)
41	3,144 ,,	(630·9 lb.)	195 ,,	(39·2 lb.)

One *deben* equals 9·1 grammes or 0·293 oz. tr.

as accidental; the tin was present as an impurity of the copper ore, which perhaps gave rise to the complex metallurgical process involved in the manufacture of cast bronze tools and weapons.

Tin appears as an alluvial metal, as a black sand on the bottom of river beds, or as a 'tin-stone', a mineral known as Cassiterite (SnO_2). The alluvial tin is commonly associated with gold, and when 'panning' for gold, ancient as well as modern prospectors would come upon heavy black Cassiterite nodules among the gold dust. But by the time bronze had become established as a tool material, the requirements of tin had exhausted all placer deposits and whence the new supplies were obtained remains something of a mystery. Egypt, having no tin at all, had to import it, perhaps by way of the slave routes from the large deposits in central Africa, perhaps from the East.

With the advent of the Phoenician sailors and traders, the ancient world became supplied with its most important strategic material from sources which this remarkable people developed in Spain, Brittany and Cornwall. The town of Gades (Cadiz) was established as a shipping port for tin in about 1100 B.C. Very little is known about this early mining except for a brief remark by Diodorus that in Spain 'they dig it up and melt it down in the same way as they make gold and silver'. Of the tin obtained in Britain he states: 'These people make tin, which they dig up with a great deal of care and labour; being rocky, the metal is mixed with earth, out of which they smelt the metal and then refine it.'

From the admittedly brief references by classical writers it is permissible to assume that mining from earliest times has been an industrial undertaking requiring men, capital and the vision and enterprise of contractors. The mineral deposits of Spain were being worked during the entire Bronze Age for gold and silver; the peninsula's copper and tin were developed by the Phoenicians (1500–1000 B.C.), the greatest mining entrepreneurs of the ancient world: nearly all mines adjacent to the sea were prospected and developed by their miners. The Spanish town of Cartagena (New Carthage) in southeast Spain became one of the important centres for silver mining. Here the custom originally developed of naming the tunnels (German *Stollen*) after the discoverer of the lode or the overseer driving the tunnel.

Thanks to Pliny we know of one such tunnel which came to play an important part in political history, since the silver mined in the stopes at the end of it provided Hannibal with the means to conduct his military operations. The name of this tunnel, which extended 1,500 paces into the rock, was Baebelo, and through it was removed

ore which yielded 300 lb. of metallic silver per day. But it was a wet
working, and to carry out the mining it was necessary to maintain
a human chain of bailers who, working in torchlight day and night,
year in and year out, kept water away from the face. This mine is
believed to have been situated north of Cazlona where Hannibal
married his rich wife Himilce, and it appears that she brought him
the mine as a dowry.

Polybius (204–125 B.C.) gives some interesting statistical information about the silver mines of New Carthage. They were situated
20 stadia from the town and enclosed by a circuit of 400 stadia.[2]
Some 40,000 miners were employed by the Roman state, and the
daily output was worth about 25,000 drachmae. Strabo (63 B.C.–
A.D. 24) also refers to this Spanish mining range, but by his time the
mines had lost some of their former importance.

Fire-setting

Throughout the long history of hard-rock mining, fire-setting remained the most important method of breaking rock wherever there
existed a supply of timber in the neighbourhood. It was developed in
the Bronze Age mines and continued to be used in a few German
and Scandinavian mines until the late nineteenth century, that is,
some 270 years after explosives were first applied to mining.

The method was poetically referred to in the Book of Job, subsequently also by Agatharchides (see p. 8), but it was Pliny who made
the statement which later produced such a lively and enduring
debate among the learned. He writes (XXXIII:21): 'Occasionally a
kind of silex [quartz] is met with which must be broken with fire and
vinegar, or as the tunnels are filled with suffocating fumes and smoke
they frequently use bruising machines, carrying 150 librae [approx.
130 lb.] of iron.' Elsewhere in his book Pliny dwells on the usefulness
of vinegar for salad dressing as well as for breaking rock. In his
belief in the rock-breaking property of vinegar, Pliny has apparently
been influenced by Livy (50 B.C.–A.D.17), who appears to have
created the myth, or at any rate put it in writing, when describing
Hannibal's crossing of the Alps. This is how the amazing feat was
accomplished:[3]

'They set fire to the timber when a wind had arisen suitably to
excite the fire, then when the rock was hot it was crumbled by pouring on vinegar (*infuso aceto*). In this manner the cliff heated by the
fire was broken by iron tools, and the declivities eased by turnings,

[2] One Roman stadium = 607 feet.   [3] Livy, XXI: 37.

so that not only the beasts of burden but also the elephants could be led down.'

This account of crossing the Little St. Bernard Pass in force in 218 B.C. was written 200 years after it happened, and when Pliny repeated it vinegar was accepted as an efficient rock explosive. The strange thing is that the rock-breaking qualities of vinegar have been debated in all seriousness ever since, despite the debunking of Gibbon, Lavalette, and others.

A long line of distinguished military writers, fascinated by Hannibal's genius, have accepted the vinegar passage. A few have been worried about it and suggested that it was a code word for a secret explosive invented by the Phoenicians. Herbert Hoover, thirty-first President of the United States and, what is more important in this context, an erudite mining historian, dismissed it as sheer nonsense but made a half-hearted attempt to explain it as a text corruption; instead of *infuso aceto* it might originally have been written *infosso acuto*. Hoover admits that the latter makes wretched Latin but it would make some sense from a mining point of view.

But vinegar blasting still lives on. In the 1940's, a leading American technical journal referred to the passage without comment, and ten years later the house organ of a Swedish manufacturer of mining equipment attempted to explain the use of vinegar by Hannibal's engineers as a solvent of limestone.

It seems strange that the numerous writers who during the past 2,000 years have stumbled across the Livy vinegar passage have not thought of the most obvious explanation. Hannibal, like all commanders in the past, recruited miners for use as engineers. When clearing a passage between the boulders and other erosion debris on the summit and slopes of the Little St. Bernard Pass they would use fire-setting as a matter of course to break up the cohesion of the rock so as to be able to dispose of the large boulders with steel bars and wedges. For the pyres they would cut down timber on the slopes and use it immediately in the raw state. Burning any wood, particularly unseasoned timber, will produce dry distillation in the heated centres not yet touched by the flames. This yields pyroligneous acid, also known as 'wood vinegar', consisting largely of acetic acid and methyl alcohol. A wood distillation plant can be detected several miles away by the strong vinegar smell: dousing a large timber fire with water will also produce a powerful odour of vinegar.

What seems to have happened on Hannibal's famous march across the Alps can be put briefly as follows: his miners cleared the obstructions ahead of the main army in the conventional manner, by heating the boulders and outcroppings by timber pyres. They doused the hot rock with water, thereby also extinguishing the remaining fires, and dumped the broken pieces down the slopes. Presumably, the work of bulldozing the Little St. Bernard Pass in this manner was done ahead of the main host; it is difficult to conceive of one of the most famous commanders in history bringing his whole army across the Alpine crags without being sure of a road. But being a good commander he would certainly see to it that there would be regular troops protecting the miners while engaged in clearing the pass. And these guards —hundreds, perhaps thousands of men—not knowing anything about mining would have felt the sting of vinegar in the air. Later, when the amazing feat became admired and discussed, the clearing of the mountain road across the Alps was attributed to the use of vinegar as a blasting agent. In short, it was a 200-year-old veterans' tale that Livy repeated when he wrote about the Punic Wars.

Hallstatt Salt Mines

During the Bronze Age, copper was mined in many other places in Europe besides Spain—in Austria, Germany, France, Hungary, southern Russia and, above all, in Tyrol, the cradle of continental mining. Everywhere, the deposits were mined either from adits driven into the hillside or by shafts 3 to 6 ft. in diameter and provided with tree-stem ladders, the way mining ladders continued to be used throughout Europe until well into the seventeenth century A.D. The galleries extended 300 ft. or so in length: they were timbered when necessary and sometimes lagged with moss and clay. When hard rock was encountered it was fractured by fire-setting. The tools used by the Tyrol miners included picks, wedges and hammers made of hard bronze. The ore was crushed and graded underground and carried to the surface in leather bags or wooden troughs. Simple machines, such as windlasses, were occasionally employed.

What kind of people worked these mines in isolated Alpine valleys, far removed from the splendours of Thebes, Babylon and Sidon? Were they the same wretches that slaved in the desert gold-mines of the Pharaohs? Apparently not, judging from the remains at Hallstatt.

Deep in the heart of Salzkammergut, in the Austrian Alps, lies a small curving lake from the shores of which the mountains rise steeply to about 6,500 ft., modest as the Alps go but nevertheless wild and difficult of access. On the western shore the small town of Hallstatt clings to the hillside, barely able to hang on to the precipitous incline and for three months of the year subdued by the bone-chilling shadow of the mighty mountain. It is an isolated place, the first road to the town having been built as late as 1875; previously the only access to it had been by boat across the lake or by laborious mountain trails. In fact, to all outward appearances, Hallstatt would seem a most inhospitable place for the seed of civilization to take root in and flourish.

And yet that seems to be what happened. On a steep incline some 1,300 ft. above the town, on a little wooded spur, a man probing the ground for gravel in 1846 turned up a human skull and a bronze ear-ring. Further digging revealed a whole skeleton, and then others, until finally, eighteen years later, 993 graves had been discovered and 6,084 objects of all kinds had been recovered. On this steep hillside was the ancient cemetery of the Hallstatt salt-miners. Two thousand men, women and children had been buried in their finest clothes, along with their weapons and metal ornaments, armlets, rings, necklaces and brooches, most of them made of bronze, a few of gold. Every man bore arms; some had long swords with the hilt made of carved ivory, others had short swords with beautifully forked hilts. The men who worked the salt mines at Hallstatt around 1000 B.C. certainly were not slaves.

The Hallstatt miners have given their name to an epoch denoting the breakthrough in Europe of the art of iron working. Here, around Hallstatt, the technique of mining, smelting, forging, and steeling iron, originally discovered in the Near East, got its first foothold in Europe. At least, so the archaeologists claim. Perhaps it is so; nevertheless, when standing on this ancient miners' cemetery, with the salt mountain towering in the rear, and viewing the narrow valleys hemmed in by Alpine peaks and not leading anywhere, it is difficult to visualize how such an advanced culture could take root and flourish under such rigorous topographical conditions. There is simply no room for it. It seems more reasonable to assume that the wealth found at Hallstatt had been traded against one of the most desirable commodities that exist—salt. These fortunate people had found in their distant and isolated mountain fastness an inexhaustible source of wealth, and they knew its value. The weapons and ornaments of Hallstatt, like the ancient wealth of Scandinavia, are of the same character as the art accumulated in American museums, to wit, trade goods.

It appears that the salt deposits at Hallstatt were worked as early as 2500 B.C., and since the lode is still mined Hallstatt can claim a mining history extending over 4,500 years, truly a record. For the first 1,500 years it was a matter of working easily accessible outcrops in a more or less fortuitous manner, but by about 1000 B.C. people settled permanently at the foot of the mountain and began to work the deposit in an organized fashion.

These professional miners drove tunnels (or *Stollen*) into the hillside, at angles of from 25° to 60° to the horizon. When salt was reached, galleries were driven in different directions. Some of the underground workings extended nearly 1,300 ft. from the portal and

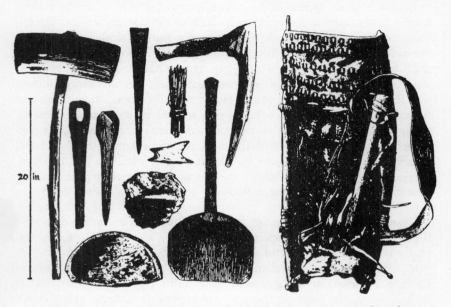

Fig 10. Well-preserved tools, used nearly 3,000 years ago, found in the Hallstatt salt mines.

were at their extremes 330 ft. below the surface. In places, the galleries were widened into 40 × 40 ft. rooms with a height of 3 ft. 3 in. The roof was supported with timber.

The tools used were bronze picks and chisels provided with wooden hafts. Not unexpectedly, a number of wooden tools, such as mallets and shovels, were employed. As later in the northern mines, illumination was obtained by burning bundles of resinous sticks tied together with rough linen. The salt deposits are veined with Triassic rock and anhydrite, which wear down tools fast; before the advent of pneumatic drilling machines, a salt-miner dulled ten steel picks in an eight-hour shift. The wastage of bronze tools must therefore have been tremendous, necessitating extensive foundries above ground. But there are no traces left of these, which is not surprising since mining has been going on practically without interruption up to our own times. A working mine holds nothing of interest to archaeologists.

None the less, enough has been saved in recent centuries to convey a fairly detailed picture of the miners, their tools and manner of working. The salt has preserved not only the metal tools but also the wooden ones, the leather sacks in which the mined salt was carried, clothing, shoes, a miner killed in an accident, and the excrement left by the miners in the galleries. The perfectly preserved body of a Bronze Age miner was found in 1735 but was removed and given a Christian burial. So we have to make do with what is left, including the ordure which, when analysed, has revealed what they ate. One miner had had a number of hefty meals consisting of millet, barley and broad beans followed by apples, quite a good diet for a hard-working man. The clothing found was made of sheep's wool and the feet were covered with a leather shoe of slipper type.

What does it all add up to? Was Hallstatt just another of those odious mining operations where men slaved so that a few could grow rich and deck themselves out with the trappings of power? Who knows? One likes to think that here in the mountain fastness of Salzkammergut, the miners were free men possessing good tools and skills and the dignity that comes from wealth honourably earned.

Greek Mining

For something like 4,000 years copper had been the metallic mainstay of the river cultures. The native copper had been used up in the settled regions before 4000 B.C.—turned into artifacts, remelted and used time and time again. At about the middle of the fourth millennium, new supplies of metal were obtained from other sources. Oxide ores were reduced with the development of new and more complex smelting and refining methods. A few centuries later, at the turn of the millennium, the art of alloying copper with tin and making hard tool and weapon bronze, had been mastered. Before the second millennium B.C., both the native tin and copper, as well as the oxide ores, had been exhausted in the Fertile Crescent and in Europe. Not only were the metals exhausted, but timber, for fire-setting and in the form of charcoal as a fuel for roasting and smelting, was also depleted over wide areas. In many regions the timber gave out before the mineral deposits. Thus began a concentric movement, heading towards the north and west, to virgin lands with an untouched wealth of metals but, of greater importance, with unbroached sources of timber for fuel. Once started, this search for new lodes and new sources of fuel has never ceased.

The Greeks had a word for it—*metallao,* to search: and indeed the quest for metals is never ending. But in those prehistoric times it was directed at finding other suitable tool material besides the costly bronze. Eventually, this was found in iron. The late development of iron metallurgy, which appears to have occurred around 1200 B.C., probably in Armenia and the Caucasian mining ranges, is one of the mysteries in the history of technology. After all, iron ore in the form of easily reduced oxides, as magnetite, haematite, not to mention the ochres, must have been available nearly everywhere, and particularly in the ancient mining ranges. Meteoric lumps of iron were also to be had by anyone who looked for them in the desert. Sumerians called it the heavenly metal, Egyptians black copper from heaven.

However, to turn iron into a useful tool and weapon material is no easy matter, particularly since it is not possible to apply the knowledge acquired in melting and working copper to iron. Briefly, there were four distinct processes—slagging, hammering, quenching and tempering—that had to be mastered in their innumerable combinations in order to obtain a stable, or reasonably stable, production method that could be applied to the best ores.

This technical revolution was brought about some time prior to 1400 B.C., by the Chalybes people living in the Armenian mountains and at that time subjects of the Hittite kings, who for two centuries maintained a close monopoly on steel. It was a period of great unrest; the political structure of the Near East crumbled under the incursion of the Thraco-Phrygian people which among its other political consequences brought about the downfall of the Hittite empire. Many tribes, including the steel-working ones, were driven southwards and eastwards. The iron-working Philistines settled along the coastline of Canaan (Syria) and the Medianites near the iron deposits of Edom, to mention but a few.

In this manner the know-how of steel-making spread widely within the brief span of 200 years, from 1200 to 1000 B.C., into Syria, Palestine, Cyprus, Crete, southern Italy, and also to Persia and Transcaucasia. Of importance for subsequent developments, the new metallurgy became known in Greece, the Balkans and the eastern Alpine ranges. Here, in Noricum, as the Romans came to call it, were deposits of spathic iron, the best base material that exists for the direct method of iron manufacture, since it is free from all obnoxious impurities and contains traces of manganese, most helpful in primitive steel-making. All the fine steels of antiquity—the wonderful magic swords swung by the heroes of the immortal poets, the 'seric' steels of the Romans, the Damascus and Toledo steels of the 'Moors'

—they all derived their magic from the fortuitous presence of manganese in the ores.

Mining for copper and tin in distant lands continued; mining for gold and silver, and the remelting of the slags left by ancient smelters near home kept on unabated. To the mining of the conventional metals was now added that of iron. More fuel was required, but far more suitable tools had become available and virgin timber ranges went down before the steel axes in order to provide fire-settings in the new mines or were converted into charcoal for roasting and melting the iron ores and turning them into blooms. The ancient countries in the Near East had exhausted their timber resources, and could only await the economic and political catastrophes that were to come. The price of maintaining a culture built on metals is high: it means, eventually, complete collapse. The depletion of the timber range upsets the natural balance, and a land that began as an arboreal abode for foraging men and beasts finished as a useless wasteland scourged by the sun and scoured by floods, with an interesting past but no future. To eat the apple of metallurgical knowledge is a sure way to close the gates of paradise.

And while the dust storms howl over the Bronze Age mines and the smelters in the once Fertile Crescent, we turn to greener pastures, to the Greeks opening up new mines on the western shores of the Aegean Sea.

The Mt. Laurion Mines

The Mt. Laurion mining range near the southern end of the Attic Peninsula can be chosen as an excellent example of Iron Age mining. But these metal mines are important for a number of other reasons. They were worked in the second millennium by the Mycenaeans for silver and then abandoned, whereupon the Athenians opened them up again in about 600 B.C. It can be argued with good reason that the existence of the Laurion mines changed the course of history at one important juncture. In the critical year 484 Athens obtained 100 talents (83,700 oz. troy) of silver from the mines, and the Athenian assembly voted the entire output to the building of the fleet which defeated the Persians at Salamis four years later.

The Greeks abandoned the Laurion property about A.D. 100, after which the slag dumps were worked over for a couple of hundred years. Finally, in 1864, the ancient mines were once more opened up and worked for zinc and lead by a French company. In 1962 the Laurion range produced 90,000 tons of ore containing 3·5 per cent of lead and 5 per cent of zinc. Thus the history of Mt. Laurion covers something like 3,500 years of time. Only the salt mines at Hallstadt can lay claim to such a life-span.

The old Mt. Laurion deposits consisted of silver and lead which occurred along the contact zone of horizontal beds of limestone and slate, overlaid with schist. At the outcrop the galena, blende and pyrites gave place to other minerals such as lead and zinc carbonates and iron oxide. The latter was used as the base material for the iron tools employed in working the lead-silver deposits at the lowest plane of contact, some 330 ft. below the surface.

Fig 11. Greek miners at work in a stope, as depicted on a Corinthian clay tablet from the sixth century B.C.

As is usually the case, the early workings at Mt. Laurion were open-cast, followed by rather short adits, or tunnels driven from the hillside towards the ore bodies. But unlike Hallstatt, the lowest—and richest—contacts could not be mined in this way, and throughout the centuries some 2,000 shafts were sunk and connected by galleries. The deepest shaft had reached 386 ft. when ground water, here at just about sea-level, was reached and stopped further sinking.

The Laurion shafts were excavated to a standard size of 6·2 × 4·2 ft. and cut with hammer and gad. The centre line of the shaft is nearly vertical, which is to be expected from a geometrically gifted people, but the shafts exhibit a feature characteristic of Greek mining. On every 10-metre (33-ft.) level the cross-section is twisted by about 10° so that the bottom of the shaft is rotated 90°, using the top as a datum. The reason for cutting the shaft in this manner was to make room for the ladders which, in the Laurion as in subsequent mines, consisted of tree trunks with steps cut into them. They were placed at one of the short sides of the shaft rectangle and therefore did not interfere with the hoist cable descending approximately along the centre line of the shaft. A shaft of this nature was sunk at an estimated rate of 15 ft. per month.

When the ore shoots in the contact zones were reached, galleries measuring 3·3 × 2·5 ft. were driven into and along them, following every caprice of the siliceous contact. But when a large ore body was found, it was stoped in a systematic fashion, either by overhand stoping, i.e., progressing upwards and filling the cavity as the work progressed; or by underhand stoping, i.e. by working downwards and leaving pillars of ore to support the roof. There are 'pillar-and-room' stopes, supported by pillars nearly 33 ft. high, from which some 100,000 tons of ore have been excavated.

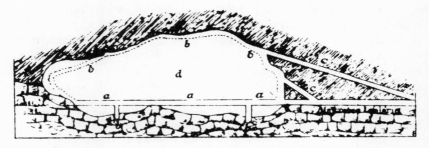

Fig 12. Arrangement of a stope in a Mt. Laurion mine: (a) horizontal gallery; (b) exploratory galleries; (c) connecting galleries; (d) mineral deposit.

The galleries driven from the shafts had frequent crosscuts between them to aid ventilation, and some of them still show grooves in the sides where 'weather' doors were placed to direct the passage of the ventilation air. Although no fire-setting was employed, fires were used to induce an upward draught, as an aid in ventilating the deep workings.

Mining in the Laurion range was conducted with steel picks with wooden handles, hammers of modern patterns, and wedges. Each miner had a lamp, apparently of the amphora type, which he placed in a small niche cut in the gallery close to his place of work.

The ore was sorted underground and, depending on the location of the stope, carried up to the surface in trays or hoisted up in buckets. Above ground it was crushed in stone mortars, measuring 16 to 24 in. in diameter. The crushed ore was milled between stones, like old-time flour mills, and sifted. The oversize was returned to the mills, while the accepted product was passed to a washing plant consisting of sloping masonry structures containing basins and channels some seven metres in length and surfaced with a layer of fine cement, sometimes riffled. The ore was concentrated by gravity, the heaviest fraction collected almost at once, the rest sorting itself out owing to the different mass of the metallic components over the inclined surface of the washing table. The water was collected and re-used; but water was a scarce commodity and numerous cisterns were constructed to catch rainwater for use in ore concentration.[4]

Although the Greek writers and philosophers usually did not concern themselves with technical details, the wealth of the Mt. Laurion mines excited their interest. Aristotle referred to them, as did Xenophon. Demosthenes orated against Pantaenetus and Phaenippus for having robbed the ore pillars and thus invited the risk of collapses. Later, a leaseholder Diphilos was condemned to death for the same offence.

The Greek mines were worked by slaves.[5] Even the overseers (mine superintendents) were slaves, albeit expensive ones. One claim-holder at Mt. Laurion is recorded to have paid one talent (about 58 lb.) of silver for a good one. This would be the equivalent of an annual

[4] Of the 2,000 shafts said to have been sunk in the Laurion range, only about a hundred are still open (1962). On one existing ancient site, situated on a level plateau to the north of the mountain range at the tip of the peninsula, there are two 2 × 3-metre shafts about 50 metres apart. The shafts are still regular in shape, with straight perpendicular walls joined by sharp corners. All that has happened to these accurately chiselled shafts since they were sunk some 2,500 years ago is that the wall surfaces have become somewhat knotty—as if covered by a coat of rough plaster—due to the exudations from the rock.

Near by one of the shafts is a heart-shaped water reservoir, about 15 metres across and very deep, cut into the rock and lined with a cement composition. Close to it is the foundation of what appears to have been a rectangular washing-table, provided with deep trenches along the longitudinal sides.

A few metres from the washing-table is a disorderly pile of stones cut into segments and with a 10-cm. circular and scalloped groove on top. It appears that by placing the segmented stones in order one would obtain a circular structure about six metres in diameter, with a circular channel in the top. By putting a stone runner in the channel and joining it by means of a wooden arm to a vertical post placed in the centre of the circle, in the manner of a horizontal horse-whim, one would obtain a simple *Kollergang*, of the kind still commonly used to mill hard minerals, driven by animals or slaves. The location and shape of the stones suggest that ancient Greek miners milled their ore in some such fashion, as well as between milling-stones.

[5] In the small but invaluable mining museum in the town of Laurion, which completely vanished during the German occupation 1941–45, there were two skeletons of miners, found in the ancient workings, that were chained together with leg irons.

salary for a president of a major mining company in modern times, or something like $40,000–$60,000. Whether, as has been suggested, the Athenian state hired out slaves to the mine operations is not known with any certainty. What is definitely known is that free Athenians formed companies, or at any rate purchased shares, for the purpose of financing the operations of mines in the Mt. Laurion range. This manner of financing mining developments later became common practice in Rome where wild speculation in mining shares among the wealthy aristocrats was not unusual.

The second decline of the Mt. Laurion mines set in at the beginning of the third century B.C. when, under the domination of Philip and Alexander of Macedonia, Greece became flooded with coinage and silver bullion from the new mines in Thrace. By the beginning of the Christian era the old slag heaps were being re-worked, and by A.D. 100 the range was abandoned.

Roman Mines

The art of mining in its widest sense, i.e. the method of tunnelling into ore deposits, had not undergone any major changes in the

Fig 13. A Roman mining team, as depicted on a stone relief. The men wear wide leather belts and carry tools similar to those shown in Fig 15.

Greek ranges. Neither did the Romans bring about any new departures, although they introduced a number of machines into the mines. These consisted of water-raising wheels and *cochlea* (water snails) or Archimedian screws, both applied for draining. There is also mention of a battering ram provided with a 150-lb. iron head, used for breaking quartz. The extensive hydraulic construction works indulged in by the Romans also contributed to increasing the output of the mines because there was always an ample source of water available for concentrating the ore.

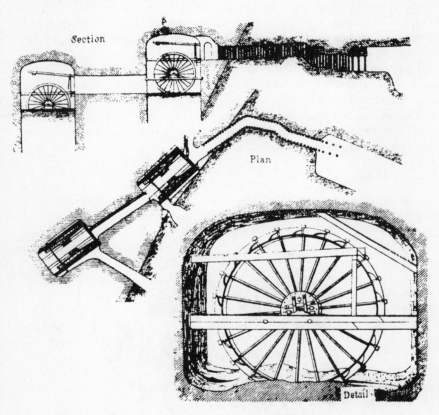

Fig 14. Layout and detail of Roman drainage installation employing water-raising wheels.

With the above draining devices the Romans succeeded in working flooded mines or lowering the levels of ancient workings. In the old Spanish and Portuguese copper mines, such as the Rio Tinto, Roman engineers installed a series of 15-ft. water-raising wheels placed above each other at different levels. Each wheel was driven by a couple of men treading it with their feet.

The tunnels or adits leading from the hillside into Roman mines were very narrow, just wide enough to permit a man to walk, but above the waist they widened sufficiently to accommodate a burden, be it a sack, batea, or pick. However, 16-ft. wide drifts were excavated in some major mines.

Fig 15. Roman mining tools from the first century A.D. Similar tools have been used well into recent times.

The rock was broken with wedge and hammer; fire-setting although known was not practised, according to Pliny, because of the 'steam and smoke'. The tools were of course made of iron and of a composition and shape familiar today. During the Republic, the mines were worked entirely by slaves, but in the first century A.D. these appeared to have been replaced by freedmen supervising condemned criminals for the heavy unskilled work. Working conditions were regulated by law, and the Emperor Hadrian (A.D. 117–138) issued detailed regulations governing the installation of pithead baths, including the times of the day when they were to be used by the miners and when by their women. This appears to have been the first recognition of the need for caring in some measure for the physical wellbeing of the miners. While they were slaves there was not much interest in social legislation, although it must be presumed that having paid one talent of silver for a good overseer the Athenian syndicate previously referred to would be anxious to keep him alive and healthy as long as possible.

THE GOLDEN AGE OF SAXON MINING

The foregoing account of ancient mining has been accumulated from scraps of archaeological evidence, brief references to mining by classical writers, a certain limited experience in the manual methods used to break and excavate rock and the tools available for the purpose, and an appreciation of the inertia, or the enduring conservatism, characterizing mining and metal working generally before the industrial revolution.

From now on we are on firmer ground, since European mining

begins to be illuminated by documentary evidence, although sketchy
at first. The first mine known to have been opened up in the so-called
Dark Ages was the one at Chemnitz in A.D. 745. The lead mines at
Goslar in the Harz were being worked in 970, the silver mines at
Freiberg in Saxony were opened up in 1170. Charters, royal and
episcopal, codifying the rights and obligations of miners, began to
be issued. The earliest charter known was that given by the Bishop
of Trent in 1185. The Harz miners obtained their charter in 1219,
the miners working the Falu copper mine in distant Sweden received
their charter from King Magnus in 1288. However, the most interesting of these early charters is the one issued by the town of Iglau in
1249 because it confirms the so-called 'Apex' form of title, whereby
the miner obtains the right to follow a vein on its dip to any depth
or distance even though it may enter adjoining land.

Backed by these legal rights and privileges, the mining industry in
Germany, Hungary, Austria and Bohemia rapidly developed along
sound lines and became a prosperous and technically highly developed business that eventually came to have far-reaching influence
on mining developments in nearly all European countries. Now we
leave the darkness of the long tunnel extending back into prehistoric
times and, emerging into the sunlight of the Golden Age of mining,
meet Doctor Georgius Agricola.

Georgius Agricola

This learned doctor and scholar is indeed worth knowing. He was
born Georg Bauer, and after some years of study at the Universities
of Bologna, Venice and Padua he settled in 1527 as a mining doctor
in the booming mining town of Joachimsthal, in Erzgebirge, at that
time the major mining centre in Europe. He became a good friend of
Erasmus who at the time was the editor of the Froben's Press in
Basle, where his many books on mineralogy and metallurgy were
printed. It was here his magnum opus *De re metallica* was published
in 1556, one year after his death.

Agricola's *De re metallica* is truly a gigantic accomplishment.
Before its publication all the references to mining and metallurgy by
classical and medieval writers could have been compressed into a few
pages. With its publication the whole body of knowledge bearing on
metals, geology, mineralogy, mining law and administration, prospecting, mining practice, assaying, surveying, ore dressing and smelting of all the recognized metals became available to the practical
miner, the administrator, and the scholar. Whereas before there did
not exist a single useful picture of mining machines, the book is

profusely illustrated in such a way that any traditional as well as newly invented machine could be reproduced.

Agricola's *De re metallica* remained for nearly 200 years the standard handbook on mining and metallurgy. Some of his theoretical views on geology are actually in closer agreement with modern science than many of the ideas that supplanted them during the eighteenth and nineteenth centuries. The only thing to be regretted is that Agricola, steeped in the Scholastic tradition, wrote in Latin, and consequently had to invent many new words and terms which have confounded his translators and readers to this day. Had he written in his native German he would no doubt have been able to communicate his advanced ideas and tremendous technical knowledge more efficiently.

The concluding pages on medieval mining are based entirely on Agricola, and the woodcut illustrations are taken from his famous book. Although some of the machines described, such as the ore stamps, were inventions of his time, the methods and tools discussed are much older. Some of them were to continue unchanged into the present century, although admittedly only in singularly backward mines.

Before entering into the details of underground work let us consider briefly how, according to Agricola, a mining range was organized and administered during the Middle Ages. Since the metal deposits according to the concept of regalian right belonged to the ruler, they could be worked only upon payment of a tithe and they had to be worked continuously. To ensure the enforcement of these regulations, the ruler appointed a *Bergamtsmann* or mining prefect. The day-to-day administrative duties were delegated to a *Bergmeister* assisted by a clerk and a number of *Geschworenen*, or select men, with duties not unlike those of the laymen judges in Scandinavian courts. Then there was the ubiquitous tax collector, called *Zehender*, tithe gatherer, and the *Bergschreiber*.

Having settled the legal formalities of a claim, there arose the matter of financing its development. A *Steiger* or mine manager was appointed and given full responsibility for running the mine. During the development stage he exacted the cash contributions of the shareholders so as to be able to pay the workers and suppliers. This he did once a week, in Agricola's time four times a year. Similarly, when the mine began to yield he paid the owners according to their shares; there were times when a share earned 1100 oz. troy[6] of silver. However, in the case of a yielding mine, the tithe gatherer advanced the

---

[6] Equivalent to 92 lb.

workmen's wages and paid the suppliers. He had to render account to the *Bergmeister* each Saturday night of the advances made. The mine manager had to be present in person when the ore was being smelted, and the weight of metal extracted was entered into the book kept by the tithe gatherer.

The actual mining work was directed by the *Schichtmeister*, literally 'master of the shift'. Besides being a miner he was also skilled in timbering and was held personally responsible for maintaining the structures, shafts, ladders, drifts and stopes in a safe condition. On the foreman fell the entire responsibility for the safety of the men. But he could not discharge a man for incompetence and negligence without the approval of the *Steiger* and the select men. The foreman ordered the men to work and kept them under his supervision. He provided them with tools and other supplies, such as oil for their lamps. When a shift came to an end, the men surrendered their lamps with whatever oil was left in them to the foreman. He was also responsible for the safe keeping of the ore mined and saw no pilfering was done from the stores. Whereas a *Steiger* usually was responsible for several mines, a foreman could not be in charge of more than one.

The men working the mines were divided into a number of trades. The actual miners were called *Berghauer*, literally 'rock cutters', those transporting the ore down in the mine, or the muckers, were *Berganschläger*, the men at the windlass were *Hespeler*, the ore sorters *Ertzpucher* and the washers, buddlers and sifters were named *Wäscher* and *Seiffner*.

The legal requirements satisfied and the financing secured, the development work would get started, using at first a couple of miners and windlass men. The top soil would be stripped and a 2 × 2/3 fathom shaft sunk, usually at the junction of a stringer and the main vein. A windlass was erected above the shaft and a shed built around it 'to prevent rain from falling in and protect the windlass men from being numbed by cold and rain'. In this shed the miners stored their tools.

At a little distance from the shaft house was erected a building for the foreman and the workers, for use later as an ore store. 'To prevent small boys and strangers falling into the shaft the two houses are placed some distance apart, or else a wall is erected between them.' Usually the shaft had to be timbered. In the four corners of the rectangular shaft, long end-posts were placed which at different levels were joined by wall-plates and dividers, whereby the shaft was divided into two parts, a hoisting and ladderway screened off by means of lagging. If the ground was loose the entire shaft was lagged in. 'The lagging prevents fragments of rock from dropping into the shaft terrifying and injuring the miners who go up and down the ladders from one part of the mine to another. The lagging between ladders and haulageway shuts off the ladders from rock falling from the bucket and makes the arduous and difficult ascent seem less terrible, and in fact less dangerous.' A little above the bottom the shaft was provided with wickerwork, except for a narrow open space

Fig 16. Longitudinal section of a transport drift or tunnel in a sixteenth-century German mine. The letters apply to the construction details, as described by Agricola. The system used is similar to timbering by square sets, as still used.

through which the bucket passed. In this manner the shovellers and other workmen at the bottom of the shaft were protected from falling rock.

Either simultaneously or before the shaft sinking, a tunnel was driven from the hillside aiming at the bottom of the shaft. The tunnel was usually 7½ ft. high and 3¾ ft. wide. Two miners excavated the tunnel, one removed the upper half and the second one, following him, the lower half (i.e. 'heading and bench').

The development work, as well as the ore mining that followed, was done in seven-hour shifts, one hour being reserved for the change of crews. The first shift started at four o'clock in the morning, the second at noon, and the third at eight at night. However, the third shift was never imposed by the *Bergmeister* unless absolutely necessary. No miner was allowed to work two shifts. When the time came to go to work a big bell in the village tolled. It was also rung at the end of a shift, when the foreman stamped on the woodwork of the shaft and called to the men to come up. Those who heard him struck the rock with their hammers and signalled the others. Actually, every man underground knew when the shift was about to end, because the oil in the lamps was getting low.

No work was done on Saturdays and usually not on Sundays and annual festivals. But when 'necessity demanded it, a rush of water or a rock fall, then it was not considered irreligious to work on holidays'. But except for the days mentioned, the work had to go on all the time without interruption, because if it ceased for a duration of three days (later the period was extended) the claim-holder would lose his title and the property would revert to the king.

The steel tools used by the miners consisted of wedges, iron blocks, plates, hammers, picks, crowbars, pikes, hoes and shovels. Each tool had a name of its own. The rock-breaking gads were of four sizes, with one end broad and square, the other wedge-shaped. All but the largest were hafted. The hammers were of two kinds, one for one-hand work and the other for double-handed work. A set of one-handed hammers included three sizes, the double-handed ones came in two sizes of which the heavy one was used to drive wedges into the rock. The tools were efficiently hafted 'so that the workmen can strike more powerful blows by the hammer's full weight being concentrated'. Most ores were mined cold with the aid of these tools, each one being used for one particular purpose. But occasionally, the miners ran into veins so hard that they could not be broken with iron tools. Then the rock was fractured by fire, provided that the neighbouring claim-holders permitted it. If such permission was not obtained the last resort was to select some part of the seam lined with small cracks. The miners drove a number of iron blocks into the fissures, and between each pair of blocks they hammered in a wedge until the vein cracked, and a block weighing several hundred pounds came tumbling down.

If permission for fire-setting was given, the hanging wall or foot-wall was hollowed out with iron tools and one or two fires were lit under the vein. The heated rock was then broken into with crowbars, and large lumps were torn out of the vein. Such heated rock was easy to work, but in many mining ranges the *Bergmeister* refused permission to use fire-setting, 'because the heated veins give forth a foetid vapour and the shaft and tunnel are emitting fumes so that no workmen can go down into the mine lest the stench affect their health or actually kill them'.

Fig 17. Wheeled transport was not used until late medieval times. To the left is a wheelbarrow used in German mines at the middle of the sixteenth century. To the right is a truck with two large wheels and casters as employed in tunnels provided with a smooth plank floor. A blunt pin ran in a groove between the planks sloping towards the portal and kept the truck on its track. The use of this truck required a smooth and uniform floor.

The ore, excavated cold or hot, was broken up in the stope and loaded in wheelbarrows or in a $4 \times 2\frac{1}{2}$-ft. two-wheeled truck called a 'hound'. Besides the two wheels and a set of casters it was provided with a blunt pin which ran in a groove in the plank floor of the transport drift or tunnel. When little ore needed to be carried out, a wooden tray, measuring 3 ft. in length, was used, borne either on the shoulder or slung from the neck. 'But this causes great fatigue and involves much labour and has therefore been abandoned.'

When wheeled to the shaft, the ore and rock were loaded by boys into a wooden bucket or hide basket. Depending on the depth of the shaft these were hoisted up by two men working the windlass, in deep shafts by a horse-whim. In the very deepest shafts hoisting was performed by water power.

Wet mines were drained in numerous ways, by hoisting up the water in leather bags through the shaft, or by different types of pumps. Since the tunnel into the deposit was driven on a slight incline, it was provided with a covered drain in the floor. However, in ranges suffering from much water, a more radical method was resorted to in order to drain the entire area. A large tunnel was driven through the entire range at a level below the lowest workings to drain all the properties and the ground above the tunnel.

These long and large tunnels were the most expensive undertakings

Fig 18. Early mine mechanization was first applied to hoisting. In this installation from the early sixteenth century the large wheel was provided with a double set of buckets and could be run in opposite directions by supplying water to either one or the other of the two rows of buckets. The hoist was controlled by an operator who manipulated levers opening and closing the water gates. This large hoist was a mechanical marvel 400 years ago.

in medieval mining and a great many encouragements were offered to have them built. The tunnellers were given the right to all the ore they encountered while advancing the tunnel, irrespective of the surface claims. The owners of the properties under which the tunnel passed were required to pay one-quarter of the cost. But there were few individuals able to finance such long and costly developments and they were usually divided into a large number of shares; the one in Joachimsthal had 128 shares, of which 126 were in private hands, one held by the State and one by the Church. However, they were safe and profitable investments, and shares were reserved for the support of the sick and needy of the population in the mining villages dotting the district.

The mining methods used differed with the nature of the deposit. But there was nothing haphazard about the layout; a medieval Saxon development followed strict geometrical laws, and the mine became an *architectura subterranea*. There are passages in Agricola that hint at methods that did not come into common use until at least a century later.

Conclusion

Medieval Saxon mining as it emerges from the pages of *De re metallica*, represents a cultural attainment of the highest order. Never before or since has underground work attained such human dignity and technical distinction. The last centuries of the Middle Ages and the transition to the new age were indeed the Golden Age of mining.

The working conditions seem to have been better than in any underground work before or since. A shift was seven hours, for five days a week. One hour between shifts was reserved for 'portal time', for one shift leaving and another entering the workings. A tolling bell in the village called out the shift change, managers and foremen had to obey the working rules, strictly enforced by the king's *Bergmeister*.

The mine manager was responsible for the economic management of the mine. He had to pay the men on Friday night, and see to it that he collected his payroll from the shareholders. The foreman had *his* duties to perform and woe to him if he neglected the safety measures required to protect the life and limbs of the workers in his charge. He was responsible for timbering vulnerable shafts, tunnels, drifts and stopes, for keeping the ladders in good repair and the workings free from water.

Also the health of the miners was the concern of the management and authorities. As already mentioned, fire-setting, with its noxious

and always unpleasant smoke and odours, was not allowed unless
permission was obtained from the neighbouring mines and the *Berg-*
meister, and even then was restricted to just before the end of the
evening shift on Friday so that the smoke could clear before the
morning shift on the following Monday. The door to the main frame
must face away from the north, to prevent ice forming on the top
rungs. Special protective clothing was prescribed for the working of
deposits containing arsenical ores. Each range had its doctor. It was
during his practice as a mine doctor in Joachimsthal that Agricola
became interested in the various aspects of mining.

From a purely technical point of view medieval Saxon mining was
well-nigh perfectly adapted to the scale of mining practised at the
time. A finder's claim (about 10,600 sq. ft.) was well suited to the
equipment available, the tools, horse-whim, or water-wheel. The
hand tools were as far developed as they could be. They have never
been improved upon.

The miners themselves, although engaged in heavy and fatiguing
labour under confined and hazardous conditions, were a privileged
group and seemingly happy with their lot. 'They lighten their long
and arduous labours by singing, which is neither wholly untrained
nor unpleasing,' writes Agricola. But a better sign of their psychology
is no doubt to be found in their superstitions. The Saxon miner
earned his living in a darkness filled with the uncanny noises of
settling rock, timber groaning under shifting loads, water dripping
and swirling down the drain, the flickering light from his lamp bringing forth blood-chilling spectres. Did his imagination conjure forth a
parade of evil spirits intent upon his destruction?

Indeed it did not. In his lonely labour at the vein the Saxon miner
was in good company. Behind him were his friends, the goblins or
Kobold as he called the knee-high creatures dressed like himself and
always busy; but although they pretended to work and mimed everything he did they never accomplished anything. At times they
annoyed him because they would not leave his tools alone. The carefully arranged set of tools was always in disarray at the end of the
shift. Yet an experienced man had learned to keep an eye open for
their meddling, because if the tools strayed in certain ways it was time
to get out fast. That was a sure sign that the roof was about to
come down.

It was a Golden Age of mining, pleasant to contemplate. But it
did not last long. When Agricola wrote his book Luther had nailed
his thesis on the door of the church in Wittenberg, Zwingli and
Calvin had put the match to the powder barrel that set off the
religious wars. Agricola himself became a victim and upon his death

the intolerant Protestants of his own town refused him a decent burial.

Although Saxon miners were invited to open up new mines and invigorate old ones with their superior knowledge, they were too few to influence the legal, social and moral conditions in the remote communities where they settled. With few exceptions they were soon submerged by local customs—or the lack of them—official attitudes, brutality and meanness. The pendulum swung back towards the Egyptian way of mining: prisoners and captives of war were thrown, in chains, to labour in the King's mines. By the time the pendulum swung back again, after nearly 400 years, it had swept over all the human miseries that the quest of mineral wealth inevitably seems to bring when pursued by the wrong people.

Chapter 3

THE QUEST FOR WATER

'He cutteth out rivers among the rocks; he bindeth the floods from overflowing.'

'BY ASSUR, my Great God, I swear that with these few men I dug the canal, and in a year and three months I finished it.'

If justified, this boast of Sennacherib, son of Sargon II and King of Assyria, engraved in the rock of a river gorge near Bavian, where the canal began, can be accepted as an all-time record of construction. The canal referred to was 49·6 miles long, extending from a tributary of the Greater Zab River to Nineveh. The canal that conducted drinking-water to the Assyrian capital was 65 ft. wide and the bottom was laid with a pavement of limestone blocks measuring 25 × 17 × 17 in. Some two million such blocks were quarried in the hills and transported along the bed on wheels or rollers. In spite of the hurried work the bed was carefully laid and waterproofed. On a one-inch bed of bitumen a 16-in. layer of concrete (made of one part lime, two parts sand and four parts limestone aggregate) was poured, on which the blocks were laid with a gradient of 1:80. At the beginning of the canal a dam provided with sluice gates was built to store and regulate the water supply.

What Sennacherib meant by 'these few men' has not been discovered, but they must have run into tens of thousands to accomplish this mighty work in 450 days. Not only did they excavate the canal, quarry and transport two million blocks of stone, and pour some

24·4 million cu. ft. of concrete, but they also built an impressive stone aqueduct at Jerwan where the canal crossed a valley. This piece of construction was 900 ft. long, 70 ft. wide and 23 ft. high.

Of this mighty fresh-water canal not a trace was seen until 1932 when in the neighbourhood of the former Jerwan in Iraq an archaeologist found an old man sitting on a stone bearing an Assyrian inscription that was deciphered as 'bridge'. Subsequent excavations uncovered the aqueduct and the canal.

Fig 19. Sewer tunnel under the Palace
of Nimroud in Nineveh.

The Nineveh Canal had no need for tunnels. But in the extensive network of irrigation and fresh-water canals that criss-crossed the Fertile Crescent and Egypt there were many instances where the topography forced the engineers to go underground and conduct water by tunnel. As a matter of fact, for reasons that will be dealt with in detail below, drinking water was usually conducted through tunnels leading from the springs into the towns.

In Egypt the work of canal-building went on century after century, dynasty after dynasty. The provincial governors of the Old Kingdom had the title 'Diggers of Canals' because their chief duty was the administration of the extensive hydraulic system in their areas. The national water administration sat in the Labyrinth, the Pentagon of Egypt, situated on Lake Moeris. It was a huge building, containing some 3,000 rooms, erected during the reign of Amenemhet III (*c.* 1850 B.C.) south of Memphis on the west bank of the Nile. Herodotus and Diodorus Siculus visited the place and were suitably impressed by what they saw. The lake was an immense catchment basin with a 400-mile shoreline and 50 (?) fathoms deep. 'Now this lake is clearly artificial,' writes Herodotus, 'for nearly in the middle of it rise two pyramids which stand 300 ft. above the water, and there must be an equal depth below the surface, and each pyramid is surmounted by a stone carving of a man sitting on a throne.' Lake Moeris was connected to the Nile by a supply canal 80 stades (5,054 ft.) long and 300 ft. wide. Of the 3,000 rooms in the Labyrinth about half were underground, excavated out of the rock, connected by a honeycomb of galleries. There were twelve large courtyards and innumerable small ones. Herodotus was shown some of the rooms above ground and made a note of the immense slabs of gleaming white marble with which the walls were faced. He also states that from the lake extended a long water tunnel to Syrtis in Libya. Needless to say no trace has been found of this tunnel.

Underground Quarries

Except for the legendary Moeris tunnel, there has been no mention of water tunnels in Egypt and none has been found. But the cliffs along both sides of the Nile valley and the escarpments surrounding the Delta abound with tunnels excavated in the rock to reach the best beds for building-stone. The Egyptian quarry tunnels offer an excellent means of studying the ancient ways of hard-rock excavation and warrant for this reason a brief diversion from the quest of water. Needless to say, similar tools and methods would have been applied also to water tunnels had there been a need for them. The methods and tools used depended on the nature of the rock prevailing in the different parts of the country. Nearly everywhere there was limestone and sandstone of varying grades, all quarried underground. Hard granite was obtained at Aswan and Wadi Hammamat, alabaster at Hat-Nub, near El-Amarna, and basalt, one of the hardest rocks, at Fayum.

The common method employed in advancing a quarry tunnel was to cut a deep recess, with enough headroom for a man to work in it, in the crown of the tunnel and then sink a trench along both sides. It was a method of tunnelling that much later became known as the Centre Core Method. The bench outlined in this fashion was then removed by cutting a four-inch groove across the top at a distance from the face equivalent to the required thickness of the slab. By placing wedges in the groove, the slab was sliced loose from the rock bench. In soft rock, wooden wedges were used which after having been driven into place were soaked with water. When the wood swelled, the wedges exerted enough pressure on the rock to break loose the slab. There were no doubt times when as a further aid in removing the slab, wedges had also to be placed along the sides and bottom.

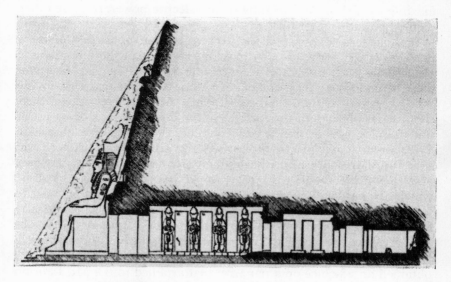

Fig 20. Longitudinal section of Abu Simbel as it appeared to a contemporary artist when it was freed of its protecting coat of sand a century ago. This famous monument to pharaonic megalomania was chiselled out of the sandstone on the west shore of the Nile 30 miles north of the second cataract.

Tunnelling in hard rock, such as granite and basalt, cannot be done in this fashion. The modern conventional way of splitting so-called dimensional stone from the mother rock is to drill up a line of shallow holes and then place steel wedges lined with 'feathers', i.e. thin wrought-iron strips, in the holes. With all wedges in place the mason taps lightly with a hammer on each wedge in succession, and after a while the rock cleaves, leaving a straight and smooth surface. By knowing from long experience how a rock behaves, a quarry worker can break out a large quantity of dimensional stone in a day. Obviously, some such method was employed also by the Egyptians when excavating building stone in hard rock. Fire-setting, the ancient method of fracturing rock, was out of the question owing to the lack of fuel and, more to the point, it would destroy the desirable properties of the building stone.

The methods used in quarrying the pink and grey Aswan granites have been something of a mystery, which has left the door open to numerous fanciful speculations about lost arts and techniques. It has been suggested, for example, that the Egyptians knew how to harden and temper copper, that the work was done by milling and grinding machines which were driven by steam, electric power, or some other method now long forgotten.

It is here suggested that the excavation and quarrying of these hard rocks did not entail any more mysteries than those familiar to skilled hard-rock masons of recent generations. Given the Egyptian tools of 2000 B.C., they could have tunnelled and quarried in the Aswan granite without difficulty. They would have drilled their usual series of holes in the rock using the Egyptian type of bow drill and tubular copper and bronze bits aided by available abrasives. They would have placed bronze wedges with copper feathers and split the slabs loose from the mother rock in the manner outlined above. For the rough work they would have used dolerite balls—which are harder than granite—either held in the hand or fixed to a wooden beam and used as rammers. Naturally, they would also have made use of chisels, although the major output would be obtained by wedging. By trenching and undercutting and by taking advantage of any fissures presenting themselves they would have obtained an advance on a par with that attained in the Mt. Laurion mines.

The methods briefly suggested would apply to the quarrying of building-stone underground. For crude tunnelling, however, a much simpler excavation method would be applied. There is no record of this method having been used, but it is so obvious to a man skilled in hard-rock work that it inevitably would have been employed. Confronted with a solid rock face presenting no cracks or fissures, i.e. no weak points of attack, there is no other method than to cut a roughly conical hole in the centre of the face. Today, this 'cut'—wide on the surface and sloping inwards—is obtained by drilling a number of obliquely set holes and charging them with explosives. Having blasted out this cone-shaped cut in the centre of the face, the surrounding rock is blown into the free space left by the cut. But such a cut could be made by using tubular drills and abrasives and chiselling out the rock enclosed by the circle of holes. Or it could be chiselled out without the use of holes, or ground out by banging a diorite ball against the face. If the ball was mounted as a head of a wooden rammer suspended in a leather thong or rope attached to a beam wedged to the tunnel side, a simple enough invention, the work of pulverizing the rock would be faster and less fatiguing to the poor wretches working for the Egyptian state building monopoly. Having obtained the cut there would be no trouble wedging out the remainder of the rock face. By the time the face had been removed to the bottom of the cut the cycle would begin all over again.

There is no need to squander power. Given time and human skill in adequate supply, anything can be accomplished, including tunnelling through the hardest of rock.

Water Tunnels

There are two major reasons for conducting water through tunnels. One is topographical: the sources of good drinking water are usually found in the mountains where the water has not yet been adulterated by silt or impurities, whereas the places of the major consumption of drinking water are situated in the plains. Occasionally, it is possible to build an open canal, like the one supplying water to Nineveh, or a surface aqueduct connecting the source of supply with the place of consumption. However, there is an important point to consider when arranging for gravity transport of water. From the springs to the distant city the channel must slope, the conduit must be given a certain gradient, not too slight because then the water is liable to stagnate and become unhealthy or be lost altogether by evaporation. But the slope cannot be made too steep, because then the rushing water will erode and destroy the trough carrying it. There exist, therefore, certain limits of gradient to which a water conduit must be built. If there were hills intervening between the source and the termination, the ancient engineers had no other alternative than to tunnel through the obstacle and continue in open trough downstream from the hill. Most water tunnels derive from such technical necessities due to the topography of the country.

The other major reason for putting a water conduit underground is strategic. This applies with particular emphasis to the settlements in ancient Palestine, which were placed on a hill for security, near to a source of water. The town site would be enclosed by a wall, whereas the spring, emerging at the foot of the hill, would be outside the fortifications. The customary procedure was therefore to cut a stepped subterranean passage from the citadel to the spring outside the wall. Subsequently, the reverse practice came into vogue: the water was conducted by tunnel from the spring into the citadel. The technical consequence of this solution was that a deep shaft had to be sunk from the top of the hill down to the grade of the tunnel, with a stepped descent permitting the inhabitants to fill their water vessels.

One of the best-preserved examples of this type of strategic water tunnel is the one that supplied the citadel of Mycenae from the spring of Perseia, but in many of the ancient cities of Canaan the inhabitants likewise had to descend deep into the ground to satisfy the daily requirements of water.

But there was also a third reason for the ancients to go underground with their water conduits, and that was evaporation. Of the tunnels excavated for the purpose of water conduction the majority were so-called *qanaats* which are still found in great abundance in Persia, northern Syria and North Africa, having been extensively used throughout the entire ancient world.

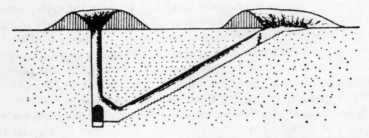

Fig 21. Section of a *qanaat* seen in the direction of the tunnel axis and at the junction of a stepped inspection adit, also used for drawing water. The mounds of excavation debris around the shafts mark the route of the water tunnel on the desert floor.

A *qanaat* is a sloping tunnel of modest capacity which is usually advanced from the water-bearing gravels of a hillside to a settlement in the valley some distance away. In the floor of the tunnel is a trough conducting water at the rate of a few gallons per second. Considering the tremendous labour invested in a *qanaat*, this trickle seems a wholly inadequate return. But when the very life of the communities depends on getting unpolluted water and preventing the modest supply from vanishing under the cruel sun, there is no point in weighing the cost.

A *qanaat* may have a length of 7½ miles—like the one supplying Aleppo in Syria—and be excavated to a gentle grade some 300 ft. below the surface of the ground. It is provided with vertical shafts every 50 yds., originally used for hoisting the excavated material up to the ground but also serving as ventilation chimneys. For this reason a *qanaat* can be followed across the desert by the muck-heaps around the shafts. At certain intervals the tunnel has a stepped oblique shaft used for inspection as well as for the removal of silt and drawing of water. If the village or town at the end of the tunnel is situated in the plain, the *qanaat* terminates in a deep well.

This type of water-conducting tunnel is closely related to the mining tunnel pioneered by Armenian miners. From Armenia as a centre the aqueduct version spread in all directions, originally by the use of free Armenian miners. Later, during the Persian hegemony, the *qanaat*-builders became a privileged caste which in the reign of Darius (521–485 B.C.) built a number of such tunnels in Egypt, the Kharga oasis and across the Sahara to southern Morocco. In northern India there was a special administration for the construction and maintenance of the numerous *qanaat* aqueducts.

Fig 22. Stone tablet in cursive Hebraic commemorating the breakthrough in the Siloam tunnel some time around 700 B.C.

Of the strategic aqueducts, the one constructed by Hezekiah, King of Judah (*c.* 715–687 B.C.) is perhaps better known than others and for two reasons: first for the troubles experienced by his engineers, and secondly for the inscription commemorating the holing through, which is regarded as the oldest known cursive written in the Phoenician alphabet. The Siloam tunnel, as it is called, brings water from the so-called Virgin's Spring in the Ophel hill to the Pool of Siloam inside the old fortified Jerusalem. The tunnel was excavated in the face of a pending siege by an Assyrian army and appears to have been completed about 700 B.C. Although the straight line distance from the spring to the pool is only 366 yds. the engineers ran into many obstacles which forced them to angle a number of times, whereby the actual length of the tunnel increased to 583 yds. They had no facilities for measuring and recording such deviations, and the two teams burrowing to meet each other got lost several times and had to drive vertical shafts to the surface to see where they were in relation to each other.

Before leaving the ancient empires in the Fertile Crescent one has reason to wonder what became of the tremendous number of irrigation canals, aqueducts and tunnels of antiquity. What happened, for instance, to the Red Sea Canal, described by Herodotus as having been started by the Assyrian vassal Necho and completed by King Darius of Persia?

Of course, most of the canals, including the present Suez Canal, were dug in sand and needed continuous maintenance to prevent them from silting up. By the time of Antony and Cleopatra, who were in such sad need of it, the Red Sea Canal had completely vanished in the sand. When the Arabs followed the Romans they, contrary to the common conception, not only kept the existing canals in good order, but the Abbasid caliphs in Baghdad continually added to the ancient net of irrigation canals. Then in 1258 a Mongol army commanded by Hulagu, brother of Kublai Khan, burned Baghdad to the ground and scourged the land in a thorough fashion. Hulagu's horsemen rode along the soft canal banks; the banks crumbled, and a few centuries later nothing remained of the hydraulic civilization begun some 3,000 years earlier.

Greek Conduits

From earliest times the Greeks were aware of the intimate relation between good water and good health, individual and public, and their settlements and cities were supplied with clear mountain water conducted over long distances. At first they adopted the *qanaat*, and the first conduit supplying Athens with water from Mt. Pentelicus was of this type. Later, they relied on pipelines provided with siphons to bring water across intervening hills, thereby avoiding tunnelling and the long tortuous loops needed to maintain the gradients of gravity-flow ducts. Although sophisticated from a technical point of view, the siphon lines caused a great deal of trouble since suitable materials were lacking to keep the lines tight under the heavy pressures acting on the pipe joints at the low points in the valleys.

But many of the water supply systems in the Greek homeland, as well as in the city states from Sicily to Asia, incorporated tunnels. One of the better known of the water tunnels is the one excavated on the island of Samos in the sixth century B.C. Herodotus regarded the Samos tunnel as one of the three greatest engineering feats in the

Greek world.[1] He also gives the name of the engineer—Eupalinus of Megara. The Samos tunnel is of an altogether different character from a *qanaat*. The tunnel forms the subterranean part of a water conduit which ran in the open until it encountered a 900-ft. hill. To overcome this obstacle Eupalinus drove a tunnel through the base for a distance of over 3,000 ft. The lined tunnel has a sectional area of about 19 sq. ft. Water was conducted through a line of clay

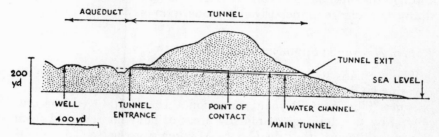

Fig 23. Longitudinal section of the 1,000-metre-long water tunnel on the island of Samos, built in the sixth century B.C. by Eupalinis of Megara, the earliest engineer known by name in the ancient world.

pipes laid in a trench in the floor and then backfilled except for inspection pits at intervals. According to available information the trench at the upstream portal was dug to a depth of 8 ft., whereas the downstream end was not less than 28 ft. below the floor. This means a gradient of 1 : 166, which seems rather foolish, but then there were many foolish things done when driving this tunnel, so greatly admired by Herodotus: for one thing, a serious error was committed in advancing the tunnel, and it would seem that a Greek geometrician should have known better. The tunnel was advanced from both ends and although it ran in a straight line through the hill the two teams managed to miss each other by not less than 16 ft., an error of 0·5 per cent. The surveying devices available to Eupalinus should have produced a much more accurate result.

From prehistoric Greece are handed down the remains of one of the most impressive drainage feats achieved in ancient times, that of the 140-sq. mile Copais Lake situated in a mountain-girt basin in Boeotia. This lake, formed by the streams from the Parnassus and Helicon Mountains, was drained by the Minyae, at a time when

[1] The other two were also on Samos, namely its breakwater, extending for a distance of 1¼ miles and forming an artificial harbour, and its temple, the largest one built by the Greeks.

Mycenae was in full flower, by means of an intricate system of trenches and canals leading to natural crevices and tunnels cut through the hills. In historic times when, for various reasons such as earthquakes and landslides, the tunnels were choked up, the basin turned into a lake in winter and an unhealthy reedy marsh in summer. Alexander set his engineer Crates to drain the lake anew and numerous shafts were sunk preliminary to driving drainage tunnels through the hills, but the work was never completed. The area is now drained by a large tunnel driven in modern times.

Roman Hydraulic Engineering

The Romans were more active in draining marshy land, or recovering land from the bottom of lakes, than any other people before or since. The early Roman expansion through Italy was accompanied by the drainage of marshy areas of land far removed from Rome. In the city itself the Cloaca Maxima was dug by Tarquinius Superbus, seventh king of Rome, as a drainage canal, although later it came to serve as a sewer.

Another of these early drainage canals still remaining is the one dug by the Consul Manius Curius Dentatus (*c.* 280 B.C.) through the marshes at Rieti, the Sabine capital. The 2,624-ft.-long canal was partly cut in rock and was deliberately led to a sheer precipice where the waters threw themselves in an impressive waterfall into the river Nera. Attempts were subsequently made to drain the Pontine marshes, south of Rome, although better results were obtained in the north, in the Po valley around Bologna, Piacenza, and Cremona. The Adige was canalized between Ferrara and Padua. Ravenna was also turned into a habitable place. Many of these drainage projects made use of tunnels. Lake Albanus was drained by a 6,000-ft. (1,500 paces) tunnel 5 ft. wide and 8 ft. high, driven through hard lava. Fifty shafts were sunk to grade and the tunnel was finished in one year.

However, historically the best-known and most interesting of the Roman drainage schemes is no doubt Lake Fucinus Emissarium, started in A.D. 41 in the reign of Emperor Claudius, as a speculative venture to reclaim land around the lake (now called Celano). The project was an old one that had been turned down by Augustus as being impractical, since it involved connecting the lake with a 3½-mile tunnel emptying into the River Liris.

The Fucinus Emissarium was driven from a large number of vertical and sloping shafts called *putei*, spaced one actus (120 ft.) apart, and some of them 400 ft. deep. According to Livy the dimensions of the tunnel were 9 × 19 ft. When parts of the tunnel were cleared in the latter half of the nineteenth century, an eye-witness estimated the height as 20 ft. and the width sufficient for two carts to pass. Where the tunnel was driven through solid rock it was unlined, elsewhere the crown was lined with ashlar.

Some 30,000 men and thousands of horses laboured in the Fucinus tunnel for ten years, excavating nearly ½ million cu. ft. of rock which was hoisted to the surface in copper buckets by windlasses placed across the shafts.

Upon the completion of the tunnel in A.D. 51, Claudius arranged an opening celebration befitting such a major feat of engineering. A gigantic sham naval battle was held on the lake preliminary to draining it, and about 19,000 prisoners are said to have taken part. The 30-mile shoreline was patrolled by detachments of the Praetorian Guard to prevent any of the participants from escaping. The sham battle went off according to plan, whereupon the Emperor gave the signal to open the sluices to the tunnel. But then something went wrong; not a drop of water entered the tunnel and the Emperor and his party returned to Rome in fury over the failure. However, Narcissus, the chief engineer, was given the chance to redeem himself. Another year was spent in deepening and correcting the grade of the long tunnel, and another opening party was laid on. At the downstream end of the tunnel tables were set for a magnificent banquet, with guests from all parts of the Empire. After a gladiatorial combat the Emperor again gave the signal to open the gates up at the lake. This time everything worked all too well. The water came roaring out of the downstream portal with such force that it flooded the tailrace canal and swept the banquet tables with it. The Empress Agrippina screamed at Narcissus, accusing him of graft and everything else she could think of, and the furious engineer retorted with some ill-chosen comments on her personality and wayward life in general.[2]

The waters subsided and thus ended the largest single tunnelling development carried through in Roman times. The successful draining of the lake added 50,000 acres of farmland to the imperial estates.

Claudius's successor Nero, not to be outdone, also threw himself into gigantic hydraulic projects, although nothing came of them. He began a canal through the Isthmus of Corinth but abandoned it after half a mile had been dug, apparently owing to bad auguries. Another of his pet projects was an inland canal from Naples to Ostia, which no doubt was more practical as, if realized, it would have meant much to the Roman economy, improving the supply situation and reducing the price of grain kept high by the cost of land transport.

[2] Suetonius.

Inexplicably, the Romans never invented a harness suitable for draught horses, neither did they shoe their horses. For harness they simply used the type applied to oxen, which choked a horse when pulling hard; thus they never got the full use of their horses which, instead of pulling twenty times more than a man, pulled only four times more.

From this poor ratio derived two consequences: since the food consumed by a horse is four times that eaten by a slave it paid to keep four slaves instead of one horse, which explains the extensive use of slave labour in Roman farming; and because of the inefficient road transport due to the faulty harnessing, the cost of wheat increased by 100 per cent for each 100 miles carried. For this reason farmers in the Italian homeland raised fodder grain and drove their fatted cattle and pigs to market, whereas wheat was imported from North Africa and Egypt. These grain cargoes were landed at the exposed port of Ostia, instead of the sheltered port of Pozzuoli, in the Bay of Naples, simply to avoid the long and costly road transport to the capital.

Nero's inland canal was thus one of the really sound ideas to emerge from his perverted mind. He put two of his best engineers, Severus and Celer, who had distinguished themselves in the rebuilding of Rome after the fire, to making the plans for the inland canal, and he decreed that all prisoners in the Empire should be shipped to Italy and put to work on it. Work did start on the canal but was abandoned on Nero's death in A.D. 68. Some 1,500 years later workers draining Lake Avernus, where the canal was to end according to the plan, came upon a tunnel—all that remained of this grandiose project. That tunnel marked the end of Roman canal-building, as indeed it was the end of Roman hydraulic construction in a wider sense.

Roman Aqueducts

Few major cities have been provided with a better water supply than Imperial Rome. It has been calculated from available information that about one million cubic metres (over 35 million cu. ft.) of water were brought to the city every twenty-four hours by means of eleven aqueducts, some of which united before entering the city. If the population of Rome in A.D. 100 is put at half a million, the consumption per head works out at 2,000 litres.[3]

[3] This is equivalent to about 500 gal. per head of population. There are small towns in England where the supply does not exceed 20 gal. Many industrial towns in the U.S. would be happy with a supply of 100 gal. per head per day.

There is a familiar modern ring to the boast of the incumbent *Curator Aquarum* in Rome at that time, Sextus Julius Frontinus, when he exclaims: 'With such an array of indispensable structures carrying so many waters compare if you will the idle pyramids or the useless, though famous works of the Greeks.'

All that has been written on the subject of the Roman aqueducts during the past 450 years derives from Frontinus' work *De Aquis Urbis Romae*, written during his term as Curator Aquarum from A.D. 97 to 104. The following brief account is typical.

According to Frontinus the Romans drew their waters from the Tiber, and from wells and springs until 441 years after the founding of the city (viz. 312 B.C.). That year the first aqueduct, built at public expense, was completed by the censor Appius Claudius Caecus, who had previously engineered the paving of the Appian Way from Porta Copena to Capua, east of Naples.

The intake of the Appian aqueduct was on the Lucullan estate, east of Rome, and ran entirely underground for 10·6 miles; only 290 ft. ran on structures above ground. Just outside the city it was joined by the Augustan aqueduct and continued, entirely by underground tunnel, for a further 5·9 miles to the foot of Clinus Publicii (close by the Gemelli). The Appia delivered about 700 quinariae[4] of water to seven wards inside the city. The area of the water duct inside the tunnel was 5 × 1·75 ft., or 8·75 sq. ft.

The next aqueduct, completed forty years later, was given the name Anio Vetus. It tapped springs up in the Sabine hills and had a length of 43,000 paces (41 miles), of which 42,799 paces consisted of tunnels. The cost of construction was financed by booty captured from Pyrrhus. The capacity was 1,600 quinariae and it served ten wards in the eastern part of the city.

These two aqueducts were adequate for 127 years, by which time they were badly in need of repair. A great deal of water had also been diverted by illegal taps. The praetor Marcius was therefore commissioned by the Senate to repair the existing ducts and build a new aqueduct if a suitable source could be found. He was voted 180,000,000 sesterces (say, $7.3 million in gold), said to derive from the booty taken at Corinth and Carthage.

The Marcian aqueduct tapped a deep green pool of water, also situated in the Sabine hills to the north-east of Subiaco. It had a total length of 58·4 miles, about seven-eighths consisting of tunnels of a varying area; at the upstream end the section was 8 ft. 2 in. × 5 ft. 7 in. The capacity of the Marcia was 3,000 quinariae and it

---

[4] Something like 4·2 million gal.

served ten wards to the west of the Palatine hill. With Marcia the water supply of the city was doubled.

A century later the Emperor Augustus repaired the existing aqueducts and constructed new ones, Julia, Augusta and Virgo. The work of building and maintaining the Roman water system was in 9 B.C. entrusted to a water board consisting of an Aqua Curator with consular rank and two technical members. The first incumbent was Marcus Vipsanius Agrippa, who put his own slaves to work on maintaining the structures. Upon his death he donated the trained slave force, consisting of 240 men, to the state.

Finally, the Emperor Caligula started construction in A.D. 38 of the two aqueducts which under the name of Claudia were completed by Claudius fourteen years later. Aqua Claudia had a length of 46,406 paces (44 miles) of which 36,230 consisted of tunnels and the remainder of surface structures. The water trough was 6 ft. 7 in. × 3 ft. 3 in. Claudia sprang from a source in the Sabine hills not far from that of Marcia, and of its total capacity of 5,625 quinariae 3,800 were distributed to all the fourteen wards of Rome.

The total cross-section of the ducts carrying water to Rome has been estimated at 80·7 sq. ft., and their total length at 217 miles, of which only 29 miles consisted of surface structures. The entire system, from the springs to the consumer was based on gravity flow. From the source the water was conducted to a settling tank with two compartments. The clean water then entered the underground conduit, which frequently ran 50 ft. below the surface and had a cross-section varying from 5·4 to 32·3 sq. ft., depending on the capacity of the duct. The water trough consisted of a 16·5-in. masonry structure which was lined and was also waterproofed with 'opus signimum'— ground pottery shards mixed with lime mortar. In tufa and stone no masonry was used, but in soft ground the entire tunnel, including the trough in the bottom, was lined with masonry.

The slope or gradient of the aqueducts varied, from 1:200 to 1:1000. They entered the city at different elevations and four of them—Anio Novus, Claudia, Julia and Tepula—terminated high enough to deliver water to the highest points of the city. The old aqueducts, owing to a combination of faulty levelling and the gradual rise of the hills due to the rubble left by frequent fires, were able to serve only the low-lying wards.

Outside the city were covered catch basins which also served as settling tanks, from which the water was conducted into the city and distributed to a number of service tanks. The Appia had twenty such service tanks and Anio Vetus ninety-two. The total for the city was 247. During Frontinus' incumbency he had all tanks connected with pipes so that in case of a shutdown of one aqueduct the wards served by it could be supplied from another source. In these service reservoirs were placed a number of outlets of definite *ajutage*, or size. At the bottom were three outlets for water used in public buildings, baths and fountains. Since the system was based on continuous consumption the reservoirs occasionally flowed over, and this overflow was free to anybody who could use it. The surplus was employed in flushing sewers and also drove water wheels. But the mains were of course tapped illegally by secret pipes with the aid of the public watermen, a racket that Frontinus tried to suppress.

The water engineer in charge of each reservoir charged consumers according to the *ajutage* of the delivery pipes. At the time of Frontinus the Roman architect Vitruvius had devised a modular system of standardizing pipe on the basis of the quinarium, i.e. a pipe formed by a strip of lead 5 digits (3·5 in.) wide. By applying this module a series of twenty-five pipe sizes, rising from one to 120 quinariae, was made available.[5]

Administration of the Roman Water Laws

In view of the critical situation confronting many western countries in matters of water supply, with the large-scale pollution of streams and water sources, including the poisoning of the ground water, it is tempting to devote some concluding remarks to the legal aspects of the Roman water supply system.

Before Augustus, the Roman system was administered by annually elected *aediles*, or magistrates, but in 9 B.C. the Emperor established a permanent administrative tribunal consisting of a Curator Aquarum with consular rank and two technical members. The water tribunal employed a staff of engineers, architects and inspectors. The first Curator was Marcus Agrippa, who trained 240 of his slaves to the various skills required for building and maintaining the works. Later, during the reign of Claudius, a further 460 men were turned over to the tribunal. The imperial work force was apparently also made up of slaves.

The distinction between the two labour forces was maintained up to the term of the seventh curator, or Frontinus. Both the municipal

---

[5] The quinarium was not a measure of volume but of capacity. It indicated how much water would flow through a pipe of a certain size, assuming constant pressure. This pressure naturally varied with the head, and the actual volume delivered therefore remains unknown. It has been estimated, however, that a one-quinarium pipe would deliver on the average about 5,000 gal. per twenty-four hours.

and the imperial labour forces consisted of specialists, such as reservoir keepers, inspectors, pavers, plasterers, plumbers, and so on. Before Frontinus' term, gangs of these workers were frequently employed on private work, a practice to which he put a stop. Work orders were issued to each gang, and the foreman had to report each day on the work accomplished. The municipal payroll was at that time about 250,000 sestertii a year (something like $6,000 in gold) whereas the imperial crews were paid out of the Emperor's privy purse.

The repairs carried out on the aqueducts by the municipal and imperial water crews arose, according to Frontinus,[6] from three major causes: (1) damage to the surface structures due to storms; (2) age; and (3) illegal building too close to the structures, and secret taps. Most of the work consisted of keeping the channels free from deposits, and repairing leaks. No channel work was done in summer since this necessitated taking a duct out of service when the need for water was at its height. Masonry work on the tall structures was done between 1st April and 1st November, except for the hottest days in summer. Leaks were temporarily stopped by placing a lead lining over the leaking section.

Some of the work was performed by contractors who at times had trouble getting access to the properties over which the aqueducts crossed. Difficulties were also encountered in obtaining from the local landlords the materials needed for carrying out the repairs. Eventually these difficulties were overcome by bills framed by the water tribunals and enacted by the Senate in the manner of the following law: 'RESOLVED: That when those canals, conduits, and arches which Augustus Caesar promised the Senate to repair at his own cost, shall be repaired, the earth, clay, stone, sand, wood, etc. which are necessary for the work in hand, shall be granted, removed, taken, and brought from the lands of private parties, their value appraised by some honest man, and each of these to be taken from whatever source it may most conveniently and, without injury to private parties, be removed, taken, and brought; and that thoroughfares and roads through the lands of private parties shall, without injury to them, remain open and their use permitted, as often as it is necessary for the transportation of all these things for repairing these works.'[7]

This enactment should bring a grim smile of recollection to numerous engineers who have been frustrated by rugged individuals insisting on their hallowed property rights and on doing as they

---

[6] Frontinus: *De Aquae ductu,* trans. Charles Bennet, London (1925).
[7] Ibid.

pleased with their own plot of land, including shutting the gates to crews and supplies and sitting down with a shotgun across their knees challenging all comers.

Another problem that haunted the Roman water tribunal was also one that seems to live eternal, and which in the end also required a Senate Act to cope with it. From the time of the construction of the early aqueducts it had been the practice to buy outright from the property owners, as a right-of-way, the strip of land required to advance a tunnel or build the surface structures. When met with refusal it was customary to buy the entire field that was to be crossed by the aqueduct, and having surveyed and deeded the strip the remainder was sold back to the original owner or to somebody else. The City of Rome held full title to a strip consisting of 15 ft. to each side of the centre line of the conduit.

What inevitably happened was of course that the owners of the land on both sides of the strip infringed on the right-of-way. Buildings and roads were constructed on it but, more serious, trees were planted or allowed to grow on or close to the strip and the roots pierced the lining of the tunnels causing it to collapse or blocking the water flow. Frontinus wrote the Bill designed to put an end to this and it was enacted by the Senate: 'That since, for the purpose of repairing the channels and tunnels obstructions must be removed by which public structures are damaged, it is decreed that there shall be kept clear a space of fifteen feet on each side of springs, arches, and walls; and that about the subterranean conduits and channels, inside the City, and buildings adjoining the City, there shall be left a vacant space of five feet on each side . . . Whoever shall contravene these provisions shall pay the penalty of 10,000 sestertii' ($415 gold).

This was followed by another enactment stipulating a fine of 100,000 sestertii($4,150gold) for 'maliciously and intentionally piercing, or breaking the conduits, pipes, reservoirs and basins of the public waters . . . with the intent of preventing them being conducted into the City of Rome.'[8]

The organization of the Roman water supply was complete, and like all ripe organizations there was nothing ahead of it but decay. When the keystone of the legal structure was being laid down there was already a flicker of barbarian camp fires on the horizon. With the rising political unrest it became increasingly difficult to maintain the water structures, and when Alaric the Visigoth sacked Rome in A.D. 412 there was no need for him to damage the surface works: the ducts were by that time clogged with silt. The centre of the world

[8] Frontinus.

entered a long period of decline. Finally, in the Middle Ages, the population of Rome was reduced to about 25,000 malaria-ridden wretches huddled around the strongholds of rude, illiterate barons. The Roman waterways and conduits had by that time vanished completely, or were ruins from which building-stone was quarried.

Early European Canals

A horse can carry 275 lb. on its back and, if provided with a suitable harness, can pull a load of 2 tons over a good road. But make a horse pull a barge on a river and he is capable of pulling 30 tons; on the unruffled water of a canal the same horse can pull 50 tons. In these figures lies the explanation of the canal-building that went on in all parts of Europe, from the end of the Middle Ages until the explosion of the 'canal-building craze' shortly before the beginning of the railway age in 1830, which in turn degenerated into the 'railway craze' some ten years later.

Since canals are inland transport arteries, it follows that there should be a large volume of goods to be moved in order to warrant the heavy investments required for canal construction. Such a volume can only be supplied by established industry and trade, which took a long time to develop in Europe after the collapse of the ancient civilizations. The history of Europe's early canals is therefore the history of Europe's early industrial and trading areas. In Flanders, Italy, Germany and France some rivers were cleared of obstacles to navigation—during the twelfth century in Flanders and Italy. Lübeck, headquarters of the Hanseatic League, was connected by a 40-mile waterway, including a 7-mile summit canal provided with navigation weirs, to Lauenburg on the Elbe in 1398.

By that time canal-building had become routine with the Milanese. After Frederick Barbarossa had laid waste their city in 1167, they enclosed the rebuilt Milan with a moat for security. Some ten years later they built a 30-mile irrigation canal from the River Ticino to a basin just outside the city. In 1269 this early canal was widened to 200 ft., but since the waterway dropped 110 ft. from one end to the other it had to be provided with numerous navigation weirs. When completed this became the famous Naviglio Grande, the greatest work of construction carried out in Italy since the days of the Romans.

When work began on Milan cathedral towards the end of the following century the Naviglio Grande was linked with the moat to permit barges loaded with building materials to be brought to the building site. This presented an awkward problem of hydraulics, since the water level of the moat was several feet above that of the canal. At first the canal was provided with a simple portcullis gate that could be raised by pulleys. When the gate was raised there was a rush of water into the canal which continued until the water levels were equalized. The waiting barges then passed into the moat, but could not move because of the shallow water. Before they could proceed they had to wait until the moat was filled up again. In 1438 this difficulty was overcome by the building of a second gate in the link canal. This was the first pound-lock constructed in Europe.[9] The engineers were Filippo from Modena and Fioravante from Bologna.

During the remainder of the century, canal construction in Lombardy proceeded at a rapid pace under the direction of the ducal engineer Bertola da Novate, who provided his canals with double gates of the portcullis type, and whose death in 1475 deprived Milan and Europe of the greatest canal builder of the time.

Six years later, in 1481, Ludovico Sforza, Duke of Milan, received one of the most outrageous letters of application ever penned. The writer asserted that there did not exist a single problem in the arts and sciences that he had not mastered. He could construct all manner of bridges, fortresses, engines of destruction, tunnels, mines, counter-mines, field pieces, mortars and machines for throwing fire. He also knew how to construct an enclosed wagon, secure and indestructible, which would enter with its pieces among the enemy and confound the largest body of men, with infantry following unharmed and without opposition. The writer remarked in passing that he could sculpt too—in bronze, terracotta and marble. He was also beyond question the greatest painter alive. If, contrary to expectation, His Ducal Highness was in no immediate need of the services mentioned, the writer hastened to add that he also knew how to conduct water from one place to another in canals. It is tempting to speculate on what reception such a letter of application would receive today, whether it would find its way immediately into the waste-paper basket, or be circulated around the office for a snigger. Duke Ludovico merely summoned the writer to Milan and gave him the job of *ingegnere ducale*. Thus, to his other distinctions the Duke can add the credit of having employed the most brilliant man of the age—Leonardo da Vinci.

We are not here concerned with the wider aspects of Leonardo's life and work. Suffice it to say that he became increasingly occupied with the upkeep and extension of the canal system in Lombardy.

[9] A similar pound-lock was constructed in A.D. 984 by Chinese engineers to permit navigation in the Grand Canal linking the Yellow River with the Yangtze. Here the gates were placed 250 ft. apart.

The so-called Naviglio Interno, that is, the moat around Milan, left much to be desired as an efficient waterway owing to the unequal flow of water; to remedy this Leonardo constructed a series of new locks, of which the one at San Marco, just below the basin of the canal which brought water to the moat, made history. San Marco was a rectangular masonry lock 95 ft. long and 18 ft. wide, that Leonardo provided with the so-called mitre gates. Each gate folded back into a recess of the masonry work. In the bottom half of each gate was a small sluice door, occupying about one-sixth of the total area of the gate, to control the flow of water. This small door could be opened by a simple latch tripped by a wire leading to the canal bank.

Leonardo has fascinated later generations with his wealth of scientific, or at any rate technical ideas, from anatomy, to physics, to gunnery, to the flight of birds. He designed numerous canal projects, including one involving driving a one-mile tunnel through a hill separating two river valleys. Nothing came of these fanciful technical speculations, simply because nothing could come of them. They were all science fiction. But his invention and actual construction of the mitre type of lock gate is enough to set Leonardo apart from the common run of engineers. The San Marco lock opened up new vistas for canal-building and the efficient time-saving use of these increasingly important internal transport lanes.

The Languedoc Canal

A few years before he died Leonardo, now in the service of the French king, François I, became involved in an enterprise exceeding anything hitherto attempted in Lombardy. It was a project for an inland waterway from the Atlantic to the Mediterranean—a *canal des deux mers* connecting the rivers Garonne and Aude.

As usual nothing came of these plans. Leonardo died and so did his patron. Strangely enough, the Languedoc Canal, which had originally occupied the greatest genius of the time without even resulting in a rough survey, came to be realized by a tax collector turned amateur engineer in middle age. He covered the ground in great detail and constructed in his own backyard a model of a canal scheme which, with subsequent modifications, became the greatest civil engineering development carried out north of the Alps.

The name of the promoter, engineer and contractor of the 150-mile Languedoc Canal was Pierre-Paul Riquet, who was fifty-eight years old when in 1682 he submitted his first plans to Colbert, Louis XIV's Minister of Finance. The idea appealed to the minister and the king, who appointed a commission to look into the scheme in detail. The plans were approved, but some doubts were expressed about the possibility of supplying the 3-mile-long high-summit section with water. To prove the soundness of his scheme Riquet dug, at his own expense, a 27-mile canal, 20 ft. wide and 9 ft. deep, in an amazingly short time, from May to October 1665. The work of building the canal began late in 1666, and three years later 8,000 men were employed. It was declared open by Louis XIV in 1681 but much work still remained to be done and the canal was not finished until 1692.

The Languedoc Canal starts from the Garonne, at Toulouse, and rises 206 ft. over a distance of 32 miles to the summit. To overcome this difference in elevation thirty-two locks are required. After running for 3 miles along the summit, which involves feeding water into the canal to keep it navigable, it descends to the Mediterranean, a distance of 115 miles with a difference of elevation of 620 ft. taken up by seventy-four locks.

Some six miles upstream of the eight-lock stairway at Béziers, Riquet ran into trouble with the commission who ordered him to take another route. But Riquet had his own idea. He put the commission's order in his pocket, dispatched his diggers to another section, and with a small, select crew he surreptitiously drove a tunnel at Malpas. This tunnel is 515 ft. long, 22 ft. wide and 27 ft. high. It was not arched until many years later. This is the first canal tunnel ever built, and it appears to have been the first one in which gunpowder was used. There were to be many more of them later, particularly in Britain, but such an outrageous solution to a topographical obstruction had never been tried previously.

The Languedoc Canal was civil engineering on a grand scale, and by the time of its completion in 1692 hydraulic engineering had reached maturity. The enormous expansion of canal-building that was to take place throughout Europe and subsequently also in America in the ensuing centuries constitutes, in a technical sense, a continuation of this grandiose project.

English Canals

The Curator Aquarum in Rome, Julius Frontinus, who has already been mentioned, built a number of military canals while serving as governor of Britain in the reign of the Emperor Vespasian. One of them, the Fosse Dike, connecting the River Trent with Lincoln, has been used up to recent times.

Although some simple canals, or perhaps more accurately ditches, were dug in medieval and Elizabethan England for the purpose of conducting drinking-water to the towns,[10] canal-building in the accepted sense did not begin in England until around the middle of the eighteenth century. By the time of their greatest extension before the advent of the railway, there were some 12,000 miles of canals in Britain which, incidentally, proved a serious embarrassment to the railway builders: to cross the patchwork-quilt system of water lanes required something like 25,000 bridges.

There is a fundamental difference between the continental and English canals: whereas the former were promoted by rulers and financed by taxes, the English canals were dug and operated by privately financed canal companies, usually lacking adequate capital. Consequently, the canals were built as cheaply as possible, meandering their way along the contours of the country. They were later reduced in distance by accepting the cost of the deep open cuts needed for grade, but since a tunnel frequently proved cheaper than a cut, tunnels became a characteristic feature of the English canals. In time, the system came to include no less than 45 miles of canal tunnels.

The vast majority of these canal tunnels were low and narrow. They lacked a tow-path along the side and progress through a tunnel was accomplished by pulling the barge along with the help of chains fastened to the walls. In some tunnels, such as the famous Standedge, of which more below, the barges were 'legged' ahead. Two leggers took up positions on the foredeck of the barge, one on each side, and lying on their backs with their legs extended over the side they propelled the barge ahead in a zigzag course by alternately pushing their feet against the sides of the tunnel. In the 3-mile-long Standedge tunnel they were paid 1s. 6d. each for their eighty-minute labour of legging a barge through the tunnel. Empty barges were poled through the tunnels, by resting the poles in notches cut in the tunnel walls for the purpose. Later, however, the tunnels were enlarged to admit a tow-path on one or both sides or by placing timber stretchers over the water.

[10] 'Myddleton's Glory', the canal dug 1608–13 for the purpose of bringing sweet waters from Hertfordshire to London, is assuredly no ditch. The canal is 10 ft. wide and 4 ft. deep and runs for a distance of 40 miles from springs at Chadwell and Amwell to Clerkenwell north of London. The canal, known as the New River, was built and financed by Sir Hugh Myddleton, scion of a distinguished Tudor family, who expended his large fortune on the great enterprise, particularly on the 50 tons of lead needed to line the aqueducts at Enfield and Islington. The old Myddleton Canal, although culverted, still brings water to London. During the Blitz, at a time when three major water-mains were severed, the old filled-in loop at Enfield was excavated to bring sorely needed water for fire-fighting.

The roster of English canal builders includes many familiar names, such as Rennie, Outram, the Whitworths and Jessops, Telford and others. Here we will consider the delightful team of James Brindley and his patron the third Duke of Bridgewater, and their venturesome building of the Bridgewater Canal.

Among the Bridgewater properties were the collieries at Worsley, near Manchester, and the Duke's father had conceived the idea of digging a canal to facilitate the transport of coal to this city, booming under the impact of new ideas of manufacture and commerce. In 1759, the twenty-three-year-old Duke succeeded in obtaining an Act of Parliament authorizing the construction of a 10½-mile canal running from Worsley Mill to Manchester; this was amended the following year. The original scheme envisaged connecting with the river Irwell by a number of locks.

This was the situation when James Brindley entered into the service of the Duke. Brindley was the semi-literate son of a crofter in the High Peak in Derbyshire, and he was making a living as a wheelwright before he turned canal builder. He began by making an 'ochilor servey or a ricconitoring' of the proposed route and reached the conclusion that the locks had better be left out of the scheme altogether because, as he sensibly expressed it, 'water is a giant, therefore lay him down on his back'. Instead of locks he suggested a 200-yd.-long viaduct to be carried on arches where the canal crossed the valley. At both ends the canal was to end in a tunnel; at Worsley it would enter the collieries so that the barges could be loaded right in the mine. He proposed that at the Manchester end the canal should terminate underground beneath Castle Hill and be joined by a shaft sunk from the top of the hill.

In this manner the Bridgewater Canal came to be laid out on a gravity course and barges could be moved along it without losing time by lockage. Despite serious criticism the Duke went ahead with the Brindley plan which worked most satisfactorily. The canal was opened for traffic in 1761, but without Brindley being present; he preferred to hide in bed until notified that his daring scheme had proved successful. The tunnel into the mine was extended over a mile into the workings. By 1878 there were 40 miles of tunnels in the mine.

Brindley's Bridgewater Canal has been termed the beginning of the new age of industrialism. From having been a costly commodity in irregular supply, coal became available at half its former price. Owing to the Worsley Canal, Manchester was now assured of a practically unlimited supply of fuel at 3½d. per cwt., the lowest price anywhere in England.

On the successful completion of the Worsley Canal, Brindley was put on the Manchester–Liverpool Canal, also financed by the Duke and later known as the Duke of Bridgewater Canal. But this undertaking proved too expensive even for such a wealthy man, and the canal was never finished as planned. The abandonment of this scheme was partly due also to another major canal development, connecting the Trent with the Mersey, sponsored by Josiah Wedgwood. The so-called Grand Trunk Canal was projected by John Grundy in 1761 and built by Brindley. This was civil engineering on a grand scale, the greatest undertaking up to that time in Britain. The Grand Trunk Canal had a total length of 139·5 miles, including the junction with the Birmingham Canal and the River Severn.

Fig 24. The 'English System' of tunnelling used to advance the late canal and early railway tunnels. A description of the method is given in Chapter 5.

Starting from the Duke's Canal at Preston on the Hill, the Grand Trunk Canal passed the summit at Harecastle where Brindley drove a 2,280-yd. tunnel through the hill before the canal descended to the valley of the Trent. He had to drive four more tunnels before the canal was completed: Hermitage (130 yds.) Barnton (560 yds.), Saltersford (350 yds.) and Preston on the Hill (1,241 yds.). These four were 17 ft. 4 in. high and 13 ft. 6 in. wide, whereas the long Harecastle tunnel was only 12 ft. high and 9 ft. wide.[11] Owing to the tunnels the canal took eleven years to build, as against four as originally planned. The Harecastle tunnel delayed the opening for two

[11] Samuel Smiles: *James Brindley and the Early Engineers*. John Murray, London (1864).

years, and the canal was not completed until 1777. The tunnel was driven by miners who sank a number of deep shafts down to grade. At the bottom of each shaft the tunnel was driven in both directions. The tunnel appears to be the first one in England where gunpowder was used for the excavation.

Brindley encountered considerable trouble in advancing the Harecastle. He struck a number of springs which flooded the workings and drowned the men, and in the end a drainage heading had to be advanced to permit work in the main tunnel. Despite the numerous shafts, ventilation was poor and fires had to be lit under some of the shafts to improve the circulation.

In spite of the cost and the time expended, the first Harecastle tunnel proved a bottleneck from the very beginning. Lacking a tow-path, every barge had to be legged through a tunnel distance of 2,280 yds., and each passage required not less than two hours. To improve the over-all traffic efficiency of the entire canal, it was necessary to drive a larger tunnel through the hill. The second Harecastle tunnel was driven parallel to the first at a distance of 26 ft. from it. It was 2,926 ft. long, 16 ft. high and 14 ft. wide, and along one side ran a 4 ft. 9 in. tow-path, leaving 9 ft. 3 in. of clear water. This tunnel was finished by Telford in 1824 without incident.

James Brindley did not live to see the completion of the Grand Trunk Canal, as he died from overwork on 27th September 1771 at the age of fifty-five. His life's work must have gladdened the hearts of the canal sponsors, particularly Josiah Wedgwood: with the Grand Trunk in operation the shipping costs from Liverpool to his potteries at Burslem were reduced from £2 10s. a ton to 13s.

Brindley was the pioneer both in respect of canal-building and tunnel advance. After his death new canals and new tunnels continued to be built at a rate that made his early efforts seem modest.

Towards the end of the century there were canals north and south of the Pennines and it was decided to join the two systems by cutting through the Standedge Ridge between Marsden and Diggle by means of a tunnel whereby direct connection would be established between the east and west coasts. The survey was carried out by Nicholas Brown in 1793 and parliamentary sanction for the Standedge tunnel was granted the following year.

Work on the first Standedge tunnel (there were to be three more) started in 1794. The tunnel was 3 miles, 171 yds. long, its width 9 ft. and total height 17 ft., but since the depth of the water was 8 ft. the useful height to the crown was 9 ft. At four places in the tunnel were so-called 'wides' where two barges could meet. They were called Brun Clough, White Horse, Judy and Red Brook.

Since the Standedge was a summit tunnel it had to be supplied with water which was obtained from two reservoirs at each end. The water was drained from the moors. Benjamin Outram was the engineer until his death in 1805.

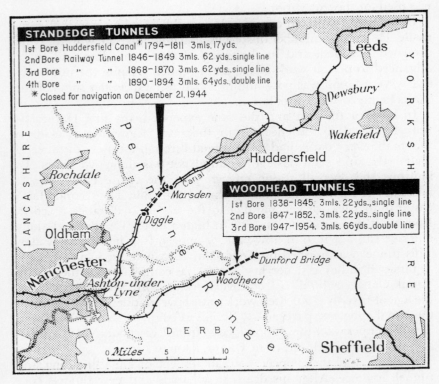

Fig 25. Tunnels through the Pennine Range.

The Standedge was driven from numerous deep shafts, the deepest being 220 ft. In advancing the tunnel, drilling and blasting with powder were used in the hard rock when encountered. Considerable trouble was experienced, in part due to the hard and difficult grindstone grit which slowed down progress, in part owing to the failure of the stockholders of the Huddersfield Canal Company to meet their obligations. Many fatal accidents also occurred before the tunnel was opened for traffic on 4th April 1811 after seventeen years of work. The total cost came to £123,803, or £23 per yd. The Standedge canal tunnel was closed to navigation on 21st December 1944. By that time the water depth had become reduced to 5 ft. owing to crumbling rock and silt. In the hard rock the drill holes were still to be seen, but elsewhere the spalling rock had created large caverns during the 150 years the rock had been exposed to water and air.

Fig 26. The Frindsbury Tunnel, built in 1819, on the Thames and Medway Canal.

But by the time the Standedge tunnel was completed, the era of British canal-building had reached its culmination, and although few realized it at the time the canals were soon to be replaced by a more efficient but hardly as pleasant mode of transport. There was one man who saw the end of the canals, and that was the third Duke of Bridgewater, who had started it all. In his old age, while watching the barges loaded with coal from his collieries sedately flowing by, he saw what was coming. 'They will last my time,' he said, 'but I see mischief in those damned tramroads.'

Continental Canal Tunnels

Before leaving the canal tunnels, some reference should be made

Fig 27. The Tronquoy Tunnel on the St. Quentin Canal was built in 1803. It was the first tunnel to be driven through soft ground, and to overcome the difficulties a new system of tunnelling had to be devised. The core was left *in situ* until the lining had been put in. A further description of this 'French System' of tunnelling is given in Chapter 5.

to canal construction on the Continent and to the long tunnels required to link up the various sections of the waterways. The experience derived from these French and Belgian canal tunnels greatly influenced the future construction of railway tunnels all over the world. Under Napoleon, the French undertook the construction of the 60-mile St. Quentin Canal on which were three major tunnels, the Tronquoy being the most interesting. It is the shortest of the three, having a length of only 3,603 ft., but it was the first tunnel

Fig 28. The Charleroi Canal in Belgium has a tunnel which was driven through quicksand in 1828. To tunnel through this treacherous material the engineers devised a method of working which became popular among tunnellers during the rest of the century. A description of the method is given in Chapter 5.

to be advanced through soft sandy ground. A steam-engine is reported to have been used on the site in 1803. Simultaneously with the Tronquoy another long tunnel was started on the same canal, the 18,197-ft. Riqueval tunnel. The canal was opened in 1810, and twelve years later the 39,360-ft.-long Noirieu tunnel was added whereby the subterranean passages along the canal reached a total length of 11½ miles.

By that time the French boatmen had become conditioned to the tunnels. At the time of the opening of the St. Quentin Canal, in 1810, the boatmen refused to a man to enter the tunnels because they were afraid of the long dark passages. Finally, in desperation, the canal authority offered freedom from all canal tolls in perpetuity to the first boat that entered the tunnels. Only one man came forward. After making the passage with much fear and trepidation this boatman renamed his barge *Grand Souterrain* and it became the most famous and lucrative of the many hundreds of barges that came to use the canal. It was kept in service for nearly a century until the tolls were eventually abandoned.

In Belgium, the Charleroi Canal was built in 1828, also through soft ground. On this canal the engineers ran into a hill with quicksand and instead of making a deep cut decided to drive a tunnel through it. The method developed in overcoming this treacherous ground became widely used in tunnel construction during the following century and is still referred to as the 'Belgian Method'.[12]

American Canals

Canal-building got under way in the United States towards the end of the eighteenth century. The first major development was the Schuylkill and Susquehanna, or Union Canal, which was started in 1791 and completed in 1827. A long series of small canals followed, such as the Dismal Swamp Canal in North Carolina (1786–91) which was not finished, and navigational improvements were also undertaken in the Potomac, James and Rappahannock Rivers. The 2-mile Hadley Canal, and the 3-mile Montague Canal in Massachusetts were dug by companies chartered in 1792. At the beginning of the century more ambitious work got under way, such as the 22-mile Santee Canal in South Carolina (1802), followed by the 2-mile Carondelet Canal in 1805 and the 27-mile Middlesex Canal in Massachusetts in 1808. In New York State, the Champlain Canal was constructed in 1816–19. Early American canal construction culminated with the 363-mile-long Erie Canal, built 1817–25.

The first tunnel built in the United States was begun in 1818 on the Schuylkill Navigational Canal in Pennsylvania, at Orwigsburg Landing above Auburn. It had a length of 450 ft. and was cut through red shale. The width was 20 ft. and the height 18 ft. It was arched for 75 ft. from each portal.

This tunnel seems to have been driven for the sake of novelty. The height of the ridge through which it passed was only 40 ft., and a much better alignment of the canal would have been obtained farther along the ridge, whereby a tunnel would have been avoided altogether. But the Schuylkill tunnel served its purpose. It excited much interest and people came all the way from Philadelphia to

[12] The Belgian method of tunnel construction is described on p. 115.

look at the wonder, and what was more important from the promoters' point of view, they also became aware of the new transport lane. Having served its promotional purpose, the first American tunnel was done away with in 1855–56, when the cover was removed and the canal taken through the ridge in an open cut.

Fig 29. The first American tunnel built was on the Schuylkill Navigational Canal, near Orwigsburg Landing in Pennsylvania. The 450-ft.-long tunnel that was excavated in shale was removed in 1855 when the canal was taken through an open cut. The above sketch of the portal was made by the assistant engineer in 1855 before the cover was removed.

The second American canal tunnel was also located on the Union Canal. This was the Lebanon tunnel at the summit of the canal. It was originally 720 ft. long, 18 ft. wide and 15 ft. high and was arched for about 150 ft. from each end. It was excavated through argillaceous slate in 1824–26 at a cost of $30,464. Five years later work began on American's first railway tunnel on the Allegheny Portal Railroad. A new era had begun.

Chapter 4

EARLY RAILWAY TUNNELS

THOSE 'damned tramroads', as the Duke of Bridgewater called them, were not long in coming. Thomas Telford, the most civilized of engineers and Brindley's successor as canal builder, had already seen them coming at the peak of the canal boom. 'In rugged country,' he wrote in 1800[1] 'or where there is difficulty to obtain lockage, or where the weight of the articles of produce is great in comparison with its bulk, or where they are mostly to be conveyed from a higher to a lower level, in these cases iron railways are in general preferable to canal navigation.' By the time he died in 1834 the railway boom was under way and canal navigation was beginning to decline.

Telford's statement was inspired by novel experiments conducted on the Merthyr Tydfil tramway in Wales by Richard Trevithick, a Cornish mine foreman. He had built a high-pressure road locomotive, which on Christmas Eve 1801 drew the first load of passengers ever carried by steam. Another of his locomotives ran on flanged rails in the Wylam colliery at Tyneside in 1805. The engines were far from perfect, but the very fact that they ran inspired improvements by such men as Timothy Hackworth, John Ericsson and George Stephenson. Like most pioneers, Trevithick did not get much out of his historic invention. He died penniless and owing rent for his lodgings.

But although Trevithick saw little of it, there was plenty of money

[1] Quoted by J. Plymley: *General View of the Agriculture of Shropshire* (1813).

about. The wars were over, and Britain was emerging as the richest and most powerful country in the world. Iron ore could be reduced with mineral coal without the use of the more costly charcoal, and pig could be reduced by puddling, with heat also raised by mineral coal. New machines were pouring out a flood of goods to willing buyers the world over. By 1830, conditions were ripe for a revolution in transport: there was money, there were men, and there was iron in what appeared to be adequate supply.

The New Men

The canal-building decades had produced a new order of men, the *civil engineers*, to whom the future belonged. These men differed in background and professional outlook from the engineers of the past, who had been technical ancillaries to the army, trained to build fortifications, operate siege engines and work military installations and who occasionally used also to supervise non-military construction. Another breed of men were also finding their opportunities —the tinkers. These native inventive geniuses had hitherto been hidden among the mass of blacksmiths, wheelwrights, mechanics and millwrights—men with the feel of material in their bones, the foremen, master-workers who kept early industry going and, for that matter, have kept it going ever since. Some of these men now emerged as mechanical engineers, gradually becoming accepted in spite of their lack of status, so far below civil engineers because of their origin, because men with money needed them, and needed them badly. Theirs were the brains guiding the new developments. They had at their disposal vast hordes of labourers—the 'navigators' who had been engaged in large numbers on the canal works. Without this pool of wild and hard-drinking men capable of lifting twenty tons of dirt a day to a height of six feet and spending the evenings and nights in fighting, drinking and whoring, the British railways could not have been built as quickly as they were. Nor, for that matter, could any other railway, because as railway construction expanded from its homeland in ever widening circles the same species was found to grow in all countries.

Where did they come from, these labouring giants who in Britain became known as 'navvies' from their original employment, in other countries by different names? No matter where and when they appeared on the flimsy stage of the industrial revolution, their origin was the same: they had emerged from the crofts and hovels in the rural areas where a generation earlier an ample supply of cheap food, in which potatoes formed a major part, had brought about an over-supply of manpower—healthy, strong of limb and wind, courageous, illiterate, loyal to each other, true to themselves and, without property ties, as free as any man could wish to be.

In the British Isles they were recruited mainly in Ireland and from soldiers returning from the wars. They followed the railway contractors, lived in turf hovels along the track, twenty men to a gang. Their diet consisted of beef, beer and whisky, their recreation of gambling and fist fighting. The countryside lived in fear of them, and thanksgiving prayers were said in the churches when they broke camp and left.

The railway epoch has now come to a close in the western world and, as with the canals, the railways are becoming white elephants that have difficulty in earning their keep. But, in total, the railway century produced the greatest output of construction the world has seen since the days of the Egyptian state building monopoly. In retrospect, it seems almost unbelievable that these untold millions of tons of dirt were moved, thousands of tunnels excavated, bridges and viaducts erected in unknown numbers, millions of tons of steel laid— that all this tremendous bulk of work was accomplished entirely by human muscle. The Arctic railways of Scandinavia, built by men still living, were graded with the aid of a shovel which the man wielding it had to pay for himself. When working in rock he signed out for drill steel and hammers which he handed in upon completion of the work, and he was docked for the metal he had worn off. These men had to fend for themselves when they arrived in the wilderness, often in sub-zero weather. They had to build their own shacks, cook their food crowding around an open hearth, sleep in their working clothes for weeks on end. Changing underwear was, appropriately enough, termed delousing.

Such were the men who built the railways. As long as there was an ample supply of this superb rural proletarian manpower blessed with an iron constitution that could stand up to any hardship, so long was management, state or private, relieved of the need for constructive thinking. Why invest in machines, or even horses that had to be stabled and fed, why bother about building barracks, keeping people in food and preventing accidents? The job of management was to provide the cash upon the completion of a gang contract, and the measure of a good site engineer was his ability to cheat as much as he could, without risking being beaten to a pulp, when paying off the gangs.

By such mean and ruthless exploitation of labour, railway companies and governments succeeded in getting their railways built; but apart from the gruesome toll in lives and senseless wastage of limbs, the cost of this barbaric and backward system was the deferred mechanization of the construction industry for some fifty years or more. The measure of this backward state in civil engineering can perhaps be appreciated by recalling that these scandalous conditions prevailed even until the time of Henry Ford's assembly lines in Detroit.

British Tunnels

To return to the beginnings of British railway history: George Stephenson, designer of the 'Rocket', had become engineer in charge of the Liverpool–Manchester Railway, the first public railway in the world in the accepted sense of the term. This line was laid down in accordance with what subsequently became known as the Stephenson 'straight-through' concept, i.e. choosing the shortest distance between two points. This implied accepting whatever obstacles the country offered in the way of bogs, ravines, rivers and hills. The latter had to be penetrated by means of tunnels.

There was, from the very beginning, another school of railway survey fathered by Joseph Locke, pupil of the elder Stephenson, which avoided tunnels, choosing instead to go up and around the hills. All railways the world over reflect one or other of these two concepts.

There were two tunnels on the Liverpool–Manchester line,[2] one extending for 5 furlongs to Edge Hill in Liverpool and the other, a mile long, on the Wapping branch leading to the quay and rising by a gradient of 1:48, which necessitated the cars being worked by cable. It was with this second tunnel that young Joseph Locke attracted the attention of his superiors. He had left his unpaid service after some disagreement with Stephenson, but was recalled to check on the Wapping tunnel survey which had been approved by his former boss. The young man was able to prove that, if built according to the approved survey, the two headings would have passed each other under the city. From that day on, the two schools of railway engineering were spurred on by this personal rivalry of their protagonists. It was therefore something of an irony that Locke in 1845 received the unusual compliment of the Board of Trade inspector for having performed 'the finest piece of engineering ever seen'—in driving the summit tunnel between Woodhead and Dunford Bridge on the Manchester–Sheffield line.

[2] The two Liverpool tunnels were not the first *rail* tunnels built. The Terrenoir tunnel on the Roanne–Andrezieux horse line was begun in 1826 and is therefore the first rail tunnel on record.

The Sheffield, Ashton-under-Lyne and Manchester Railway Company was incorporated by an Act of 5th May 1837 and on 1st October the following year Lord Wharncliffe turned the first spadeful of sod near the Woodhead side of the proposed tunnel. The engineer of the railway, C. B. Vignoles, cut the second, and the difficult work of driving the first long railway tunnel got its official send-off. But not much progress was made with the tunnel, because a year was spent building roads over the moors and establishing camps at both ends.

The cost of the 3-mile-long Woodhead tunnel was estimated by Vignoles at £98,467, but when he was succeeded by Joseph Locke the following year the latter doubled the estimate immediately. Locke surveyed the tunnel and projected the axis on the ground from a series of tall masonry columns, each one surrounded by a stepped cylindrical structure. The theodolite was placed on a flat stone on top of the column.

The tunnel is situated on the summit of the Sheffield–Manchester line at an elevation of 1,552 ft. above sea-level. The gradient is 1 : 201 rising from the east. The average cover is 450 ft., but at one point the grade of the floor is 600 ft. below the surface of the ground.

Five 8-ft. cylindrical shafts were sunk on line down to tunnel grade and the axis transferred underground by means of two wires suspended in the shafts. The tunnel was advanced simultaneously on ten shaft headings as well as from the portals. The alignment of the headings was accurately maintained and the largest deviation was only 3 in. Locke experienced his greatest difficulties in the shaft sinking, particularly with the No. 2 shaft, which yielded at one time something like 100,000 gallons of water per day and required four and a half years to sink to grade. Although there were numerous casualties, no lives were lost in the first Woodhead tunnel.

The tunnel was driven at a time when the Chartist movement was at its most popular and there was much unrest and political trouble on the site. During the summer of 1841 serious fighting broke out between the Irish and English workers. However, despite the labour troubles and natural difficulties, the work was completed in six years. Total excavation came to 272,685 cu. yds., necessitating the expenditure of 157 tons of powder and £200,000. The total length of the first (down-line) tunnel came to 3 miles, 13 yds. On 20th December 1845 General Pasley, the Board of Trade inspector, approved the tunnel and two days later the world's longest railway tunnel was opened for traffic.

The up-line tunnel was started early in 1847 and ran 17 ft. from the down-line one. Numerous crosscuts were made to the latter which facilitated the work and no particular difficulties were encountered.

However, two years later cholera struck the Woodhead camp and twenty-eight workers died. When their coffins arrived the entire labour force panicked and abandoned the site. Eventually the contractor got the situation under control and succeeded in completing the tunnel without serious delay. Woodhead No. 2 was opened for traffic on 2nd February 1852. Its length was exactly the same as the No. 1 tunnel, which by then had lost its brief fame of being the world's longest rail tunnel, to Standedge, which proved to be 49 yds. longer.

Woodhead[3] was never a popular tunnel owing to its poor ventilation. Passing through the tunnel was an unpleasant experience for all passengers, and many were overcome by the sulphurous fumes trailing the locomotive. The bitter protests against tunnels that fill the minutes of the Parliamentary railway hearings of that time were to a large extent inspired by the lethal character of the Woodhead and other poorly ventilated long railway tunnels.

But by that time a large number of tunnels had been driven through the green hills of England in connection with the building of the great trunk lines. The London–Birmingham Railway, surveyed by Robert Stephenson, required nine tunnels, some of which caused a lot of trouble. When cutting through Kilsby Ridge quicksand was encountered, upon news of which the contractor died instantly. The tunnel was about 2,400 yds. long and the headings ran repeatedly into springs which flooded the workings. For eight months 1,800 gallons per minute had to be pumped out to keep the workings manageable. Incredible though it may seem, it has been stated that 13,000 men with hundreds of horses slaved in the tunnel day and night for thirty months. The contracted price was £99,000, the final cost £300,000.

The Primrose Hill tunnel on the same railway also gave much trouble owing to the presence of wet clay which broke the brick

[3] In 1946 the two Woodhead tunnels were in such poor shape that it was decided to advance a new double-track tunnel through the ridge, 100 ft. to the south of the down-line tunnel. More serious difficulties were encountered with the new tunnel than with the two old ones together. The original method of enlarging the 12 × 12 ft. pilot tunnel by radial drilling had to be abandoned owing to poor rock and excessive overbreak, and in June 1951 a 72-ft.-long section of the enlarged tunnel collapsed and filled the excavated space with débris from a 70-ft.-high cavity. To clear up the mess a by-pass tunnel had to be driven 50 ft. to the south of the main tunnel for a total distance of 9,500 ft. and connected to it by numerous crosscuts. Instead of using 600 men as originally planned, 1,100 men had to be put on, or nearly as many as a century earlier. The large cavity had to be left unfilled and the dangerous section arched by a 5-ft. reinforced concrete lining. The troublesome Woodhead No. 3 was completed in 1954, a century after No. 2.

lining. Shifting gravels in the Watford tunnel killed a large number of miners.

The building of the Great Western Railway brought upon the railway tunnelling scene the son of a man who knew from bitter experience what tunnelling meant—Sir Marc Isambard Brunel. The young Brunel had himself been blooded and scarred by the ill-fated attempt to tunnel through the Thames clay, and on the abandonment of the flooded tunnel he found himself without work, and replied to an advertisement for a railway engineer. The advertisement was inserted by a committee formed of wealthy businessmen in Bristol. Money always speaks loud, and a little money loudest of all. The Bristol promoters, accustomed to buying cheap and selling dear, applied the same principle to the hiring of a railway engineer. They put the applicants on the auction block and were prepared to buy the one that sold himself at the lowest price.

The committee got the surprise of its life. 'You are holding out a premium to the man who will make you the most flattering promises,' young Isambard Kingdom Brunel told them at the interview, 'and it is quite obvious that he who has the least reputation at stake, or the most to gain by temporary success, and least to lose by the consequences of a disappointment, must be the winner in such a race.'[4] Therefore, he concluded, he would withdraw his application. In view of what subsequently happened it might have been sensible if the hard-headed Bristol committee had stuck to their original intention and selected a less brilliant engineer than Brunel. As it was, they were impressed by his character and gave him a free hand. It is beyond the scope of this book to enter into the details of Brunel's amazing career as a railway engineer and his many innovations, his lovely bridges, his broad gauge and hopeless design of the permanent way, and his peculiar locomotives. Here we must confine our interest to his great Box tunnel.

The Attack Against Tunnels

Brunel began work by making a preliminary survey of the route which finally ran from Bristol, striking the Thames near Cholsey, and thence through Reading and Maidenhead to London. Near Box the railway was to penetrate the oolite ridge with a 2-mile tunnel. The total cost of the railway was estimated at £2,800,000.

The proposed tunnel came in for severe criticism. Before the Parliamentary Committee which conducted hearings preliminary to

[4] Celia Brunel Noble: *The Brunels, Father and Son*, Cobden-Sanderson, London (1938).

granting a charter, a number of witnesses gave evidence of the many evils that were sure to follow upon the building of the Box tunnel. A distinguished medical witness predicted dire catastrophe to the bodies and minds of all unfortunate wretches who had to pass through this hell-hole. Another witness insisted that the monstrous, extraordinary, most dangerous and impractical tunnel at Box would cause wholesale destruction of human lives, and that no means with which he was acquainted could prevent it.

Distrust of tunnels was common among the medical profession in England. Sir Anthony Carlisle, Vice-President of the Royal College of Surgeons, testified that passengers going through tunnels were liable to the following afflictions: common colds, inflammation of the lungs, erysipelas, rheumatism and lumbago. 'I know from experience,' he stated, 'that it is difficult to discharge a tunnel or large room of any stagnant or quiescent mass of air, and I believe that a six hundred-yard tunnel would neither discharge itself nor could it be discharged by any ordinary means.'[5] On the same occasion a Dr. James Johnson testified that the reverberations of sound are of more consequence than the vicissitudes of temperature. The noise when travelling at thirty miles an hour would be a very great shock to delicate people. As to the effect on the nerves of passing under arches thirty to forty yards long Dr. Johnson testified from his own experience: 'The deafening peal of thunder, the sudden immersion in gloom, and the crash of reverberated sounds in a confined space, combine to produce a momentary shudder, or idea of destruction, a thrill of annihilation.'[6]

The Box tunnel was to be given a gradient of 1:100, from which one witness calculated that if the brakes of the train failed it would issue at the lower portal at a speed of 120 miles an hour. Behind the opposition to the tunnel was marshalled an opinion against the railways as such. Dr. Hawtree of Eton believed that the railways would in the end destroy the entire classical tradition in English education. The English schoolmaster would be superseded by French governesses and mistresses. 'Homer, Virgil, Horace and other classical authors—with the exception of Ovid's *Art of Love*—would be forced into the background in favour of Rousseau, Voltaire and equally destructive writers.'[7] The Duke of Wellington was against railways, this one or any others, for one good reason: they would encourage the lower classes to move about.

Some of these views were no doubt quite sensible. A railway

[5] Richard Cort: Railway imposition detected by Richard Cort (1834).
[6] Ibid.　　　　　　　　[7] Ibid.

tunnel is not a very pleasant traffic artery, and at the time of the testimonies and much later, a long tunnel could actually be lethal to men and beasts. However, the Parliamentary Committee on this and other occasions accepted neither the sober medical views nor the outpourings of the lunatics, and the charter for the Great Western Railway, including the Box tunnel, was passed.

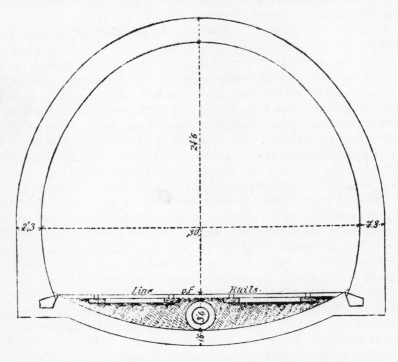

Fig 30. The famous Box Tunnel on the Great Western Railway was advanced 1836–41 by the younger Brunel.

So the work started on the Box in the spring of 1836. A large number of shafts were sunk to grade. From the east the headings were driven through the great oolite, followed by a thick bed of fuller's earth, the lesser oolite and strata of marl and lias, all of them liable to cause a great deal of trouble. This they did: water broke into the tunnel on numerous occasions, and in November 1837 the entire tunnel was flooded. Box has a total length of 3,212 yds., but it required 4,000 men and 300 horses for five years to complete it. It was opened for traffic in the summer of 1851. It was subsequently found that by a slight change in the alignment of the tunnel axis Brunel had contrived to reorientate the Box tunnel so that the sun floods it with red light at sunrise on 9th April, his birthday.

The first tunnel through the Standedge ridge was opened for navigation in 1811. As subsequently proved, the experience gained from driving the canal tunnel saved the Leeds, Dewsbury and Manchester Railway a lot of trouble and something like £100,000 when the time came in 1845 to drive a rail tunnel through the ridge.

The geology was known and by making crosscuts from the parallel canal tunnel 50 ft. away the number of shafts could be reduced, and some of the debris was removed by forty barges. Thomas Nicholson, the contractor, had steam-engines installed in the few shafts sunk, one of the early instances on record where steam was used in tunnelling. The work of advancing the tunnel began in February 1846 and the tunnel was completed in January 1849, a record performance in early tunnelling. Total length of the Standedge rail tunnel came to 3 miles, 62 yds., which made it the longest rail tunnel in the world, a record it held for several decades.

The highest number of men employed by Nicholson was 1,953, and he used 150,798 lb. of candles to light the workings. The total cost of Standedge No. 2 came to £201,608 12s. 3½d., to be exact, but since £30,605 was spent on the approaches, the cost per linear yard was about £32.

The third Standedge, another single-line rail tunnel, was started in April 1868 and completed in October 1870. One memorable incident in driving Standedge No. 3 was the tremendous fight between miners and muckers that broke out on Whit-Sunday 1869 and kept the village of Marsden in a state of siege for over a week. But except for this fracas the work was completed without trouble. There was one fatal accident when a boatman succeeded in blowing himself to bits by his careless handling of powder canisters.

The third Standedge has exactly the same length as the second, or 3 miles, 62 yds. It was lined with 16 million bricks and its total cost, including the lining, came to £120,000 or roughly £22 10s. per linear yard, surely an all-time bargain as tunnels go.

The old canal tunnel was to prove its worth once more. In 1890, a double-track tunnel was driven parallel to the down-line tunnel from 13 crosscuts extending into the canal tunnel. The debris was removed by barges and the water encountered was also drained into the canal. The London and North Western Railway carried out the work with 1,800 men and 120 tons of gelignite, at a cost of £508,000, or £93 per linear yard.

Since then Standedge has been left in peace. A suggestion made in

1935 to drive a motor tunnel through the ridge was not taken seriously.

Early Continental and American Tunnels

Railway building on the Continent also necessitated the driving of numerous tunnels during the 1830's. From available material it appears that the first to be built was the Cumptieh tunnel in Belgium,

Fig 31. The Köningsdorf Tunnel on the Dresden–Leipzig line was driven in 1837. In this tunnel the foundation for the lining was placed first, after which the masonry lining was put in. With the lining in place the central core was removed.

begun in 1835. Other tunnels rapidly followed in France, where the first was built on the St. Germain line in 1837. On the Versailles, the Gard and the Rouen lines the tunnels had a total length of 42,105 ft. By the middle of the century France had 126 railway tunnels totalling 135,000 ft., of which half were under construction. Among the notable early French tunnels were Nerthe, Arschwiller, Rilly, La Motte, Lormont and Alouette.

In pre-Bismarck Germany the early railways also required a good deal of tunnelling, the first one being the Oberau tunnel on the

Leipzig–Dresden line, commenced in 1839. In Austria, the Gumpoldskirch tunnel was the first. In 1856, the Austrian railways had sixty tunnels totalling 43,300 ft. in length. One of the early Italian railways, the Naples–Castellamare line, had numerous tunnels, all of them finished by 1840. By 1856, the Italian railways had 32,600 ft. of tunnels. In Switzerland, subsequent scene of the most dramatic tunnel-building of the railway age, the Hauenstein tunnel was begun in 1854 and completed four years later.

Fig 32. The Gumpoldskirch Tunnel, on the Vienna–Gloggnitz line, was built in 1839. For a description of the method used see Chapter 5.

In the United States the first railway tunnel was built in 1831–33 on the Allegheny Portage Railroad. It was 701 ft. long, a 25 × 21 ft. double-track summit tunnel through which the canal barges east of the range were transported to the headwaters of the Ohio-Mississippi system. The cost of excavating the tunnel was $1.47 per cu. yd. Miners were paid $13 per month with all found. The total cost was $37,798. This tunnel stands to this day, although abandoned, in the mountains near Johnstown, Pennsylvania.

The second American railway tunnel was built in 1835–37 on the Philadelphia and Reading Railroad. This was the first American tunnel advanced from shafts sunk on line. To prevent deviating from the course, a pair of 7-ft. shafts were sunk just outside the 19-ft.-wide tunnel at a distance of 100 ft. from each other. By 1850, there were twenty-nine tunnels on the American railways and sixteen on the Croton aqueducts bringing water to New York.

By 1850 a respectable number of canal and railway tunnels had been built in England, on the Continent and in the U.S.A., and a great deal of experience in tunnelling had been accumulated.

Whereas in nearly all countries miners were at first employed to advance the tunnels, now everywhere there were men skilled in driving tunnels of much larger areas than those used in mining. Special methods had been developed, particularly in respect of

Fig 33. The first Swiss tunnel was the 8,198-ft.-long Hauenstein Tunnel on the central railway between Bâle and Olten. This 25·6 × 19·7 ft. tunnel was built 1853–8 by the famous British railway contractor Thomas Brassey.

timbering, to overcome the obstacles encountered underground. Books began to be published, and the methods were analysed and criticized.

Manual methods were used to advance all these early tunnels. The majority were hacked out with mattocks and picks or else scooped out by men wielding spades. Occasionally, gunpowder was used to gain a few inches per day in hard rock. Then a new kind of labouring man entered upon the tunnelling scene—the steel-driving man at the front, on whose prowess and endurance the success or failure

Fig 34. An early timber-lined American rail tunnel as it appeared at the middle of the nineteenth century.

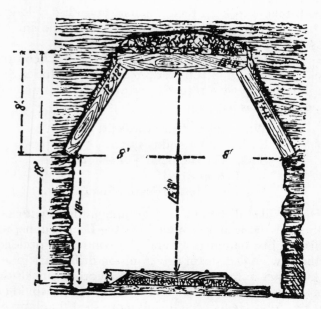

Fig 35. A sketch by Benjamin H. Latrobe showing his method used in building the tunnels on the Baltimore and Ohio Railroad.

of the tunnel enterprise rested. It is tempting to leave the main track for a moment to record some of the feats performed by these labouring giants preserved in the ballads of railroading.

Steel-driving John Henry

From a strictly historical point of view the deeds of John Henry do not belong to the early phase of railway tunnelling. His chief claim to enduring fame comes from his having placed his bulky frame in front of advancing mechanization, challenging it to stop. This Negro hero of the ballads of American construction and mining camps, in the working chanties sung across the continent before singing was submerged in the cacophony of engine exhausts and shrieking air tools, is fashioned out of Homeric clay and John Henry, black of skin and only a few years removed from slavery, has become the everlasting symbol of the dignity of labour regardless of race.

John Henry, then, drove steel. But not in the manner of common mortals. He placed his muscular frame five feet from the drill and swung one hammer with each hand. He used sheepnose hammers, each weighing 10 lb., with switch handles 4 ft. long. The handles he rubbed with tallow to keep them flexible, and all day long he kept the two hammers flashing in the air. Nothing could interrupt the beat of his flailing. Nobody could stand up to him.

In this manner John Henry drove steel in the Big Bend tunnel on the Chesapeake and Ohio Railroad, near White Sulphur Springs in West Virginia in the year 1870. Or, as one of the innumerable versions of the ballad has it:

> When John Henry was a little baby,
> Sitting on his daddy's knee,
> Says, 'The Big Bend Tunnel on the
>   C & O Road
> Is going to be the death of me.'

John Henry, like all heroes, had an appointment with fate. Progress in the one and a quarter-mile-long Big Bend Tunnel was slow, despite his mighty hammering, and the contractor decided to try some of the newfangled steam-driven piston drills. But John Henry, just like his mates in the Big Bend and in all other tunnels the world over, was not impressed. He vowed that no machine would ever beat him, that he, John Henry, could sink more steel than any ol' steam drill.

'All right,' said the foreman, 'you show us you kin do it. If you kin beat the steam drill you win a hundred dollars.'

So a race was arranged between John Henry and the machine, or as the ballad has it:

> Captain told John Henry,
> Says, 'A man ain't nothin' but a man;
> If you beat that steam drill down,
> I'll lay a hundred dollars in your hand.'

Whereupon John Henry made his fateful boast:

> John Henry told the captain,
> Says, 'A man ain't nothin' but a man;
> And if I don't beat your steam drill down
> I'll die with a hammer in my hand, Lawd,
> Lawd.'

But before he entered the contest John Henry insisted that he needed a pair of new hammers:

> John Henry told the captain,
> Says, 'When you go back to town
> Bring John back a ten-pound hammer
> And he'll sure whip your steam drill
> down.'

So came the day for the historic tournament. John Henry had his new hammers and had the switch handles carefully tallowed:

> John Henry went up to the mountin
> He come down on the side:
> The rock was so tall, John Henry was so
> small,
> That he laid down his hammer and cried,
> 'Lawd, Lawd.'

But John Henry regained his courage and faith in his own prowess; he picked up his hammers and stood up to the ol' steam drill:

> Put John Henry on the right-hand side,
> That ol' steam drill to the left,
> 'Before I let that steam drill beat me
> down
> I'll hammer my fool self to death.'

> John Henry said to his shaker boy,
> Says, 'Boy, you better pray,
> For if I miss this six-foot steel
> Tomorrow'll be your burial day.'

> The man who owned the ol' steam drill,
> Thought it was mighty fine,
> But John Henry drove fourteen feet,
> And the steam drill only nine.

So John Henry won his legendary race with the machine, beat it by sinking fourteen feet against nine in thirty-five minutes. But it proved too much for him. After collecting his hundred-dollar stake he went to his shack and complained to his wife that he felt something a-roaring in his head:

> John Henry said to his loving little
>   woman,
> Says, 'I'm sick and want to go to bed;
> Fix me up a place to lay down, chile,
> I got a rolling in my head.'

John Henry died in the night and next day his loving wife went to the scene of his Herculean labour:

> John Henry had a pretty little woman,
> The dress she wore was red;
> She went down the track and she looked
>   back,
> Says, 'I'm going where John Henry fell
>   dead.'

The ballad ends with John Henry's widow leaving camp:

> John Henry had a loving woman,
> The dress she wore was blue;
> She went down the track, she never
>   looked back,
> Says, 'John Henry, I'm leaving you.'

But for days afterwards his black mates refused to enter the tunnel. From inside they kept hearing the ring of steel as John Henry's ghost kept on flailing his mighty hammers. It was only after the captain had proved to them that it was water dropping from the roof that he could get his bereaved crew to take up their labour in the Big Bend tunnel.

Challengers of John Henry

Although many tried, no double-jack driller succeeded in breaking John Henry's apocryphal record of driving fourteen feet of steel in hard rock in thirty-five minutes. For two generations or more, giant men, masters in wielding heavy hammers, met in drilling contests each year in the West, from El Paso to Butte. Hand-drilling as performed by such champions as the Tarr brothers from Idaho Springs or 'The Turrible Swedes' from Ouray was a precision sport which required as much careful preparation and training as a prize fight. Tens of thousands of dollars changed hands in betting and prize money, and no record was recognized unless made in Gunnison granite from Colorado. Large blocks of this standard granite were therefore shipped to the scenes of the great drilling contests.

The contests were run in fifteen-minute sets; double-jack teams used $\frac{7}{8}$-in. steels and single-jack performers $\frac{3}{4}$-in. jumpers. Since the steels dulled after a minute or so, changing steel became a sleight of hand performance, the shaker removing the dulled steel and putting in a new one between two blows without the hammer men slowing down the beat of ninety blows per minute. Likewise, members of a two-man team changed places in a split second, the hammer not missing a beat during the fifteen-minute match.

Many amazing records were set. The Tarr brothers sank 44 in. to become El Paso champions in 1903; Kinsella and McLean beat that record with $46\frac{5}{8}$ in. at Bisbee the same year. At Butte in 1912, the Tarr brothers seem to have set an all-time record of 59·5 in. The single-jack record set at the same drilling meet was $45\frac{1}{16}$ in., obtained with a beat of 144 strokes per minute.

But such drilling skills were not for sale to mine operators and tunnel contractors. They had to be satisfied with far slower performance, but it nevertheless took many years before manual drillers admitted defeat by the machines.

Chapter 5

METHODS OF TUNNELLING

*'He setteth an end to darknesse
and searcheth out all perfection:
the stones of darknesse and the
shadow of death.'*

IN UNDERGROUND work it is comforting to know that all ground, except quicksand, possesses a natural arch. That is why tunnelling can be accomplished at all. The essence of the tunneller's art is to disturb the natural arch as little as possible while excavating the material. In good, homogeneous rock the arch takes the shape of a semi-ellipse spanning the entire width of the tunnel and forming a durable vault against collapse. To repeat, in good rock the protective ellipse is always there, at any depth. It does not matter whether the tunnel is driven with a rock cover of 50 ft. or 5,000 ft.—the area is spanned by the vaulting. It may be disturbed locally and temporarily by blasting, but eventually the vault accommodates itself to the void and will keep the tunnel intact for ever if no earthquake alters the static balance. This is the reason why the gigantic rock excavations carried out in the Scandinavian rock for the purpose of placing power-houses, factories, air-raid shelters, etc. in the bowels of the earth have been such a success.

But such solid primeval rock is not often met with outside Scandinavia and Canada. Elsewhere, tunnelling has to be done in entirely different ground, in decomposed and badly fissured rock, in soft ground, in water-logged calcareous rock, in clay, silt, shale, etc.

There exist today numerous methods whereby such difficult ground can be made to change its character, to turn more stable so as to permit tunnelling through it with speed and safety. Some of these methods will be briefly dealt with in another context. However, a hundred years ago and later, in fact during the entire period when the majority of the world's railway tunnels and, in the cities, the transport, water and sewage tunnels were being built, these methods were unknown, and the tunnellers had to deal with whatever ground they encountered by applying their art and skill. Perhaps it is not superfluous to recall in this context that nearly all the railway tunnels up to and including the Simplon were constructed without the aid of electric power.

The body of this chapter will be devoted to a brief review of the classic tunnelling systems developed and brought to perfection during the nineteenth century, but by way of introduction a short note on the dangers and hazards involved in underground work is not out of place.

Rock Hazards

Most of the dangers in tunnelling arise from natural causes and the failure to realize in advance what will happen when the structure of the rock is disturbed by excavation. As stated above, if the rock is solid and homogeneous nothing will happen. But often rock is

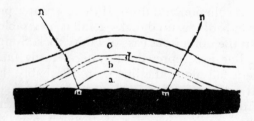

Fig 36. Danger of collapsing rock owing to undermining the folds a, b and c. Water percolating through the faults m–n will dissolve the binder holding the blocky rock in place.

folded or dislocated or badly fissured, and that is when danger lies ahead of the miners attacking it.

A common case of danger not observed except by an experienced eye is illustrated in Fig 36. After a heading has been advanced through what appears good rock, the folds *abc* have lost their footing owing to the excavation. Water, percolating through the fault (mn) will sooner or later dissolve the binder holding the layers together. The blocky rock will lose its coherence and suddenly drop into the cavity.

Horizontal stratifications also spell trouble. If the roof of the tunnel, as shown in Fig. 37, is left unsupported for too long, the blocky

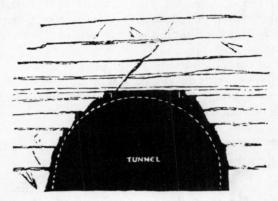

Fig 37. Horizontal stratifications are also risky since a blocky layer will lose its cohesion.

layer will lose its cohesion and drop. If there is water present—which there always is in badly fissured rock—a fall is inevitable.

Then there is the ubiquitous case of faulty rock. Suppose, as shown in Fig. 38 the line o–o represents a water-bearing fault, then there is bound to be a fall along the line (x–n). Probably the whole mass below the fault will come down.

A change from one type of strata to another also means trouble. In Fig. 39 the heading has passed through firm rock (M) and struck soft rock (K). At the junction there is a strong likelihood of a fall; if there is a fault in the soft rock there is assurance of a bad fall.

Sometimes foreign material has been injected in the natural rock by the working of percolating water, as shown in Fig. 40. This is a particularly nasty case because with water present the entire mass (P) will come loose and drop into the excavated cavity below.

These are the more common causes of tunnel collapse, to which can be added more exotic types of trouble, such as running close to or into a natural cave in the rock. Such a case is shown in Fig. 41

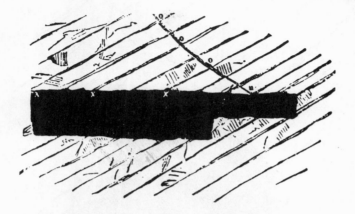

Fig 38. Faults are encountered in all rock and mean trouble. A water-bearing fault such as o–o will eventually cause the blocky ground in the roof to collapse.

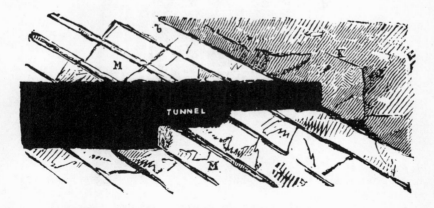

Fig 39. Changing ground is also risky. When passing from the firm rock M to the soft rock K there is likely to be a fall at the junction. If the soft rock is fissured a fall is certain.

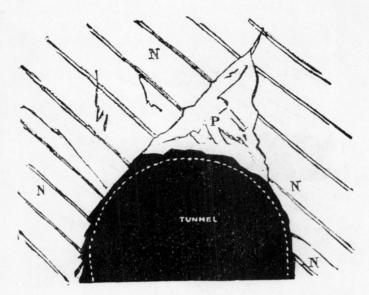

Fig 40. Foreign material deposited in country rock, such as at P, will always spill into the excavation.

Fig 41. Natural caves were sometimes encountered by the early railway tunnellers and caused a great deal of trouble.

where a tunnel on the Karst Railway in Austria ran into a series of caves.

Of the numerous bad falls recorded in nineteenth-century tunnelling history, many were due to one or a combination of such causes as these. The collapse of Dom Pedro No. 3 on the Dom Pedro Segunda

Fig 42. The collapse of the Brazilian Dom Pedro 3 Tunnel in 1859 is shown in this sequence of contemporary sketches. The tunnel was driven through stratified rock (upper left) which suddenly collapsed and filled the entire excavation with rock (upper right). The tunnel was recovered by trussing up the roof (lower left), gradually extending the timbers to the floor of the tunnel as the loose rock was removed.

Railway in Brazil was the worst of all, according to the consensus of opinion eighty years ago when tunnellers had ample material for comparison. Dom Pedro Segunda was a very short one-track tunnel of no particular interest. Its length was only 300 ft. and its section 14 × 17 ft. Work on the tunnel began in 1859, and owing to the

Fig 43a. Two bad spills in the tunnels on the Vienna-Trieste line. Top sketch shows how one fall was restored in blocky ground, the lower one how a break-dam was placed across the cavity.

Fig 43b.

apparently good granite it was excavated full face. The contractor noted some fissures in the roof and recommended that the tunnel be lined, but the engineer held to his original opinion that no lining was needed. One portal of Dom Pedro No. 3 is shown in Fig. 42, as well as the strata of the rock. No sooner was the tunnel completed and the rail laid than the stratified rock suddenly lost its cohesion and the entire tunnel caved in. The whole hillside followed and filled the length of the tunnel with a mass of stones, earth and large chunks of rock.

Unbelievable as it may appear today, the contractor succeeded in recovering the tunnel. Not only had he to excavate it anew, he also had to widen it 2 ft. on each side in order to accommodate the lining that should have been put in from the outset. In Fig. 42 is shown how a top heading was driven through the rubble filling Dom Pedro. The posts holding up the roof are 18-in. rosewood trunks. To the left is indicated how a run was stopped by heavy timbering. The roof being secured in this fashion, trenches were excavated to grade and the tall posts erected, after which the bottom part was cleared. The walls and the arch were built with ashlar, the roof timbers being arched in and the space between the top of the arch and the timbering backfilled with rock. Recovering Dom Pedro No. 3 was a terribly slow and dangerous job but it was carried through without a single accident. The work was done by slaves, who, after some training, did an excellent job; they spent about six months driving the original tunnel and three years clearing up the fall.

The Karstbahn Wien–Trieste, built in the early 1850's, had a run of bad luck with all the six tunnels on the line. Tunnel No. 1 struck a natural cave, as previously noted, and in three of the others there were bad falls. Fig. 43a shows how one fall was restored in the blocky ground, highly dangerous work when done in this fashion. The recovery of Tunnel 6 is shown in Fig. 43b: here the tunnellers succeeded in placing a so-called break-dam across the cavity that had spilled crushed rock into the tunnel. Then, before the debris in the lower part of the tunnel could be moved, heavy timbers had to be placed under the sill. Clearing up such falls belongs to the most unpleasant aspects of underground work; in many countries today the mine-inspection authorities would prohibit this kind of salvage work.

Forepoling Heavy Ground

The tunnellers of the past spoke of 'heavy ground' in which they bracketed four different types of material, all of them difficult and dangerous to life and limb. There is, to begin with, the worst, *run-*

ning ground consisting of dry or water-bearing gravels, sand, silt and mud. In tunnelling through such material the heading has to be enclosed by lagging and supported by timbering almost as soon as the spade has been stuck in the ground.

Soft ground includes squeezing clay, soft earth, damp sand, decomposed rock, etc. The walls of a tunnel driven through such materials will stand upright for a few minutes but the roof has to be supported immediately.

Firm ground will stay intact a few minutes after a heading has been driven through it, but it also will have to be timbered. By firm ground is meant firm clay, shale, cemented sands and certain rocks.

The best in this disreputable company is *self-supporting ground,* such as packed clay, shale, sandstone, cemented sands and gravels.

These were the common materials encountered by the canal builders and the early railway tunnellers who devised a number of different systems for dealing with them. But whatever systems were used, they all embodied a common feature known as *forepoling.* It may be defined as a working cycle consisting of numerous phases, whereby the heading was timbered with 'square sets' and enclosed with lagging placed in a definite sequence so that the miners were always protected against falls and runs.

Forepoling is not easy to describe, but since it is fundamental to tunnelling an attempt will nevertheless be made to explain it briefly, omitting many of the phases. The profile of a forepoled heading is shown in Fig. 44. Planks sharpened to a chisel point and about 6 ft. long are driven ahead into the ground at a slight angle. First the roof planks are driven half-way and firmly wedged in place. Then the side spiles are driven half-way, with a slight outward pitch. With the roof and walls enclosed in lagging in this manner, the top breast-board against the face is removed and the material is allowed to run into the heading. Then the next breast-board is removed, and perhaps also the next. In the niche thus formed a temporary support is placed under the top spiles and the face is secured with the face boards, as shown in Fig. 44. This being done, the top spiles are driven to their total length and then the side spiles. The ground ahead is now enclosed by the spiles, which form a protective roof while the side ones stop lateral runs. After quickly removing the breasting the ground enclosed is excavated. The new breasting is held in place by braces to the square set, while a new set is being placed behind the breast-boards.

In really difficult ground it would not have been possible to remove the full face in this manner. Then only the top of the enclosed bench would have been scratched out sufficiently to place the new forward cap (of the square set) in position, supported by a short post resting on the bench. A pair of heavy oak timbers, about 10 ft. long, would have been put under the cap and, pivoted on a post placed behind the set, used to cantilever the forward cap. The two booms,

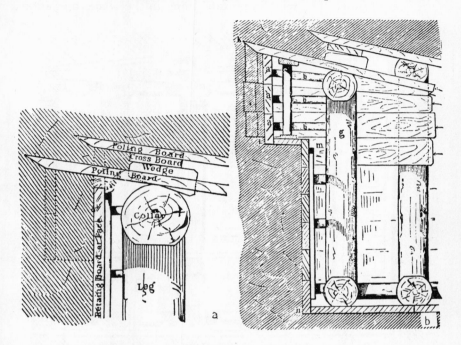

Fig 44. The lost art of forepoling. At left is shown the first phase of the working cycle with six-foot splines driven halfway into the soft ground. At right is shown a later phase prior to excavating the ground in front of the square set (g) and substituting the breast-boards (a) with a square set close to the face.

taking the weight of the top splines and secured by a beam wedged to the sides, would permit the bench to be removed and the legs of the forward set to be placed under the cap. The position of the heading at the beginning of the new cycle would be as shown in Fig. 45.

This, then, is the way a small tunnel, intended to carry a sewer main, for example, would be driven under a town built on soft ground. The tools used would be of the simplest kind—spade, hammer, pick and wedges. In the early stages of the advance the material would be carried out; later, rail would be laid in the finished part of the tunnel and the material loaded into small wagons pushed by men or pulled by mules or ponies. If a locomotive were used, sidings had to be excavated in the sides of the tunnel at certain points.

But such a forepoled working could equally well serve as the pilot heading which would subsequently be expanded into the full size of a railway tunnel. The most important thing in the whole operation

Fig 45. A forepoled heading entirely enclosed by lagging and supported by square sets.

is to excavate a hole in the ground without causing any runs. Should the balance of the material outside the lagging be disturbed in any way it will result in a run that will expose the timbering to local pressure and bring about its collapse. Such a run can under certain circumstances progress to the top of the ground and collapse the foundations of buildings and other structures.

In tunnelling through running ground it is vital to keep the breasting intact all the time, until the miners learn about the nature of the ground on the other side of the boards. There are numerous instances on record where carelessness in removing the boards has resulted in tragedy. A small mining drift advanced through rock in this fashion in a Silesian mine ran into what appeared to be running ground and the miners hurriedly boarded up the heading and hesitated about what to do next. A furious foreman came running down the heading cursing the men for the delay. He grabbed an axe and smashed the breasting, whereupon a flood of mud gushed into the heading and drowned the mining crew. It was subsequently discovered that the crew had struck a cavity in the rock filled with mud to a height of 146 ft., all of which drained into the drift.

Before proceeding any further it should be noted that no tunnel would be driven by means of forepoling today. For one thing, there probably exist throughout the western world no men capable of driving a heading in this manner: it is a lost skill. For another, advancing a tunnel through heavy ground could be accomplished in a number of different ways depending on local circumstances. The heading may be driven with a shield, or the running or soft ground may be firmed up with compressed air or, more likely, the character of the ground will be changed altogether by freezing it or by chemical injections. Moreover, by engaging a capable geologist it is possible to avoid such difficult ground entirely, by choosing a slightly different line.

None the less, the old-time method of forepoling gives in a nutshell all the pertinent aspects of tunnelling, and all the various modern techniques are in actual fact sophisticated variations of this basic theme.

Breaking Out

An old-time mining tunnel, or drift, seldom exceeded an area of 10 × 10 ft., whereas a single-track railway tunnel used to be given an area of 16 × 22 ft., and a double track 28 × 22 ft. (modern tunnels are larger). The conventional practice used to be to advance a small pilot heading first in the forepoling manner described—if in heavy ground—and subsequently expand it to full size in some way or other.

The method of breaking out from the safe, wholly enclosed pilot tunnel is one of the central problems in tunnelling and was endlessly debated throughout the last century. As a matter of fact it is still an issue that has to be argued as a preliminary to any tunnelling scheme, because if it is not correctly settled beforehand men will lose their lives and the contractor his capital.

During the last century a number of different tunnelling systems were evolved which derived their names from their national origin. These were the English system, the Belgian system, Austrian system, German (actually French) system, and the Italian so-called Cristina system. The Americans also laid claim to an independent system.

The English System

Of these different methods the most daring is the English system, which seems to have been developed before the construction of the Bleechingly and Saltwood tunnels during the 1830's. With this system a centre heading is driven along the crown of the tunnel some 16 to 24 ft. ahead of the masonry arch. The pilot heading would have, say, a width of 10 ft. and a height of 18 ft. and extend 3½ ft. above the crown of the finished arch. In dangerous ground the heading would be forepoled and timbered with square sets. Two 30-in. timbers 20 to 25 ft. in length would be placed in the crown, the forward ends resting on a pair of props and the rear ends atop the finished masonry. These so-called crown bars would be used throughout the length of the tunnel and, as it advanced, they would be slid ahead for the distance chosen as a section, which was always less than the length of the crown bars.

To repeat, in the English system of working, the fully excavated tunnel was immediately lined with masonry, and ahead of the masonry lining was driven the small pilot tunnel which was never permitted to go beyond the length of the crown bars. The lined section was of course safe; the forepoled advance heading was also safe until the time came to expand it to full tunnel width. As a preliminary to erecting a protective roof over the advance heading, the two crown bars were pushed ahead and placed on two props, as shown in Fig. 24.

With the two crown bars in place, the crown part of the pilot tunnel was widened somewhat to allow two further drawing-bars to be pulled ahead. In widening the section, the lagging had to be removed along the length of the heading and it became necessary to put it back in place before the next step. Now followed the most hazardous excavation along the shoulders of the tunnel to permit pulling ahead the lowest pairs of drawing-bars, whereupon the lagging was extended down to the shoulder line of the section. These six bars, then, the space between them filled with lagging, formed the roof over the top part of the advance heading permitting the rest of the excavation to proceed in relative safety.

The tunnel excavation proceeded in several steps. First, the upper part was taken out to the floor of the pilot tunnel. Then followed the tricky manœuvre of transferring the load on the crown bars from the vertical posts on to battered props footed on blocks placed on the floor. A heavy horizontal timber, called a sill, was placed across the entire width of the excavated top of the tunnel. Short props radiating to the six bars were placed on the sill and firmly secured. The remaining part of the crown was excavated for the entire length of the section.

The next step involved sinking a trench half-way down towards the bottom, followed by the sinking of two sloping holes down to the grade of the finished tunnel. In these holes were put rakers to brace the top sill. Having transferred the weight resting on the top sill to the rakers, the part of the tunnel area extending from the sill and half-way down was excavated along the entire section. As the excavation proceeded, additional rakers were put in place until in the end the top sill was resting on twelve props.

Now the middle sill with its saddle was put in and provided with rakers placed in holes sunk down to the tunnel floor. Twelve props were wedged between the two sills, before the remaining bottom bench was removed and the bottom sill placed. The same number of props as above were placed between the bottom and the middle sills and wedged firmly in place. Along the walls stretchers were placed between the end of the masonry and the forward props, and the sides were lagged against runs. This just about concluded the mining job. A whole tunnel section some 20 ft. in length would thus have been opened up and be ready for the masons to put in the lining. While the lining was being extended, the miners advanced the next section of the pilot heading preparatory to a new break-out cycle. The complete timbering is shown in Fig. 33.

The English system possesses a number of excellent features. The principal advantage is the large unobstructed space for the masons to work in. By the drawing and re-using of the six crown bars, the system is economical in timber and the debris can be removed easily and cheaply. Finally, there is no interference between the miners and the masons. For these reasons the system was employed from the 1830's in nearly all English tunnels. It was also used in the United States and New Zealand. On the Continent it was occasionally employed, having been introduced there by the famous English railway contractor Thomas Brassey when driving the Hauenstein tunnel in Switzerland in 1853–58. In America, the well-known Hoosac tunnel (to be discussed later), the Allegheny, Pittsburg, Baltimore and Lydgate tunnels were built on the English system.

The Belgian System

The system in vogue on the Continent up to the time of the St. Gotthard was the so-called Belgian system that had been developed in 1828 when a tunnel was being driven on the Charleroi Canal, as shown in Fig. 28. This was the system applied on the first two long

Alpine tunnels, Fréjus and Gotthard, but as a consequence of the catastrophe in the latter it lost favour among the engineers and went into a decline from which it never recovered. The great advantage claimed for the system by Belgian and French engineers is the speed whereby the roof of the tunnel can be secured, which of course is highly desirable when advancing a tunnel through poor rock.

As seen in Fig. 46, the advance begins by a top heading being driven which measures, as in the St. Cloud tunnel, $6\frac{1}{2} \times 9$ ft. This

Fig 46. The early phases of the Belgian System of tunnelling. To the left is the pilot tunnel driven along the roof of the tunnel. To the right the pilot heading has been enlarged and two props resting on a sill have been placed.

pilot tunnel is supplied with square sets and lagged if necessary. The pilot gallery is then immediately enlarged both vertically and laterally and two props resting on a mud sill are put in, as shown in Fig. 46.

With the two initial props in position, the pilot gallery is expanded to the full tunnel width, the miners placing radiating props on the mud sill as the excavation proceeds towards the sides. In the spaces between the square sets, additional rakers are put in to support the roof, as seen in Fig. 47a. Centres for the masonry are then placed and the lining is advanced in short sections by striking the timbers immediately in front of the arch. In Fig 47b the arch is being built.

Having secured the roof by first building the masonry arch of the tunnel, one can remove the remaining bench in several ways. A trench can be sunk down to grade along the centre of the tunnel, or else one can be sunk along each side. This side trenching implies, of course, that as the arch is undermined by the excavation it has to be underpinned as the masonry is being extended down to grade. With the masonry work completed to grade on both sides, the timbers are struck, whereupon the bench remaining in the centre can be removed without difficulty.

Fig 47. Putting in the arch lining of a Belgian tunnel.

The advantages of the Belgian system are more theoretical than real. It suffers from the disadvantage that the masses to be excavated are not available in a large coherent body, and working

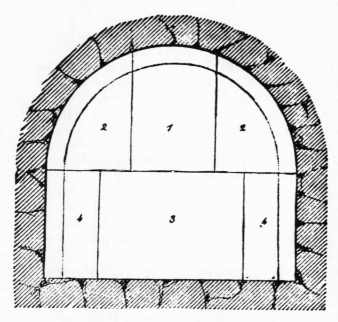

Fig 48. An early sketch indicating the sequence of excavation according to the Belgian System.

the pockets becomes expensive. But the really serious fault of the system, as it became clear in St. Gotthard, is the necessity for under-pinning the arch. In yielding ground the timbers give way, resulting in cracking or total collapse of the masonry arch.

The German System

The German or Centre Core system is said to have been developed from the method used in excavating the broad Bavarian beer-cellars. However, French engineers also lay claim to the system since it was first used in the excavation of the long Tronquoy tunnel on the St. Quentin Canal in 1803. This tunnel had a width of 26 ft. and was driven through soft ground.

The system developed for the excavation is shown in Fig. 27. First, a bottom heading was advanced and the abutments of the arch put in. Above the first heading and slightly off centre a second heading was driven, and above that a third. The arch was successively carried up through the three headings and laid on a core of well-rammed earth. Having extended the lining of both sides of the tunnel in this fashion, the top was excavated and the arch was struck, on a mound of well-rammed earth. Having completed and back-filled the arch, it was then a small matter to excavate the bench enclosed by the lining.

This was the French origin of the system which was later improved by German engineers in driving the first German railway tunnels, particularly the Königsdorff tunnel on the Dresden–Leipzig line advanced in 1837. Here the two bottom headings were driven along the sides and the foundation for the lining laid. At intervals, the two headings were united by crosscuts in which the invert was built. Then a top heading was advanced and the arch turned. With the lining in place the centre core was removed.

Although the obvious weakness of the German system was brought into the open in the Triebitz tunnel, built six years later, a large number of tunnels continued to be built in this manner on the Con-tinent, until it was eventually abandoned. The trouble with this system is, of course, the confined working space which prevents good masonry work being done. In the Triebitz the lower portions of the lining failed owing to faulty bonding, and had to be rebuilt. Also the arch had to be reinforced, whereby it came to occupy so much of the tunnel area that the original double-track tunnel could only be used for one-way traffic. For this reason, the Triebitz became the costliest tunnel built in Europe up to that time, at something like $290 per linear foot.

There is another objection to the centre core method as such that was not appreciated at the time. Instead of distributing the pressure as in all sound timbering systems, it concentrated on the core. A heavy wet core will sink at the top and sag at the sides, whereupon the roof timbers will become loose and sink.

Fig 49. Collapse of the Cžernitz Tunnel due to the sagging centre core.

The German system came to its calamitous end when applied to the Cžernitz tunnel, as shown in Fig. 49, where everything went wrong. Here, the headings, with their timbering, settled in the quicksand and the pressure was transmitted to the centre core. The sills carrying the top timbering were slewed out of place and the timbers broke. The result of the swelling ground is shown on the right, where 14-in. timbers have been broken and crushed by the tremendous forces developed by the swelling core.

The Austrian System

The second tunnel on the Leipzig–Dresden line, the Oberau tunnel, was built according to entirely different principles. This tunnel is 1,680 ft. long and was advanced in 1837–39 through marl, gneiss and seamy granite.

The tunnel was excavated full face, i.e. the full cross-section, or area of the tunnel, was mined in short sections. The pressure of the roof was taken up by a cap and two slanting legs, footed in notches cut in the rock, a method known as spar timbering. When the rock footing of the rafters proved poor, a horizontal brace was placed across the tunnel. If these timbers did not give the desired stability longitudinal bars were placed under the cap, or atop the brace, and props were added to the rafters until in the end a timbering system as shown in Fig. 32 was developed.

This, then, was the method of timbering selected when building the first Austrian tunnel, the Gumpoldskirch tunnel on the Vienna–Gloggnitz line in 1839. Here, a bottom heading was advanced for some distance, followed by a top heading which was timbered so that the caps served as parts of the full timbering system. Longitudinal bars were placed under the caps and propped up at their fore-end, while at the back they were carried on long legs extending to the floor of the tunnel. After these timbers were in place, the arch was broken out as before and raftered. When finished, the tunnel section appeared as in Fig. 32, which shows the centre in place and the arch about to be turned.

A number of Austrian tunnels were built according to this system during the ensuing decade, when the weakness of the timbering system began to be evident. The spars holding up the roof proved to be too long and were difficult to place in ground exerting much pressure. As will be seen from Fig. 32, a tremendous lot of ground had to be removed above the haunches of the arch and the space backfilled again after the arch had been turned.

Fundamentally sound as it was, the early system proved inadequate on numerous tunnelling developments where heavy pressure forced the sills and props out of alignment; with the yielding timbers, the pressure kept increasing until in the end timbers up to 2 or 3 ft. in diameter proved unable to take it and the heading was thus lost.

For this reason the Austrian system was about to be abandoned about a hundred years ago, instead of which it came under theoretical review resulting in a number of improvements which turned it into the most sophisticated of the old-time tunnelling systems. It was found that one of the principal troubles lay in the long sections being taken out together, which created areas of heavy pressure. It was also found that it was advisable in all cases, but particularly in wet ground, to drive a bottom heading first. By this means the ground above, and also the sides, would be drained and facilitate the subsequent mining. The use of tall props, extending from the bottom of the tunnel to the roof, was of course also abandoned in favour of dividing the area with a sill and using short props. In soft ground the timbering was steadied by rakers.

The improved and final version of the Austrian system is illustrated in Figs. 50 to 54. A bottom heading (see Fig. 50) is driven first, either part-way or along the entire tunnel at once. This pilot tunnel serves to ventilate the workings, to drain the surrounding area, and as a transport adit. It also aids in establishing alignment. The heading is heavily timbered, the cap will serve as the future middle sill and the side props as the legs of the centre frame. Longitudinal members are also placed as a future support of the centre frame.

Fig 50. To the left is the heavily timbered bottom pilot heading in the improved Austrian System of tunnelling. To the right a rise has been driven to beyond the crown of the finished tunnel, the timbering being carried on the pilot sets.

When the bottom heading has been advanced, the ground is usually drained so as to facilitate mining of the break-out area. The top heading is excavated, as shown in Fig. 50 (right) and timbered, the top structures resting on the undisturbed timbering below. The two headings, extending in combined height from the bottom to above the arch of the finished tunnel along the axis, will have drained the ground on both sides by the time the remainder of the tunnel is broken out.

Breaking out the tunnel to full width begins at the top, as shown in Fig. 51, and continues down to the shoulders. The rafters are propped up against the middle sill and the roof lagged. With the roof secured, the side benches are taken out in sections of 6, 9 or 18 ft. depending on the nature of the ground. When a section has been excavated, it appears as in Fig. 52. The longitudinal view of an advance showing the bottom and top headings, followed by an excavated section with centres placed for the masonry and, at the

Fig 51. In the last phase of the Austrian System the top heading is broken out to full tunnel width (left) and continued down to the shoulders of the tunnel (right). Note the large overbreakage needed to place the lining.

Fig 52. Final phase of excavation, prior to lining, in the improved Austrian System (left). To the right is a longitudinal view of a tunnel showing from left to right the top and bottom headings, a fully broken out section and, at the extreme right, the lining in place and backfilled.

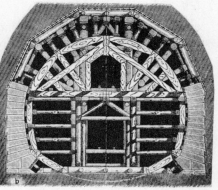

Fig 53. To the left is shown an Austrian tunnel with the centres being erected and the base of the lining in place. To the right the centres are in position and the lining has been extended up to the shoulders.

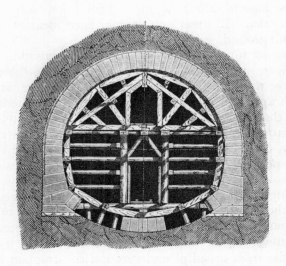

Fig 54. The final phase of advance of a tunnel driven according to the improved Austrian System. The entire lining is in place except for the invert.

extreme right, the lining in place is given in Fig. 53. The finished tunnel, except for parts of the invert, is shown in Fig. 54.

The advocates of the Austrian system claimed that it could be used in all types of ground, from loose rock to quicksand. It is much stronger than any of the previous systems owing to the fact that no large spaces are being left unsupported and the pressure is distributed over the entire timber structure. It also provides good ventilation and early drainage of wet ground.

The principal objection to the Austrian system is that it is too strong and hence unnecessarily costly for most tunnels. It requires a tremendous amount of timber, the presence of which makes the masonry work awkward and more costly than in the open English system.

The Italian System

The statement just made that the Austrian system could be used under any circumstances is not strictly accurate; no such claim will hold true because in tunnelling, ground conditions will eventually be encountered that will upset any preconceived ideas of what constitutes difficult ground.

In numerous tunnels the world over enormous difficulties have been met with and successfully overcome. The Gotthard and Simplon tunnels, as will be seen in subsequent chapters, at times presented such appalling conditions owing to the movement of decomposed rock that the workings came close to being abandoned. In some instances, ground conditions put a definite stop to the work.

However, the most horrible tunnelling ever recorded was without a doubt experienced in the Apennines on the Naples–Foggia line where six tunnels were driven in 1865–70. The tunnels were not particularly long, the shortest was only 548 ft. and the longest 10,509 ft. Three of them presented no particular difficulties; two of them caused serious troubles that were mastered by conventional means, but it was the sixth, the 4,698-ft. Cristina tunnel, that has gone into history as the most dreadful underground construction ever undertaken. Cristina will remain a monument to the skill and endurance of Italian tunnellers and civil engineers.

The material through which the tunnels were advanced consisted of a peculiar type of clay, *argilla scagliosa*—that was lacking in cohesion. It was encountered in lenticular or semi-laminated masses, wet and sliding along the contact faces. The Cristina tunnel was driven partly through this clay, partly in shaley marl. When the clay beds were disturbed by excavation, the clay would slide along the wet contact surfaces. The runs were propagated to a considerable height above the tunnel and exerted a tremendous pressure.

The tunnels were driven according to the Belgian system from numerous shafts, and the two shafts on the Cristina tunnel were located 550 yds. apart. The pilot galleries were rapidly advanced, but a few days after the ground had been opened up it began to swell and sometimes blocked the heading. The swelling gave trouble at the sides and bottom and necessitated the removal of much additional material. At times, the excess grew to about four times as

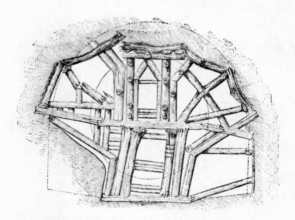

Fig 55. Crushed Austrian timbering
in the Cristina Tunnel.

much as the tunnel area. The moving ground crushed the props and broke the lining, and surface breaks appeared 160 ft. above the tunnel. Nevertheless, despite these difficulties one section after the other was completed and in May 1870 there remained only 143 ft. to be finished in the Cristina tunnel. This is the section that became historic, and the following account refers only to the work of mining and lining this short distance.

When a 6-ft.-thick arch had been repeatedly crushed, it was decided to drop the Belgian system altogether and try the Austrian. After some lengthy experiments, the new system was applied for a distance of 38 ft. divided into three sections. About 12,000 cu. ft. of heavy timber were put in, filling nearly half the excavated area. The work of excavation and timbering took 107 days.

Then the earth moved. Oak sills and caps 16 × 16 in. in section, and props 5 ft. in circumference split and shattered, the rafters collapsed and the entire timbering became disarranged and broken.

Masonry work measuring up to 5 ft. in thickness also broke. The havoc created by the moving earth is shown in Figs. 55 and 56.

The Austrian system, obviously, was not good enough for the Cristina. Something else had to be tried if the entire tunnel and the railway were not to be abandoned owing to these few feet of bad ground. But all systems had been tried to no avail. An entirely new one was needed. Such a new system had in fact been developed by L. Protche, consulting engineer on the tunnels. He had recommended

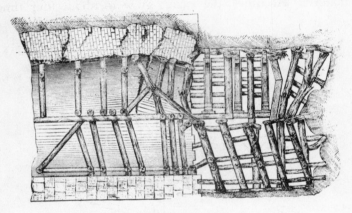

Fig 56. Longitudinal section showing the collapse of the lining and
heading in the Cristina Tunnel.

the excavation of the lower half of a section and filling it with stonework before mining the upper half. In this manner, the heavy timbers holding the roof would rest on an unyielding solid stone base, except for the narrow pilot heading in the centre. This method had worked to satisfaction in other difficult parts of the Cristina tunnel, although at a terribly high cost and slow advance, about 23ft. per month.

This, then, was the method resorted to in the last difficult section after the Austrian system had broken down. But the Protche system as originally devised was changed to the extent that the section was reduced to 6 ft. 6 in. in length, and the timbering greatly strengthened. The modified method, as shown in Fig. 57, worked for the first section; when advancing the second, the timbers were crushed and the heading was reduced to about 3 ft. square necessitating removing the materials in baskets.

So it went on for months, one failure following another, until in the end the final section was bridged by building an arch over the lower part of the tunnel, leaving a narrow transport and ventilation adit in the centre. By that time 97 ft. of top heading remained to be excavated and it was thought that, with the lower half practically filled with masonry, it would be safe to drive this distance and expedite the arching by obtaining more points in which to erect the masonry.

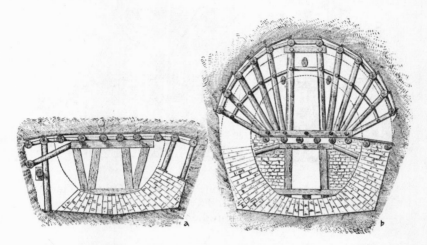

Fig 57. Another attempt to bridge the running ground in the Cristina Tunnel. A heavy stone base was put in (left) and filled with masonry so as to get a stable support for the timbers carrying the roof (right).

The decision was disastrous. One of the intermediate top sections opened up brought on a movement far worse than anything previously experienced. A 17-ft. depression developed on the surface and the run continued 230 ft. through the ground down to the tunnel and broke the arch. The adjoining finished lining was also broken, and in order to prevent total ruin all the excavated intermediate spaces were filled with masonry. The broken heavy lining is shown in Fig. 58. In the end, by carefully excavating a short section at a time and putting in a heavy invert, such as that shown in Fig. 59, the Cristina was made secure. It was accomplished by filling most of the excavated areas with masonry, but despite the heavy masonry lining, the ground pressure continued to deflect the lining, reducing the width of the tunnel so that no train could pass through it. It became necessary to trim the intrados so as to permit a train to squeeze through. The rails were bent to conform to the curves in the tunnel walls.

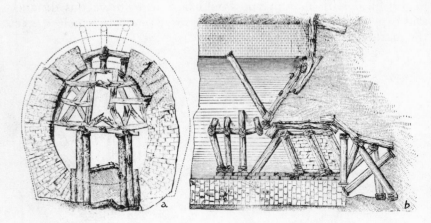

Fig 58. Failure of the heavy stone lining in the Cristina Tunnel owing to the moving ground. To the left is shown the broken lining, to the right a longitudinal section of the collapse.

Fig 59. The fully developed Cristina System of tunnelling. The excavated section was filled with ashlar, beginning with the invert, as soon as the clay was removed.

So the Cristina tunnel was at long last completed, and it was opened for traffic in 1871, three years later than estimated. The cost came out at $780 per linear metre, which is not surprising considering the heavy lining, as shown in Fig. 60.

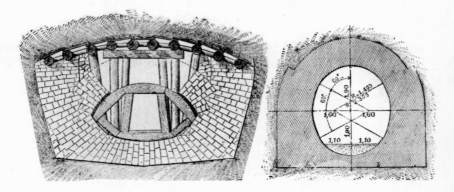

Fig 60. By filling in the excavated space with stone, leaving only a small pilot tunnel open in the centre, the Italian tunnellers finally succeeded in stabilizing the ground (left). The finished Cristina Tunnel is merely a small opening enclosed by a tremendous stone structure. But even this structure did not prove wholly stable and it became necessary to trim the sides to enable a train to squeeze through the tunnel.

As far as is known there has been no further occasion to apply the fully developed Cristina system of tunnelling, i.e. building a temporary arch and filling the lower half of the area with masonry in order to get a solid support for excavating and lining the top half. Some thirty years later a bad section of the same kind was encountered in the southern half of the Simplon tunnel, but the difficulty was overcome by heavy steel structures. Nowadays, such running ground would be mastered by freezing or by chemical means.

However, the Cristina tunnel is a useful reminder that in tunnelling too much reliance must not be put on orthodoxy. Or, as Signor G. Lanino, engineer on the site, summarized the tunnelling troubles he had known: 'In life the best system is not to be too systematic.'

The American System

At the time when the grand European tunnelling systems were in full flower, nobody recognized the tunnelling methods used in the United States or indeed took any notice of them. However, in view of the current developments in subterranean construction, which derive to a considerable degree from the American practice, a brief reference will be made to the rise of a typically American system of tunnel driving.

The American system has also been referred to as the 'block system' of timbering. It was a fully developed system when the Oxford tunnel was driven on the Delaware, Lackawanna and Western Railway in 1854. In its simplest form it resembles the rafter timbering used in the Oberau tunnel, i.e., it consists of a cap and two batter legs footed in a notch cut into the rock. The space between the sets is lagged with planks. This simple method of securing the roof was used in American railway tunnels from the 1830's. One such tunnel on the Baltimore and Ohio Railroad is shown in Fig. 35.

With the building of the Oxford tunnel in 1854, the system was further developed by the use of nine wooden voussoirs for the arching carried on stringers supported by 12 × 16-in. posts, as shown in Fig. 34. The voussoirs consisted of 5 × 12-in. planks. Above the arch and on the sides, 2½-in. timber lagging was placed when necessary. These wooden tunnels were sufficiently large to permit a masonry lining if needed at a later date.

Many such timber-lined tunnels were built through the United States in the decades around the middle of the century, most of them in the south-western States. The wooden tunnels, as shown in Fig. 34, as well as other timber structures used on the American railways, were from the beginning regarded as temporary measures to be replaced by permanent structures when the railways began earning profits. However, the interesting feature of these early American railway tunnels is that most of them were driven full face, i.e. the entire tunnel area was excavated, although in poor ground the top half was taken out to the full width and the roof secured with rafter timbering and lagged. When, subsequently, rock-drilling machines became available and the use of explosives became better understood, it was this naked and, compared with the complex European systems, primitive American method that proved most suitable to the 'full face' method so characteristic of modern underground workings.

In conclusion, it should be noted that the classic tunnelling systems briefly discussed are no longer used. Even in their hey-day they were threatened with extinction owing to the huge quantity and high cost of the timber used. A tunnel driven by the Austrian system in heavy ground would require a whole forest or, more accurately, the best timber selected in vast tracts of forest land. Where would be found today oak timber measuring 2 ft. or more when adzed to squares? By the time the Bessemer, the open hearth, and the Thomas processes of steel-making made cheap steel available for construction needs, steel—usually in the shape of profiles—began to be used as supports for tunnels and the wood lagging was replaced by pressed steel liner plate. Similarly, masonry—formerly the only type of lining used—became too awkward and costly, and concrete linings gradually began to take the place of masonry and ashlar.

It would indeed be difficult to find a tunnelling engineer today capable of accounting for the purpose of the different members forming a constituent part of, say, the Austrian system of timbering. It would be still more difficult to find a foreman capable of erecting the timbers. However, the names of the different systems, or at any rate the Austrian and the Belgian, live on, little though they signify today.

Chapter 6

THE FIRST ALPINE TUNNEL

*'He putteth foorth his hand upon
the rocke; he overturneth the
mountaines by the rootes.'*

BY 1850, the national railway systems on the Continent had been
extended across the frontiers and joined up. North of the Alps, the
French, German, Swiss and, in part, the Austrian railways were
linked together; south of the Alps, Italian railway construction proceeded seemingly unimpeded by political sub-divisions and revolutionary upheavals.

Between the embryonic northern and southern systems lay the
impenetrable barrier of the Alps. It was not only a physical barrier,
it was a cultural, religious and psychological one that from the
beginning of time had divided Europe in two. To the south of the
inaccessible peaks and deadly glaciers were the lands of the sun, the
heirs of Paradise gained and lost, of culture and sophistication. To
the north were the impenetrable forests, and in the bone-chilling
mists rising from the bogs men vied with the aurochs, bear and wolf
for ascendancy. To the south were Christ, Augustus, Franciscus, and
Machiavelli; to the north were Valhalla, Odin, Goths, long-haired
Merovingians, Calvin and Luther. It was a formidable barrier indeed
that had to be crossed in order to link the two railway systems.

Nevertheless, the challenge had to be accepted. In the early 1850's
Stephenson and Swinburne were called to Switzerland to lend their
advice on a tunnel through the Alps. They took one look at the

country and declared that it could not be done. No locomotive could climb the gradients necessary for a railway across the mountains. They left it to the natives to muddle through as best they could.

Behind these outstanding English railway engineers was ranged a phalanx of supporting scientific opinion.[1] The geologists maintained that the temperature under the mountains would reach such heights that men would be scorched to death. The mathematicians backed them up with beautiful fireworks of calculus suggesting that a tunnel through the Alps was vulgar nonsense. On the other hand, there were leading technical authorities who maintained that it was feasible to cross the Alps with summit railways at elevations of from 6,000–9,000 ft., using, if necessary, short tunnels under the passes. But these proposals bore the marks of desk work: they seemed to ignore the climate prevailing in the Alps at such altitudes. At the heights suggested the snow lasts for up to nine months of the year and covers the ground to 13 ft. or more. It is not unusual for drifts of over 50 ft. to accumulate in exposed spots. Such snow masses could not be removed by mechanical ploughs but would have to be cleared by hand. To obtain the labour necessary for keeping a summit railway clear of snow was not possible even a hundred years ago, particularly as storms heaping up gigantic drifts often raged for weeks on end. Even with the mechanized facilities available today a summit road crossing the Alps cannot be kept open all the year round.

Snow, then, is the reason for the Alpine tunnels, the portals of which have to be placed at sufficiently low levels to enable the railway to be kept clear. Unfortunately, however, owing to the cone-shaped profile of the massifs, the farther down the slopes the portals are placed the longer the tunnels become.

As frequently happens, the problem that induced university professors in France, Germany, Austria and Switzerland to question each other's scientific competence and personal honour had actually been solved twelve years before they became aware of it. A native and former shepherd of the small mountain village of Bardonnèche, nestling under the shadow of the Col de Fréjus, had already considered the problem of linking the French and Italian railway systems and given it the benefit of his local knowledge. Having been a herdsman in his youth, G. F. Medail knew his country intimately and, not being burdened with the technicalities of railway engineering, he succeeded in picking out a lovely meandering line descending from the village of Modane, to the north of the Fréjus massif, along the

[1] Francis Kossuth, Royal Commissioner for Railways in Italy, in articles published in *Engineering* (1857).

River Arc to the banks of the Isère. South of the massif he followed a natural route from Bardonnèche to Susa along the Dora Riparia. The two lines leading up to the massif, Medail suggested, should be linked by a tunnel.

In 1838 he submitted his plans to King Carlo Alberto of Sardinia, and three years later he published his scheme and tried to get the backing of the Chamber of Commerce of Chambéry, but without success.

In 1845, after Medail's death, King Carlo Alberto commissioned a railway between Genoa and Turin, as proposed by Brunel, to be built at government expense. A Belgian engineer, Heinrich Mauss, was retained as a consultant and ordered to study a suitable route across the Alps with the idea of extending the line being built into Savoy, then part of the kingdom of Sardinia. The seven-year-old Medail plan was found eminently suited to the purpose. A geological survey of Col de Fréjus was carried out by Professor Sismonda, an Italian geologist, who found that the mountain was built of quartzites, limestone, dolomite, and a few types of schists; this having been determined, the geological report was filed away to gather dust for thirteen years.

In 1846 a new name was added to the roster of famous men associated with the Fréjus project. A young engineer, Germain Sommeiller, who had been sent abroad by the Sardinian government to study railway engineering, worked after his return on the railway which was being extended up the Susa valley from Turin.

Seen in retrospect, there could have been no possibility of penetrating through the massif in 1850. As projected by Mauss, it entailed advancing a tunnel for a distance of 39,372 ft. under a rock cover that would extend to 3,937 ft. The tunnel had to be driven from both ends, with no intervening shafts for ventilation or the removal of debris. As we have seen, there had indeed been magnificent tunnelling performances before this; but it will be recalled that all previous tunnels had been driven from numerous shafts sunk to grade from the surface. The headings of the *qanaats*, the Roman aqueducts, the canal and the railway tunnels were never far from each other. The shafts, after serving their purpose of removing the rubble, were used as draught chimneys and there was never a problem of ventilation, except of getting rid of the locomotive smoke. The cover was modest in thickness and presented no difficult pressure problems.

Fréjus was altogether different. Two headings from the north and south portals had to be driven through a rock massif for 7·5 miles. The rock cover, according to geologists, would create a heat estimated at 160° F., and there was also the problem of supplying air to the miners working at a distance of 3·8 miles from the portals. But the Fréjus scheme fascinated inventive minds in both Europe and the United States, and patents were filed in such rapid succession that it is difficult to sort them out. Mauss himself obtained 500,000 francs from the Sardinian government to develop a tunnelling machine that would grind out the entire tunnel area; but after having spent the money to no avail, he ceased to have anything further to do with the Fréjus tunnel. The Swiss physicist Colladon proposed that compressed air be used as a medium to drive the machines-to-be, and the spent air would then be used for keeping the miners alive. This compressed air was to be produced by mountain torrents at both ends of the tunnel.

By 1854 the numerous ideas and suggestions began to sort themselves out. An English engineer, T. Bartlett, had invented a steam-driven rock drill which was tried out with compressed air the following year by a Sardinian commission appointed to report on the feasibility of using compressed air as a medium for operating rock drills. The Bartlett machine worked to the satisfaction of the commission, but in the end, like many others, it was abandoned. A German machine followed, and in 1855 Sommeiller brought out a model, in part original, in part an improvement on the Bartlett machine, that finally convinced the technical commission that a compressed-air tool was a practical idea. Later, the commission visited the United States in search of equipment and methods to be applied to the Fréjus development and there found an American direct-action rock drill patented some years previously. Features of that machine, invented by Fowle of Philadelphia, were later incorporated in the improved models used for advancing the Fréjus tunnel.

By 1857 the technical aspects were apparently under control, and what remained to be accomplished was action on the financial and political plane. This seldom presents a problem in Italy where great engineering projects have a powerful popular appeal and therefore become political instruments. Cavour saw in the Fréjus a great monument to the national dream of a united Italy. His colleagues in Victor Emmanuel's government, the Minister of Finance and the blind Minister of Public Works, were also in favour of the tunnel. Together on 29th June 1857 they pushed through the Fréjus Act whereby the Sardinian government undertook to pay half the estimated cost of the tunnel, or 20 million francs. The other half was to be paid by the Victor Emmanuel Railway, which was to operate the tunnel. Since this was a state railway the entire cost of 40 million francs fell on the Sardinian government.

Driving the Fréjus Tunnel

The name of the first long Alpine tunnel presents something of a mystery. In English technical literature it has always been referred to as 'Mt. Cenis', whereas the French and Italian railway administrations and cartographers—who should know—call it Fréjus. The tunnel pierces the Cottic Alps, between Mt. Tabor in the south-west and Mt. Cenis in the north-east. It passes right under the Col de Fréjus, whereas the Col du Mont Cenis lies something like fifteen miles distant and has nothing whatever to do with it. However, there is a good reason for calling the tunnel Mt. Cenis. That was indeed the original name of the tunnel because the bore under Mt. Fréjus superseded an ancient carriage road crossing Mt. Cenis, and in its capacity as the major transport lane across the Cottic Alps the tunnel inherited the old name. Much later it came to be called Fréjus, and since the tunnel is so named on modern maps and in continental references to it, this modern name will be used in the following brief account of its building history.

The final plan of the tunnel development approved by the Sardinian government had been prepared by the two Piedmontese engineers Sommeiller and Grattoni. It envisaged driving a tunnel between two given portals, one at an altitude of 4,408·5 ft. above sea-level at Bardonnèche on the southern side of the Fréjus massif, the other at 3,945 ft. in the neighbourhood of the small mountain village of Fourneaux on the northern slope. As later determined by survey, the distance between the portals was 13,365 yds., but such details were not known accurately at the time the work began.

Once it had given its approval, the Cavour government was in a hurry to get the tunnel started. On 18th August the first round was fired in the presence of King Emmanuel and Prince Napoleon at the northern portal. On the southern side, the first round was fired on 4th November. The work of driving the Fréjus was under way. The time estimated to complete the tunnel was twenty years, and nothing —not even the Italian War of Liberation that broke out two years later—was permitted to interfere with the work. When after the end of the war Savoy was ceded to France, a treaty was concluded by which the French government undertook to pay half the cost of the tunnel, and for every year pared off the estimated building time the French contracted to pay 500,000 francs.

It was a formidable task that confronted Sommeiller and Grattoni, his second-in-command. First of all they had to devise a survey accurate enough to ensure that the two headings would meet in the bowels of the mountain some twenty years later. They had to drive

Fig 61. Germain Sommeiller, pioneer of Alpine tunnelling.

a tunnel 7·5 miles in length with a new machine which, though apparently better than any other one in existence, had not been tried under actual working conditions. This machine was to be operated with compressed air, which had never before been applied to the driving of tools. To produce the compressed air required an entirely new machine, the air compressor, which had to be invented, designed, built, and put to the test under actual operating conditions.

To these technical problems were added some ugly logistical ones. Bardonnèche, or Bardonnecchia as it is called now, was a small mountain-village consisting mostly of dilapidated stables where the inhabitants, all of them herdsmen, huddled with their flocks when the winter storms raged over the Col de Fréjus. Fourneaux on the northern slope was another herdsmen's village with some 400 souls living in filth and sharing their hovels with their animals. About one and a quarter miles downstream was the somewhat larger village of Modane, which possessed a nucleus of civilized amenities. It was into these villages that Sommeiller had to crowd some 4,000 men, and feed them.

Before Sommeiller, and indeed long after his death, the canal and railway promoters and their contractors were not much concerned with camp facilities or the feeding and hygiene of the hosts of men mobilized to do the work. These workers were left pretty much to fend for themselves under wretched conditions, and when, as often happened, a construction site was struck by typhus or other diseases generated by filth, they died like flies.

The manner in which Sommeiller mastered these formidable difficulties gives a measure of both the man and the engineer. He realized from the outset that a social rehabilitation scheme of a major order would have to be undertaken before he could hope to make any progress with the tunnel. All the existing houses in the villages were made fit for human habitation and many new ones were erected. The local building material was brick, but owing to the climate masonry work could only be carried out during six months of the year, and even then a great many working days were lost owing to bad weather. It took three years before even the key men—the engineers, clerks, foremen, etc.—could be accommodated near the northern portal. During these years they camped in Modane, walking across one and a quarter miles of marsh and morass, and in winter through five feet of snow, four times a day to reach their place of work at Fourneaux.

Eventually two new communities were built around the two portals. On each side there was acceptable accommodation for 2,000 persons. Single men were quartered four to a room, married men

Fig 62. The shepherd hamlet of Bardonnèche before the driving of the Fréjus Tunnel.

Fig 63. The village of Modane at the time when it served as the northern base camp during the advance of the Fréjus Tunnel.

Fig 64. General view of the portal installations at Bardonnèche with accommodation for 2,000 workers. Engraving from a contemporary photograph.

Fig 65. The hydraulic compressor plant at Bardonnèche which at first supplied compressed air to the rock-drilling machines.

lived in separate quarters with one room to a family. There were schools for the children, a hospital, a cookhouse, a club house, and baths. There were numerous repair shops fully equipped with machine tools, forges with air-powered hammers and other air tools, offices, compressor installations, gas works, powder magazines and powder cartridge filling shops, and so on.

Such facilities are of course now commonplace on all major construction developments, and although similar establishments were repeated on subsequent Alpine tunnelling jobs, Sommeiller was a pioneer in his grasp of these essentials. From a technical point of view as well as in logistics and social amenities Fréjus stands as the watershed in tunnelling and underground work generally. Everything that has since happened in these fields goes back to Germain Sommeiller and his magnificent work in advancing the Fréjus tunnel. But it has taken a long time for his social ideas to take root and mature. A hundred years later, in the 1960's, newspaper reporters are still amazed when they find construction workers housed like human beings.

The Advance

While the portal installations were being put in, work on the tunnel proceeded from both ends. During the first six years it was a slow and frustrating job. A pilot heading measuring 11 × 8 ft. was driven by manual drilling along the floor of the tunnel. It was raised to the full height of the tunnel, whereupon the crown was broken out to the shoulders and lined. With the roof secured, the benches left along the sides were removed and the lining extended to the floor of the finished tunnel.

The drilling was done entirely by hand. Holes were drilled to a simple pattern to a depth varying from 18 to 36 in., depending on the nature of the rock, by double-handed drilling—one man wielding the hammer and another turning the 'jumper', i.e. a drill steel provided with a simple chisel-shaped bit. The holes were charged with black powder and ignited with a fuse. The advance recorded during these early years was on the average 9 in. per twenty-four hours.

While the tunnel was being advanced in this painfully slow fashion, Sommeiller and his engineers were busy solving the technical problems of a mechanized advance. These will be discussed in some detail in a subsequent chapter; here it should only be noted that the long delay in putting the rock drills to work derived from the difficulties experienced with the first compressor installations. They had been built according to an ancient idea of compressing air by falling water advocated by the Swiss Professor Colladon. As installed at Bardonnèche, these hydraulic compressors—there were ten of them producing a total of 6,000 cu. ft. of air per minute at a pressure of 6 atm.—consisted of inclined cast-iron pipes ending in a U-shaped part provided with a suitable valving system. Water with a head of 164 ft. descending from a dam built above the compressor station impacted against the bottom of a vertical pipe, thereby compressing the air entrained in the water. By a clever valving arrangement, the air and water were separated and the compressed air delivered into an air receiver, whereas the water was allowed to escape. From the common air receiver a pipe conducted the air into the tunnel to operate the rock drills. Since these machines were used intermittently while the water columns never ceased compressing air, the supply pipe was fitted with a safety valve close to the face. When the pressure built up to 7 atm. the valve opened, releasing compressed air to ventilate the tunnel. With the rock drills working, the valve stayed shut and the heading was ventilated by the air exhausted by the machines.

It was a brilliant idea admirably executed. The trouble was that the idea was too brilliant. The water hammer pounding on the annular valve at the bottom of the column destroyed the valve and put the unit out of service. There was at the time no material good enough to withstand the tremendous impact on the valve when closing. The costly compressor plant had to be scrapped and the type of machine used on the Modane side substituted.

The new machines installed combined a well-tried prime mover with Montgolfier's water ram. Sommeiller called them 'water-spout machines'. He utilized the 164-ft. head to drive a series of seven water wheels made of iron and having a diameter of nearly 20 ft. and a width of 16 ft. To both ends of the shaft of such a wheel was fitted a flywheel with a connecting rod working a piston enclosed in a cast-iron horizontal cross-head. The reciprocating movement of the piston displaced water enclosed in the cross-head. On the forward stroke the water was forced up into a vertical cylinder joined to the cross-head, thereby compressing the air trapped in the top of the cylinder. By means of a valve at the top, the air was collected in a manifold pipe connecting all seven machines and joined to air receivers previously installed for the water-column compressors. These water-spout machines worked smoothly and reliably for years on end, with no need for repairs. The output was adequate up to 1864, when two large 164 × 6·5 ft. air receivers were added to conserve the air previously released by the safety valve and used to ventilate the tunnel when the rock drills were not working.

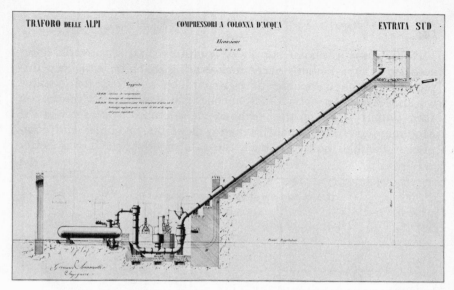

Fig 66. A contemporary drawing of the hydraulic compressor plant at Bardonnèche. Legend: ABBB, water pipe; C, water reservoir; DDDD, air delivery pipe.

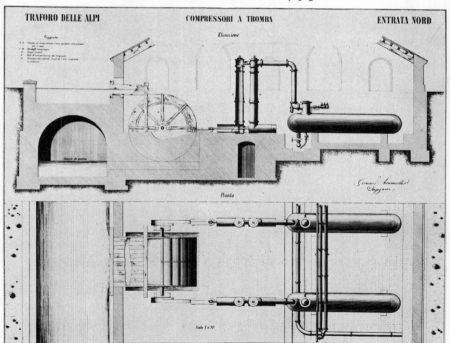

Fig 67. 'Water spout' compressors designed by Sommeiller worked without trouble at both portals of the Fréjus Tunnel for the duration of the mechanized advance. Contemporary elevation and plan. Legend: AA, air compressor cylinder; C, crosshead; D, water cylinder; E, overshot wheel; F, air pipe between air receiver; G, air delivery pipe.

By the time a reliable supply of compressed air was available on both sides, Sommeiller's early rock-drilling machine had been improved to such an extent that it could be relied on for a stable working cycle. In actual fact, mechanical drilling had started on 12th January 1861 on the Bardonnèche side and a year later at the Modane end, but frequent breakdowns of the machines and compressor troubles had held back the rate of advance; it was better

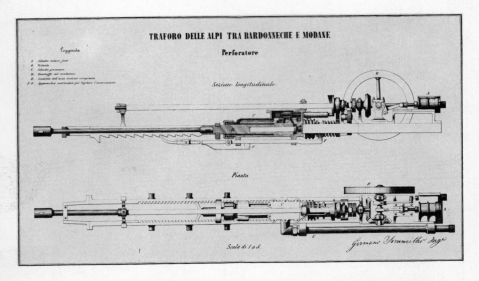

Fig 68. Sommeiller's improved rock drill, patented and put to work at both ends of the Fréjus Tunnel in 1863. Contemporary longitudinal section and plan. Legend: A, air motor; B, flywheel; C, percussion cylinder; D, piston; E, air supply pipe; F, feed mechanism.

than the manual average but not good enough to warrant the large investments in plant. The rate recorded in 1861 was 557 ft. with a best advance of 1·57 ft. per day. In 1862 the machines working at the Bardonnèche end attained a progress of 1,278·5 ft. with a best daily advance of 3·41 ft.

When the new machines were put to work in the summer of 1863 the rate of advance rose, and in 1864 it was 2,038 ft. on the Bardonnèche end and 1,529·1 ft. on the Modane end. The best daily advance that year was 9·75 ft. From that year on, the annual advance kept improving on both ends, and in 1870 no fewer than 2,917·7 ft. were chalked off at the southern end and 2,447·2 ft. on the northern end.

That year a record daily advance of 14·89 ft. was attained. Mechanical drilling in hard rock had revolutionized work underground, and there was no return to the old manual ways of excavating rock.

Sommeiller's air-operated rock drills, although troublesome to maintain,[2] possessed a number of features associated with modern machines: they were impacting, rotating and had an automatic feed. On one setting the machine drove a drill steel a distance of 31·5 in., which was the average depth of the hole drilled. A unit weighed 440 lb. and worked steels with Z-shaped bits varying in gauge from $1\frac{9}{16}$ to $3\frac{1}{8}$ in. As in all machines available during the last century, the drill steel was attached to the cylinder and followed its 8-in. stroke.

A number of these machines—varying from four to nine—were mounted on a wheeled carriage weighing 12 tons. It ran on rails which were moved up to the heading when the previous round had been mucked out. By means of screws and gears each machine could be positioned within a rather wide field of the face. They were joined with flexible tubes coupled to a distributing head at the end of the air main. The dust produced from the drilling was suppressed by dousing the face with water jets from a supply tank in the rear of the carriage.

So far as the actual drilling was concerned, the practice developed by Sommeiller resembles in many details the one frequently used today, except, of course, the number of men employed. Whereas he used altogether sixty men in each pilot heading, only six or even fewer would be employed today. It is also interesting to note that the heavy multi-unit drill carriage which he introduced has again returned in the United States, after having gone out of fashion at the turn of the century, and in Europe was applied for the first time on the French side of the Mt. Blanc tunnel.

By the middle of the 1860's, when the organization had shaken down to mechanized drilling, the underground working force was divided into three shifts of eight hours. In the pilot tunnel some sixty men were employed in drilling, charging and mucking. About eighty horses were used in hauling out the broken rock and bringing steel and lining material into the tunnel.

The drill carriage, mounting the four to nine units and nursed along by thirty men, was brought up to the face, and drilled altogether eighty holes. Three holes in the centre were of 3-in. gauge and were left uncharged. They were drilled with a $1\frac{1}{2}$-in. steel and

[2] For twenty machines in actual operation on each heading sixty were being repaired. The repair cost was something like 5 francs per metre (3·28 ft.) drilled.

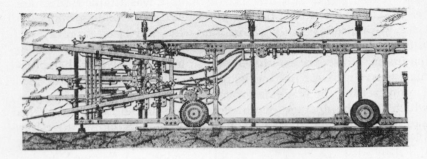

Fig 69a. Drill carriage mounting four to eight Sommeiller rock drills, as employed in the pilot headings at both ends from 1863 until the completion of the work in 1870.

Fig 69b. The drill carriage in action.

then reamed out to full size. The work at the face was illuminated
by gaslight.

The rest of the holes were drilled to a depth of 32 to 36 in., using a
drill set of $1\frac{9}{16}$ in., $1\frac{7}{16}$ in., and $1\frac{5}{8}$ in. gauge. To produce these
eighty holes required 120 steels; sometimes one hole required three

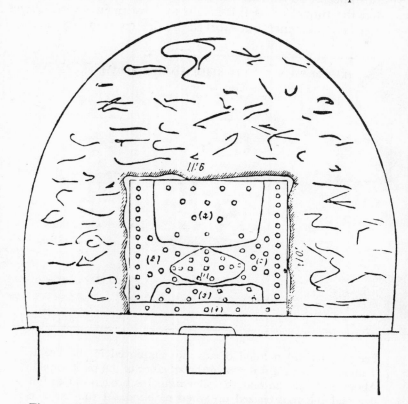

Fig 70. Contemporary sketch of a blasting pattern used in the
Fréjus pilot headings in 1862.

sets of steel. In fissured rock, the steels were provided with a
Z-shaped bit, in good rock the simple chisel bits were used. All but
the three large centre-cut holes were charged with gunpowder and
fired successively in four groups. The last row of holes was charged
and fired after the first three and after the debris had been cleared
up. The machine tenders were paid 4·50 francs per day, the miners
and muckers 4·00 francs. If a round was drilled in less than six hours
the entire gang was paid a premium equivalent to a quarter of a
day's pay; if the round was completed in less than five hours the

premium was raised to half a day's pay. Each round blasted with gunpowder (dynamite, although available towards the end, was never used in Fréjus) pulled about 20 cu. yds. and produced an advance of 6 ft.

At a distance of 80 ft. from the face 170 miners and sixty muckers excavated the tunnel to its full height and width in several stages. They used no machines but worked in the conventional manual

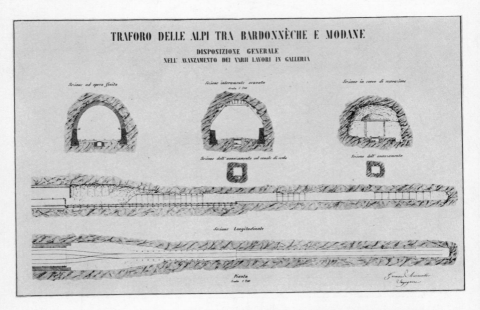

Fig 71. General method of advance employed in the Fréjus Tunnel. To the right is shown the advance of the pilot tunnel. About 80 ft. in the rear the pilot tunnel is broken out to full size and the roof trussed up when required. At the extreme left the masonry is being placed. From a drawing by Sommeiller. *Top left,* finished tunnel; *top centre,* fully excavated section; *top right,* pilot heading; *centre,* drain in floor; *below centre,* longitudinal section; *bottom,* plan.

manner. First they drove a raise to the full height of the tunnel, after which they broke out the arch on both sides down to the shoulders. When in poor rock they put in a masonry arch, thereby securing the roof before proceeding any farther. With the arch in place or the roof supported by timbering, or left unsupported, depending on the nature of the rock, they broke out the remaining benches on both sides down to the invert. In this manner the tunnel, including both headings, was advanced on the average by 7·7 ft. in twenty-four hours.

Farther to the rear a gang of twenty masons, aided by sixty labourers and ten boys, erected the lining consisting of ashlar on the sides and, at the Italian end, masonry in the arch. To keep these underground crews at work, the portal installations at each end required 570 men, in addition to a supervisory force of sixty men and some 200 transport workers.

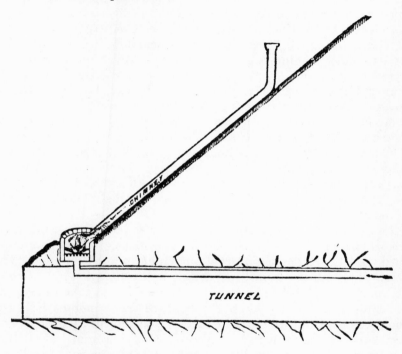

Fig 72. Furnace and chimney installed at the southern end to improve ventilation.

Ventilation proved a serious problem. The exhausted air from the machines kept the pilot headings adequately ventilated, but with the advance of the tunnel the workings in the rear became insufferable. The heat also rose, though never to the 160° F. predicted by the geologists, but at times to 80–90° F. To improve the ventilation, a 300-ft. chimney was raised at the southern end and a fire lit under it to create draught. When this proved wholly inadequate a horizontal brattice was placed along the entire tunnel from each portal. A 32-ft. fan at the southern portal drove fresh air into the lower half of the tunnel and the vitiated air was exhausted through the upper half. On the northern side, circulation was maintained by powerful exhaust pumps. The ventilation machinery was driven by overshot waterwheels.

Although by no means satisfactory, principally owing to the large volumes of carbon dioxide generated by the blastings and the not inconsiderable amount of air consumed by the oil lamps lighting up the rear workings, the measures taken in 1864 to improve the ventilation were adequate to keep the men and animals in working health, and Fréjus escaped the dreadful conditions later experienced in the St. Gotthard tunnel. The accidents were held down to a rate of which modern safety engineers could be proud. Only fifty-five casualties were recorded from 1857 to 1871, of which twenty-eight were fatal.

In 1867, when 14,386 ft. remained to be excavated, the Italian government turned the work over to Sommeiller and Grattoni at a contract price of $895 per linear metre (3·28 ft.) of finished tunnel. Three years later, at 4.25 p.m. on Christmas Day 1870, the thin partition separating the two headings was pierced by a drill 12½ ft. in length, and at 5.20 p.m. the following day the breakthrough round was fired. Signor Capello, surveyor of the tunnel and in charge of the northern end, was the first man to walk through the whole length of the Fréjus tunnel, the world's longest.

As a surveyor Signor Capello could be proud of the work done twelve years previously. The error in alignment was less than half a yard, and the difference in level amounted to about one foot. The actual length of the tunnel was determined at 40,138·3 ft. Owing to the method used, the Fréjus was nearly completed at the time of the breakthrough, and it required only three more months before it could be opened for traffic. By that time 960,000 cu. yds. of rock had been excavated after firing 2,954,000 rounds consuming 580 tons of gunpowder. The final cost came to $14,600,000 or $295 per linear foot, against an estimated cost of $6,300,000.

Fréjus, this masterpiece of tunnel engineering and breakthrough of new concepts in underground work, was officially opened on 17th September 1871 in the presence of 1,500 prominent guests invited from nearly every European country. Sommeiller was not present, having died from overwork in the fashion of all great tunnelling men, on 11th July that year.

Before the guests boarded the train that was to take them on the inaugural journey through the tunnel, they sat down to a feast on the heap of rubble outside the southern portal. There was a great deal of the type of oratory deemed suitable to such an occasion, and innumerable toasts were proposed and drunk in a torrent of cham-

Fig 73. Driving the last spike at the junction of the rails in the middle of the Fréjus Tunnel. From a contemporary engraving.

Fig 74. The inaugural train entering the Fréjus Tunnel on 17th September 1871. Note the alignment tunnel to the left. From a contemporary engraving.

pagne—but none was drunk to the memory of Germain Sommeiller. Somehow or other the assembled politicians (among them Charles de Rémusat, the French Foreign Minister and Victor Lefranc, Minister of Public Works) who exchanged flowery compliments upon this historic occasion succeeded in forgetting completely the man responsible for the feat they were celebrating. Perhaps there was some excuse for this, because this is what they ate and drank:

> *Potages: Consommé à la Royale—Purée de Riz à l'Ecarlate*
> *Hors-d'œuvre: Petites Bouchées à la Reine*
> *Relevés: Truites du Mont-Cenis—Sauce Genevoise*
>   *Filets de Bœuf à la Maréchale*
> *Entrées: Jambon d'York au Sherry*
>   *Salmis de Perdreaux des Alpes aux Truffes*
>   *Poulardes de Bresses à la Périgueux—Aspics de Fois Gras*
>   *Punsch à la Romaine*
> *Rôtis: Cailles de Vignes—Dindonneaux Piqués au Cresson*
>   *Salade Russe—Petits Pois au Beurre*
> *Entremets: Gateaux Gênois—Ananas au Vin de Champagne*
>   *Gelée de Fruits au Marasquin—Fromages Glacés*
>   *Dessert—Café et Liqueurs*

The list of wines was equally impressive: Madeira, Syracuse, Hautes-Sauternes, Montrachet, Bacolo, Gruan-Laroze, Pommard, Château-Lafitte, Chambertin, Grand Crémant, Moët frappé, Lacryma-Christi mousseux.

To complete the record, the Fréjus inauguration feast came to 55 francs per head, or about the cost of excavating one cubic yard of rock in the tunnel.

Troublesome Hoosac

While in the Alps the Fréjus tunnel was advanced in its slow but technically admirable manner, in the United States another long mountain tunnel became entangled in all the troubles and difficulties that can possibly beset a major construction project. 'When the first locomotive rolls through the Hoosac Tunnel bore,' wrote Oliver Wendell Holmes, 'then order your ascension robes.' Little did Holmes and his contemporaries realize that out of the Hoosac mess would ascend the American compressed-air industry which, during a strange twenty-five-year hydraulic interlude in Europe, took an unchallenged leadership in developing and providing the mining and construction industries with the only types of tools and machines hitherto capable of mechanizing work underground.

The idea of piercing the Hoosac Mountain in western Massachusetts was born in 1825 in connection with a canal project linking Boston with the Hudson River. The New England merchants watched with envy and apprehension how the newly completed Erie Canal brought the lucrative western markets under the control of their rivals in New York.

Fig 75. The first long mountain tunnel in America was driven through the Hoosac Range in western Massachusetts 1855–76.

The Boston–Hudson canal never left the dream stage after the railways had come on the American scene. In 1848, a petition was filed with the State of Massachusetts for a charter for a railway through the valleys of Dearfield and Hoosac to the state line, where it was to connect with a line leading to Troy in New York. The charter was granted and the Troy and Greenfield Railway Company was formed with a capital of $1 million. Six years later, in 1854, an Act was passed by the Legislature 'to enable the Company to construct the Hoosac Tunnel' and, in addition, it granted the railway company a state credit of $2 million towards the construction of the tunnel. In this manner the Yankee politicians managed to get themselves involved, no doubt to their regret, in an undertaking that immersed the State in endless trouble and expense.

The original estimate of the cost of building the Hoosac tunnel was calculated to the last dollar, or $1,948,557—no more and no less. The time for its completion was also determined in advance: completing the Hoosac would take 1,556 days—no more and no less. If, however, a central shaft were sunk, the consulting engineer was certain that the duration of the work would be reduced to 1,054 days. But there were difficulties from the beginning. For one thing, the railway company failed to raise its share of the capital, as nobody in Boston and its environs was anxious to invest in anything that would take at least 1,054 days before returns on the investments could be expected.

However, there were contracting firms willing to take the long-term view. A contract was signed with E. W. Serrel & Co. in 1855, under which some work on the tunnel was done, but the following year the first contractor had had enough of the Hoosac and bowed out. The second contractor, Herman Haubt & Co., offered in 1858

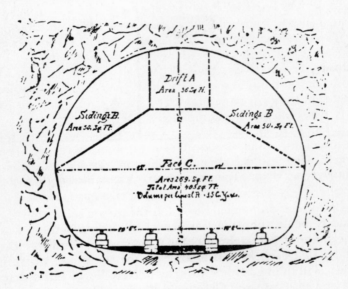

Fig 76. Cross-section of the Hoosac Tunnel and the sequence of excavations used, as proposed by A. F. Edwards in 1851.

to build the railway and the tunnel and also raise money for it provided the firm received $2 million in state bonds, plus $900,000 in railway company bonds, plus $1·1 million in cash.

The Legislature agreed, and under the contract the work was vigorously pursued until June 1861 when the state engineer refused to approve a payment, and Contractor No. 2 downed his tools. By that time a shaft 306 ft. deep had been sunk and 1,850 ft. of the tunnel advanced westwards from it. From the east portal 2,400 ft. had been excavated. The total cost to the state at that time was $778,695.

The works were left idle until October 1863 when a State Commission took over. Of the total length of 24,416 ft. of tunnel there remained 20,166 ft. to be excavated by the Commonwealth of Massachusetts. The People of the State took over the assets of the railway company, or what passed for assets, by an Act of 1862.

The State Commission put in charge of the Hoosac proceeded in a most impressive manner. While the work was stopped, the Commission sent an engineer to Europe to report on current tunnelling developments. Other reports dwelt on the development of rock-drilling machines, air compressors, explosives, and so on. It so happens that owing to these and subsequent reports the official archives of the Massachusetts Legislature form one of the best sources in the world for the study of the art of tunnelling a century ago.

For one year no advance on the tunnel was made. Instead, the time was spent in damming the Deerfield River to provide power for the new compressors. In addition, a large oval shaft measuring 27 × 15 ft. was sunk, but not completed.

The advance by means of a top heading, instead of the bottom heading previously used, began in 1865 on three faces, each heading being 15 ft. wide and 6 ft. high. At the year's end, a total of 634 ft. had been gained at an expenditure of 9,522 man-days. Other pertinent details of this classic American operation are as follows:

Number of drills dulled	153,436
Number of holes drilled	16,350
Inches of holes drilled	403,150
Pounds of powder used	11,195
Cubic yards of rock removed	2,329

The figures suggest that in the mica-schists, gneiss and granitic gneisses of the Hoosac tunnel an advance of 1·04 ft. per day was obtained in headings averaging 94 sq. ft. The removal of one cubic yard of rock required 3·6 man-days, 15 ft. of drill holes and about 5 lb. of gunpowder.

In the following year, on 31st October 1866, Burleigh rock drills were introduced in the east heading. They were supplied by a compressor delivering 148 cu. ft. of air per minute at a pressure of 42 lb. per sq. in. This mechanical compressor, as well as its successors, was designed by the resident engineer of the tunnel, Thomas Doane, who that year also began experimenting with nitroglycerine, imported from Europe. Electric firing was also introduced by him.

By using machine drilling but retaining gunpowder for blasting,

he increased the advance to 1·5 ft. per day in a 105 sq. ft. heading.
The removal of one cubic yard of rock took 4·3 man-days, 15 ft. of
holes and 6·7 lb. of powder. So, in fact, the early advantages gained
by mechanization were quite modest and cost more than manual
drilling.

In 1867, Thomas Doane had had enough of his long and frustrat-

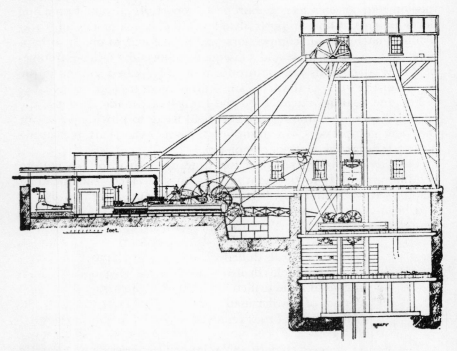

Fig 77. Installations at the central shaft of the Hoosac Tunnel
were wrecked by fire in 1867 and thirteen men lost their lives.

ing job of trying to drive the Hoosac with the State Assembly sitting
on his neck, and resigned. But it was due to his initiative and designs
that the art of American tunnelling was lifted from its primitive state
to a level from which it could spring to its subsequent technical
prominence.

Thomas Doane's successor lasted only a few months, after which
the State Commissioners took turns acting as resident engineer. The
actual work of driving the tunnel was let to a contracting firm which
lasted three months. A fourth contractor was then put on, driving
from the west portal. After seven months of work a naphtha fire

broke out and consumed the central shaft installations and caused the loss of thirteen lives. In the public outcry the contractor found it politic to surrender the contract and the tunnel was handed back to the Commissioners. Exit Contractor No. 4.

According to a report issued by the consulting engineer for 1867, the cost of driving the heading by the state had come to $24.46 per cubic yard, whereas the last contractor had performed the same work for $7.25.

In 1858, the commissioner in charge sank one of the shafts started by Doane to grade and thus obtained two new headings. In June, a drill carriage mounting five drills was introduced in still another heading from the west end, and in August nitroglycerine began to be used regularly, a factory having been established in the near-by town of North Adams. Towards the end of the year, on 24th December 1868, a contract for completing the tunnel was given to Shanly Brothers of Montreal for the sum of $4,594,268. The work was to be completed by 1st March 1874, but the Governor of the state was authorized to extend the time by six months if necessary. By the time the fifth contractor entered the tunnel, the state had spent $3,002,176 in the Hoosac hole. It may be recalled that the original estimate of 1851 called for a cost of $1,948,557.

At the end of 1868, the consulting engineer resigned leaving his testament in a report to the effect that the work was not particularly difficult. The poor rock at the west end was not so bad as the clays and quicksands encountered in European tunnels. The wet west shaft needed only pumps to be kept dry, and the east end was really a *comfortable* piece of underground work. The real difficulties were in the main due to extraneous causes that had nothing to do with the work as such. But there was no particular need to dwell on them, since now, it was to be hoped, they had been removed.

After fourteen years of work and the expenditure of five contractors, three site engineers, the consulting engineer and numerous commissioners, the Hoosac tunnel was again resumed in late March 1869, having been at a standstill from the end of the previous year.

Advance of the east heading began on 29th March, the central shaft sinking was resumed on 20th May, the west heading came alive on 2nd July. By December the contractor had 700 men at work. On 13th August 1870 the shaft reached grade. A heavy rainstorm on 3rd and 4th October flooded the west end workings and stopped operations for a month. Improved machines began to give satisfactory results and saved, according to the contractor, two-thirds of the expense of drilling. That year an advance of 1,514 ft. was made, and the monthly rate increased to 126·17 ft., as against 47·54 ft. in 1866 when manual drilling and gunpowder were still used exclusively.

As the use of compressed-air drills was gradually mastered, the monthly advances kept climbing, until in 1873 an advance of 162 ft. was attained for the best month. Breakthroughs were obtained on

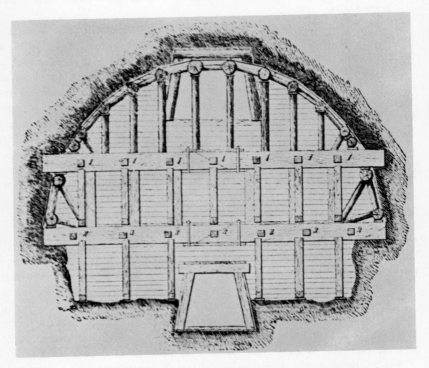

Fig 78. Timbering in the Hoosac Tunnel was according to the English System employing drawbars.

12th December 1873 on the two headings east of the main shaft, at 11,274 ft. from the east portal. The two west headings met on 27th November. After twenty-three years of trial and tribulation it was nothing short of a wonder how accurately the survey work of the tunnel had been performed. For the east breakthrough the error in alignment was 5/16 in. and the grade a few hundredths of a foot. The breakthrough in the west occurred at 10,138 ft. from the portal with an error in alignment of 9/16 in. and 0·134 ft. in level. The error in distance was trifling.

A new consulting engineer was appointed in 1871, but was succeeded after a few months by a third who remained until early 1875, when he also resigned, and was succeeded by Thomas Doane, the site engineer of ten years earlier.

Shanly Brothers concluded their work on 22nd December 1874, nearly nine months after the contract date. But this was by no means

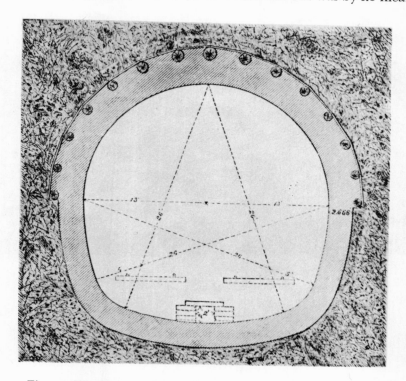

Fig 79. The Hoosac Tunnel was lined as an afterthought. In some bad spots the drawbars had to be walled in.

the end, for the Hoosac had also to be lined. Five experts were retained to report on the need for lining, and all five gave widely different estimates for lining and arching. During the long period of construction the exposed rock had become weakened by percolating water and the veins had dissolved and turned the rock into detached blocks lacking cohesion. In all, some 2,500 linear feet of tunnel had to be lined, necessitating the removal of 12,000 cu. yds. of rock. The lining was put in place by 1st January 1876.

So, at long last, the Hoosac tunnel reached completion. It was officially opened on 1st July 1876 after twenty-one years of work. The total cost came to $10 million, or $409 per linear foot. Ten years later, it has been stated, the Commonwealth of Massachusetts was still budgeting nearly half of its revenue to pay off the debt incurred for the troublesome Hoosac tunnel.

Fig 80.

Chapter 7

THE ST. GOTTHARD TUNNEL

IT WAS, of course, inevitable that Gotthard sooner or later would be subjected to close scrutiny as a possible location for a tunnel through the Alps. Through this 6,927-ft. pass, runs an axis connecting Milan via Zürich with the Ruhr and its numerous industrial centres, Cologne, Düsseldorf, Essen and many others, its extension striking the North Sea close to Amsterdam and Rotterdam. Clearly, such a costly undertaking as a tunnel through the central massif of the Alps required the traffic load generated by this wealth-producing ribbon. But from a historical point of view also Gotthard was predestined for a tunnel. The Gotthard Strasse had carried the north- and south-bound traffic from Roman times. A 13-ft. pack trail across the pass existed in the sixth century, and throughout the Middle Ages countless northern pilgrims struggled through the pass on their way to Rome.

The importance of the Gotthard Pass as a major link between north and south was recognized by the Emperor Frederick II, who issued a charter guaranteeing free access to it in 1231. The famous hospice on the summit was built in 1431 and served as a refuge from the mountain storms for nearly five centuries, until it was torn down by Napoleon's soldiers who used it for firewood. The vital importance of the pass is also evidenced by the saving of time when mail began to be carried over it in 1696. Previously, a letter from Zürich took thirteen days to Venice and fourteen days to Milan; on the Gotthard route the times were cut in half. With increasing traffic the old trail was widened to an 18-ft. carriage road, built in 1818–30 at a cost of 4 million francs. The cost of building and maintaining the summit road broke the two cantons of Uri and Ticino, which had to carry the financing alone.

In the middle of the last century, the railway hysteria struck the population in these remote mountain valleys, and in 1853 eight cantons decided to sponsor construction of a railway up to and through the Gotthard massif. Fortunately for them, nothing came of their initiative. The plans for a Gotthard railway were shelved for ten years.

A second railway conference was held in 1863, while Sommeiller was hacking his way through Fréjus, to discuss a project worked out by an engineer named Wetli. This plan triggered off a heated debate that raged for another ten years. The technical and political opinions gathered around two poles: a summit railway with a short tunnel under the pass, and a long tunnel farther down the slopes. The proponents of the summit tunnel brought up every argument possible against the long tunnel, quoting ample scientific evidence that such a tunnel could not be built. The long tunnel advocates maintained that it would be impossible to keep a summit railway open during the winter with the heavy snows prevailing at such an altitude and, moreover, that it would be uneconomical to lift the trains to such heights. A summit railway, in short, would impose a permanent burden by the excessive cost of haulage.

In the end, an international conference held in 1871 approved a plan worked out by two German engineers, A. Bech of Stuttgart and R. Gerwig of Karlsruhe, based on the original Wetli project and a triangulation survey carried out in 1869 by M. O. Gelpke. It was indeed an ambitious project, which included the building of a 9-mile tunnel through the massif, in addition to 36 miles of approach roads of which 28 per cent would consist of tunnels. On the north side, the railway would form seven almost complete loops before reaching the portal. The total length of the railway came to 163·51 miles. The cost was estimated at 187 million francs or $36.5million.

According to the St. Gotthard Convention of 1871, the cost was to be shared in the following manner: Germany was to contribute 20 million francs, Italy 45 million, and Switzerland 20 million. The remaining 102 million francs were to be raised in the capital markets of the three countries by the St. Gotthard Railway Company formed under the convention. R. Gerwig was appointed technical director of the company.

Brutal Contract

Thus, after a gestation period of eighteen years, began a tunnelling venture of transcendent difficulties and frustrations. The critics were

Fig 81. M. Louis Favre of Genoa, contractor of the St. Gotthard Tunnel.

proved right: the tools provided for building the Gotthard tunnel were altogether inadequate for the job. Although the tunnel was in fact finished, the cost in human lives and suffering came too high.

But such considerations were far from the minds of the seven optimistic contractors who bid for the work. The contract was given to the firm of Louis Favre of Genoa since he was the only one willing to guarantee to finish the work in eight years and to back his undertaking by posting $1,600,000 in forfeit money. If he succeeded in completing the work earlier than 1st October 1880, he was to be paid $980 a day as a premium; if, on the other hand, he went beyond that day he pledged himself to pay $980 per day for the first six months, and $1,960 after that. If the tunnel was not finished one year after the stipulated time, his forfeit money would go to the St. Gotthard Railway Company.

By agreeing to these terms Favre signed his death warrant. He also headed for catastrophe by his choice of tunnelling method. He had two from which to choose. Either he could proceed with a bottom heading, which had worked so satisfactorily in the Fréjus; or he could drive his pilot tunnel as a top heading, which held out certain theoretical advantages. Favre chose the latter or Belgian method. In so doing he had lost his great gamble before he began his eight-year Via Dolorosa through the bowels of St. Gotthard.

At the outset, however, Favre and his associates had seemingly good reasons for their optimism. The successful conclusion of Fréjus and the good reports of the advances made in completing the Hoosac had added to the body of tunnelling know-how; rock-drilling machines had been greatly improved and there were compressors for supplying the workings with compressed air. Above and beyond all this, Favre had at his disposal an explosive far superior to the 'black powder' used by Sommeiller, namely the dynamite recently perfected by Alfred Nobel.

The technical auspices therefore appeared promising for the successful completion of what came to be regarded as the greatest construction feat of a century not lacking in outstanding building achievements. In outline, the Favre contract involved advancing a tunnel 9 miles 452 yds. long from a point with an elevation of 3,460 ft. at Göschenen on the northern slope of the massif to a point with an elevation of 3,760 ft. on the southern slope near Airolo. The tunnel was to accommodate a double-track railway and had a width of 24 ft. 11 in. and a height of 26 ft. 3 in. From the northern portal the incline was 7:1000 to a point 25,587 ft. inside the tunnel with a summit elevation of 3,818 ft., from which it descended towards Airolo with a gradient of 1 : 1000.

The geological profile of the mountain from north to south showed firm granitic gneiss for 7,200 ft., followed by more or less schistous gneiss for 1,500 ft., limestone and marble for 1,100 ft., micaceous gneiss for 32,000 ft., mica schists crossed by veins of quartz for 2,600

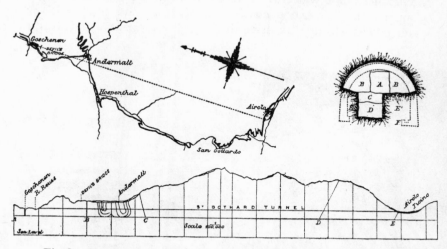

Fig 82. St. Gotthard Tunnel on the old St. Gotthard Railway pierces the Alps between the hamlets of Göschenen in the north and Airolo in the south. *Top*, plan; *bottom*, elevation; *top right*, sequence of excavation.

ft., and, towards the portal, some 4,500 ft. of serpentine, gypsum and anhydrate. Except for the Airolo end, the rock appeared to be firm, which of course was the chief reason for choosing the Belgian method.

Portal Installations

Work on the tunnel started at the southern portal on 13th September and on the northern end on 9th October 1872. Manual drilling was used at both ends while the portal installations were being put in. This took two years, during which an 8 × 8 ft. pilot heading was advanced a distance of 285 ft. at the northern end and 702 ft. at the Airolo end. The daily advance varied between 2 ft. and 2 ft. 6 in.

The portal installations put in during these two years were of an impressive order. Favre had to build, from nothing, two separate communities with housing accommodation and simple social amenities for 4,000 men, in addition to stables, hospital, stores, foundry,

repair shops, and so on. The total cost of the portal works, not count-
ing the machinery, came to $1,200,000.

In addition, he had to engage in major hydraulic engineering to
obtain the power required to mechanize the drilling and transport. At
the northern end, water was diverted from the River Reuss to obtain
a supply of 1,200–2,000 cu. ft./sec. with a head of 305 ft. This
water-power was used to drive three 2·4 m. horizontal shaft turbines

Fig 83. Compressor station at Airolo. Water power from the
Tessini and Tremola drove horizontal turbines connected to
Colladon mechanical compressors. Four turbines drove five
sets of compressors delivering air at a pressure of 88 or 100 p.s.i.
From a contemporary drawing.

delivering 250 h.p. each at 160 revolutions per minute (r.p.m.). At
Airolo, water was taken from the Tremola and diverted so as to
provide a head of 594 ft. to drive three 1·2 m. vertical shaft turbines
delivering a total of 1,120 h.p. at 390 r.p.m. However, this power
capacity soon proved inadequate for the job. The Tremola lost water
in winter, and in 1874 it was necessary to build a long open channel
to tap another mountain stream to get water for two additional

250-h.p. turbines. Two years later, a further 250-h.p. turbine was added at the northern end.

At each end the turbines drove three sets of Colladon compressors, each consisting of three units. As the work progressed additional sets were added until in 1875 there were five compressor sets, or fifteen compressors, working at each end. In the following year two additional sets were added at each end, which raised the total number of compressors to forty-two, in addition to four charging the loco-motives. The total output of the compressor plant was in the order of 90,000 cu. ft. per hour at 105 p.s.i.

As compressed air became available in the spring of 1873 by means of Sommeiller's 'water-spout', compressor and also, in the last months of the year, by Colladon's 'hydro-pneumatic' machines, mechanical rock-drilling got under way. Now, however, there was an embarrassment of riches in the way of rock-drilling machines or 'perforators', as they were called. The type first used at the southern end was known as Dubois-François, but as the work pro-gressed every available type of make was tried out. There were British, French, Swiss and Italian machines that had their brief day of glory and were discarded. In the end, three makes of machines survived: Dubois-François, McKean and, the most successful of them all, Ferroux. In view of the rapid advances made in the design of rock drills since 1945,[1] it is interesting to compare the performance of the test machines used in St. Gotthard during the 1870's. With the Ferroux perforator, one metre (3·28 ft.) of hole was drilled in 1 hr. 9 min. A Dubois-François unit required 1 hr. 31 min., whereas McKean needed 2 hrs. 1 min. The old Sommeiller rock drill took 2 hrs. 24 min. The wear of the machines was excessive and the cost of repairs came high. Ferroux, the best of the lot, cost 2·43 francs in repairs per metre drilled and the next best, Dubois-François, 4·27 francs.

The Ferroux machine was invented in 1873 by the former chief of the workshops at Fréjus and was put to work in the St. Gotthard on 8th May 1874. It differed from all competing makes principally in being fitted with a pneumatic feed cylinder which pushed the bit into the rock at a rate automatically adjusted to the speed of drilling. It was a precursor of the modern airleg machines, although differently designed and much heavier. The Ferroux was an intelligent rock drill and it remains something of a mystery why its many sound features were not further developed to make it competitive with later

---

[1] In 1961 a drilling rate of 625 mm. per minute was obtained in standard granite.

American machines. Instead, it disappeared rapidly after having performed invaluable service in the Gotthard.

The Ferroux, which came to be used mostly on the northern end, was mounted on a track-bound jumbo carrying a number of drill units, six in the pilot tunnel. The whole rig weighed 2·4 tons, and when used in an 8-ft. heading it left room for a narrow (11·8 in.) track alongside, to permit mucking out the heading while drilling the next round.

Fig 84. The drill carriage employed at the Airolo heading.

Transport in the pilot headings was done with horses, but farther in the rear the muck was loaded into trains of dump wagons driven by a compressed-air locomotive developed for use in the tunnel. Between trips the locomotives were charged with a new supply of compressed air.

Such, briefly described, were the mechanical facilities mobilized by Favre at both ends to aid his 4,000 men to pierce the 9¼-mile hole through the Gotthard massif. There was ample power, the best machines available at the time were put in service, a lot of other machines were designed and built specially for the Gotthard, camp conditions appeared satisfactory. Everything was in readiness for the big push—everything, that is, with the exception of a cemetery.

Driving the Gotthard

As previously mentioned, the manner chosen by the contractor for advancing the tunnel was top heading. A pilot gallery, varying in size from 53 to 75 sq. ft., was advanced along the crown of the tunnel. A wheeled jumbo mounting six rock drills, served by six men, drilled altogether eighteen to twenty-five holes to a depth of 4 ft. with a gauge of 35 to 40 mm. The drilling was done to a set pattern: three so-called 'cut' holes were drilled in the centre, surrounded by eight relievers and fourteen trimming holes. The holes were charged with 40 to 55 lb. dynamite and ignited in such a sequence that the centre was broken out first, followed by the remainder of the face, where-

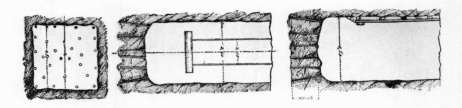

Fig 85. Blasting pattern used in St. Gotthard: the three cut holes in the centre of the face were detonated first, followed by the rest of the holes, except for the bottom row which finished the blasting sequence. *Right*, longitudinal section of heading; *centre*, plan of pilot heading with track.

upon the trimming charges outlined the heading. Such a round pulled 245 to 280 cu. ft. of rock, resulting in an advance of 3–6·5 ft. After blasting and during mucking, the valves of the compressed-air mains were left open to ventilate the heading. In this manner 5·7 million cu. ft. of air were delivered to the heading in twenty-four hours. Bell-shaped exhausters at both ends removed 16,500 cu. ft. of vitiated air per minute.

The time for drilling such a round was two and a half hours, followed by three and a half hours for mucking out the round. By working three shifts, an advance of from 10 to 13 ft. with a maximum of 16 ft. 3 in. was obtained in twenty-four hours.

In the rear, some 1,000 ft. from the face, the gallery was broken out to full size down to the shoulders, also by means of mechanical drilling. A masonry arch resting on shoulder abutments was put in before the left bench was removed. The right bench was left in place for the time being until a second track became needed. Some 3,000

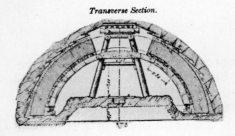
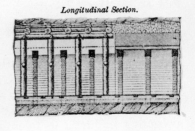

(a) Expanded top heading arched in, cross-section to the left, longitudinal section to the right.

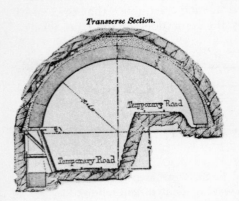

(b) Left half of the tunnel is fully excavated, with the arch supported by timbering.

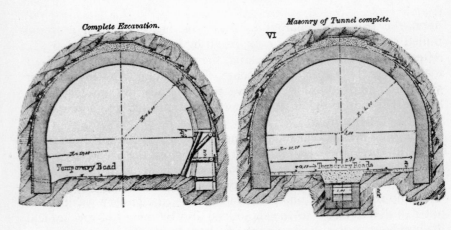

(c) Tunnel fully excavated and lined. From contemporary drawings.

Fig 86. The Belgian System of tunnelling was used in the St. Gotthard Tunnel.

yds. in the rear the remainder of the lining was put in place, which concluded the work.

To accomplish an advance of from 13 to 14·5 ft. per twenty-four hours in August 1876, 1,902 men were required at the northern end and 1,984 at the southern, or altogether 3,886 men. That was the highest number employed in the St. Gotthard tunnel at any one time.

In this fashion the two headings slowly advanced towards each other. But the trouble was that such an orderly advance could not be achieved all the time. At the northern end, water began to pour into the workings almost from the outset. At 460 ft., water flowed at the rate of 330 gal./min. and increased to 1,000 gal./min. at 540 ft. It rapidly got worse; at 1,325 ft. the rock squirted water from the roof, from the floor and from both sides, at a rate of 2,600 gal./min. Another few hundred feet farther in the discharge increased, and at 1,900 ft. the constant discharge from the tunnel ran at 2,400 gal./min. But then the water abated, and after 4,500 ft. the rock turned practically dry.

The Airolo end was worse. It was wet from the very first hole, and as the heading advanced the situation became unbearable. At 2,000 ft. water flooded the workings at a rate of 3,000 gal./min. Water on the floor reached the knees of the miners, and water jets the size of a fist in diameter breaking through the walls struck down the men with the force of a fire hose. For two years the work was conducted in a tropical downpour; to get rid of the water rising on the floor the ventilation tubes had to be disconnected at times to provide further drainage. At 4,100 ft. water still streamed in at the rate of 3,100 gal./min. The dynamite flowed out of the drill holes as a yellow sludge and it became necessary to encase the explosives in tin tubes in order to blast at all.

Nevertheless, despite these ghastly conditions the work went on, although at a frightening toll of human lives. Some twenty-five deaths and hundreds of casualties were reported each year due to accidental explosions from unignited cartridges, rock falls, train accidents, burst air-pipes, etc. More serious, however, were the diseases induced by the wretched working conditions. Rock dust, explosive fumes, exhalations from men and animals, temperatures that at times rose to 122° F. caused numerous ailments, and an untold number of men died from 'miner's anaemia'. A man became incapable of working after three to four months; if he persisted, he died or became incapacitated for life. The toll among animals was just as bad, about thirty horses and mules dying each month.

As previously mentioned, Favre kept increasing the number of compressors, and with more air, conditions improved somewhat. The water subsided and by 1875 the operations had become stabilized. By 1st May a total advance of 12,352 ft. had been obtained. There remained 36,535 ft. to be completed in sixty-five months, which would require a monthly advance of 640 ft. in order to finish the tunnel within the time limit stipulated by the contract. Since, however, a monthly advance of 750 to 850 ft. had been obtained on both headings during the early months of that year, there appeared to be ample margin to ensure success.

Financial Crisis

Now, however, the promoters lost their nerve, and a crisis arose above ground. It seems that the money was gone and that it would require an additional 102 million francs to complete the work. Disgusting squabbles broke out among the management of the railway company. The progress of the tunnel was far too slow and scapegoats had to be found; the technical director R. Gerwig had to go and was succeeded by his second-in-command, Hellwag. Rumours circulated that the tunnel could not be completed, and the shares of the company had to be supported on the stock exchanges by extensive purchases which made serious inroads in the already inadequate capital. The German Chancellery announced that the government had no intention of lending further financial aid to the St. Gotthard Company. The cost of the railway, including the tunnel, had increased to $56 million , or $19.5 million more than the original estimate.

In the end, the crisis was mastered. At a conference in 1876 the parties to the St. Gotthard Convention agreed to additional subsidies. Italy and Germany paid 10 million francs each, Switzerland 8 million francs, but only on the condition that the original ambitious plans were reduced in scope. By making the approaches one-track, increasing the gradients and paring costs on the surface structures, the estimates were brought down to 227 million francs (£9·1 million). Later that year an international commission reported on Favre's doings. The members were impressed by what had been accomplished, and in view of the new installations at both ends and the encouraging progress made in recent months, they saw no reason why the tunnel should not be completed by the date set in the contract.

By the end of 1876, everything seemed once more under control. All that remained was to settle the outstanding management squabbles, first by replacing the new technical director by his assistant Gehrlich, but Gehrlich in turn had to give way to M. G. Bridel, called in from Biel. After this bloodletting, the St. Gotthard Railway Company was fit for further action.

With good rock, a reasonably harmonious railway management, and an ample supply of compressed air, at least in summer, the advance continued through the bowels of the massif. By breaking out the rear of the pilot gallery at four points, using four machines in each one, the work of enlarging the tunnel was speeded up. By the end of 1876, the pilot headings had been advanced altogether 24,999 ft., but only 17,268 ft. had been enlarged and 7,288 ft. completely lined.

During 1877, the work progressed without interruption and 7,208 ft. were added. In the early months progress was slowed down by the hard serpentine rock encountered on the northern heading and friable rock on the southern. The pilot headings dropped somewhat below schedule and the lining work fell behind. By summer the headings were 500 ft. behind schedule and it began to appear as if something was seriously amiss.

Death of a Contractor

An indication of what was going on was given by Professor Colladon, designer of the compressors, in a paper read before the French Academy in January 1879. There was trouble with the hard serpentine, but more serious was the dearth of water at the Airolo end, which had necessitated building a new aqueduct 9,840 ft. long to tap the Ticino River. Before the new water supply became available it was necessary to drill by hand, and instead of a regular advance of 13 ft. per day it now took four days to drill 3 ft. 3 in. On the northern side, water jets had again broken through the rock with the force of a powerful fire pump.

Professor Colladon also mentioned that under the plain of Andermatt serious trouble had developed in a portion of the tunnel driven through decomposed feldspar and gypsum. The material became plastic in contact with the moist air and exerted a tremendous force that crushed timbers and cracked the arch. Colladon could also have remarked, although the subject would no doubt have been distasteful to his distinguished audience, that the diminished supply of winter water at the Airolo end had reduced the output of his compressors. In the many recesses towards the rear of the pilot headings the miners gasped for air and, in desperation, pierced the air lines. By doing so the air pressure dropped and so of course did the output of the machines—all of which contributed to slow down the advance.

The heat also was now becoming a great hindrance. The geothermic gradient proved to be 2° C. per 100 m. of vertical height (1·1° F. per 100 ft.), and in the advance headings the temperature reached 50° C. (122° F.) owing to the cumulative effects of this and other causes, such as the blastings, numerous oil lamps, and the exhalations of hundreds of men and animals. Working time was reduced to five and a half hours per shift. The contract price of $9.3 million was being exceeded.

In the summer of 1879 Favre was broken by the combination of evil forces—seven years of incessant struggle with the mountain during which he had spent days on end submerged in water up to his waist personally supervising the work, the shocks and frustrations, his long persecution by the railway management and, lately, his deteriorating economic condition. His robust health collapsed and on 19th July he was struck with a heart attack inside the tunnel. He was buried with the rest of the tunnel victims in the Gotthard cemetery at Göschenen, which had been expanded to a respectable size as the advance continued.

After Favre's death the work was carried on by his two technical assistants, Borsi and Stockalper, who drove the tunnel to completion. The breakthrough took place at 11 a.m. on 29th February 1880, at a point 4 miles 110 yds. from the northern portal. The error in alignment proved to be 12·87 in. and the difference in levels 1·95 in. The total length of the tunnel was 7·6 m. (25 ft.) shorter than calculated. The work had required seven years and five months, two months longer than the scheduled time. Exceeding the scheduled date by two months on a construction development that has taken more than seven years does not seem to be such a major sin. But that is not the full story. The really serious aspect of the situation which confronted Favre's heirs was that the lining was far in arrears. When the breakthrough occurred there remained exactly seven months until the stipulated contract date, 1st October 1880.

This is where Favre's fatal error in choosing the Belgian method, eight years earlier, reaped its ugly consequences. It can be proved by theoretical analysis that even if the work had been conducted according to schedule he would still have been ruined, because by the method chosen he could not under any circumstances have finished it by the contracted date. It would have required 15·8 months to complete the tunnel after the breakthrough, and he would have lost his forfeit sum of $1.6 mil. As it happened, the tunnel was finished twenty-one months after the contract date. Most of that time was spent in struggling with what proved the most difficult and, as it appeared for a long time, insoluble problem in the Gotthard tunnel.

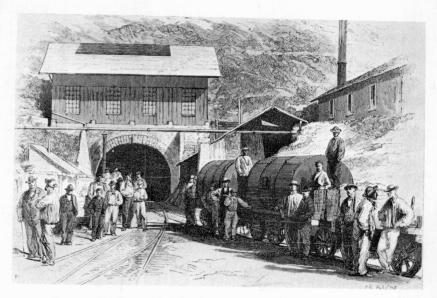

Fig 87. View of the Airolo portal showing compressed-air receivers supplying the pneumatic locomotives.

Fig 88. The first man to enter through the broken rock partition separating the two headings was the engineer François Arnaud. A contemporary artist in distant Paris visualized the historical event in this fashion.

This was the pressure section referred to by Professor Colladon in his Academy paper. For a distance of 100 yds. under the Andermatt, about 2,800 yds. from the Göschenen portal, the arch collapsed. Several years earlier the tunnelling teams had passed through this zone of decomposed feldspar and gypsum without paying any attention to its critical nature. The section had been broken out and lined. But while work in the tunnel continued, the moist air turned this section of the Andermatt rock into a plastic mass resembling clay. It began to flow, the abutments carrying the vaulting gave way and the lining collapsed. Repeated attempts to replace the lining failed. A 6-ft. thick granite wall simply sank. The Gotthard geologist Dr. Stampf became convinced that there was no way of saving the section and advised by-passing it, a course which would have required at least another year and the abandonment of half a mile of finished tunnel.

In the end, the section was saved by the heaviest construction resorted to in the St. Gotthard tunnel. A 2-ft.-thick granite invert was laid which carried walls 8 ft. 3 in. thick supporting a granite arch 4 ft. 8 in. thick. This heavy structure proved at last capable of standing up to the pressure of the flowing clay. It was a major error of the contractor to leave this section unsupported for so long. But even if somebody had recognized the danger in time nothing much could have been done about it. To secure this section the arch had to rest on firm abutments and such could only have been obtained by first securing the invert (curved floor) in order to get a solid platform capable of supporting the heavy walls needed to carry the arch. That, in effect, meant turning the tunnelling operation upside down, which could not be done without disrupting the entire programme and incurring the forbiddingly heavy costs of starting all over again.

One of the most valuable lessons learned from St. Gotthard is the critical importance of choosing from the outset the right method of attack. Favre lost his life and fortune by choosing the wrong method. The lesson was not wasted on succeeding contractors and their engineers.

Meanwhile, however, the work went on towards the finish. At Christmas 1881, 3,319 men were working night and day expanding the pilot headings and lining the tunnel. The contracting firm was by then $415,000 in arrears.

Sequel of the Gotthard Tragedy

Finally, on 23rd May 1882, the work was completed and the St. Gotthard Railway officially opened with the usual oratorical hyper-

Fig 89. The arrival of the inaugural train at Airolo on 23rd
May 1882.

bole. By that time the managing director, Alfred Escher, the toughest and most ruthless of the men behind the project, had become a shell of a man devoid of the will to live. He died seven months after the opening. His second-in-command had died before him. Of the original men directing the building of the St. Gotthard Railway, few remained alive when the work was finished.

An inquest of the St. Gotthard venture would reveal the following pertinent facts:

1. Total length of the St. Gotthard tunnel is 14,900 m. (9 miles, 452 yds.). Error in alignment was 33 cm., in levels 5 cm.
2. Total cost of the tunnel was 57,600,000 francs ($11.2 million), divided as follows:

Excavation	41,700,000 francs
Lining	13,300,000 ,,
Outside works	600,000 ,,
Ballast, rail	2,000,000 ,,

3. Cost per linear metre came to 3,900 francs ($700 per yd.).
4. Contract price per metre was 3,630 francs ($650 per yd.)
5. Cost of excavation came to 46 francs per cu. m. ($9 per cu. yd.)
6. Year of best advance was 1878, with 8,100 ft.
7. Average advance was 550 ft. per month and 18 ft. per day.
8. Explosives consumption came to about 1,000 tons of dynamite; 3·7 million lt. of oil were consumed for lighting the workings.
9. Casualties: 310 deaths (177 in the tunnel); 877 incapacitated (400 in the tunnel); 70 per cent of the men employed on the northern end fell victims to miner's anaemia caused by the intestinal worm *Dochimus duodenalis*, and an unknown number became incapacitated for life.
10. Travel time from Lucerne to Milan was reduced from 27 to 5½ hours.
11. The capacity of the tunnel was originally 30 trains per day; now 170 trains pass through it daily, and 100,000 motor-cars per year.

The job of the century was done! All that remained was to settle the accounts. The contracting firm had exceeded the contract sum by 14·75 million francs ($2,850,000) and what did the St. Gotthard Railway Company propose to do about that?

The St. Gotthard Railway Company proposed to do nothing and, having already collected the forfeit money of $1,600,000 it had come out rather well in the tunnel deal. So the disagreement between the

Company and the Contractor was brought before a court of arbitration. Here, in the detached atmosphere of the court room, well insulated from the realities of the hell-hole under St. Gotthard, the court took the easy way out. It simply kept to the letter of the contract and ignored everything else. The contracting firm was allowed 2·3 million francs as compensation; but the rest, or 12·45 million francs, the firm could regard as its contribution to the advancement of civilization.

That was the end of the Favre firm. However, as a gesture to the memory of the man who gave his life and immense fortune to the St. Gotthard tunnel, the railway company later voted an annuity equivalent to a couple of hundred francs a month to his only surviving daughter.

Chapter 8

THE ARLBERG REHEARSAL FOR SIMPLON

THE Arlberg tunnel piercing the mountain barrier between Austria and Switzerland is another long rock tunnel, measuring 6·375 miles in length, and as such occupies a prominent rank among the world's great tunnels. But its principal interest in any history of tunnelling is not so much its length as the link which it forms in the technical developments of tunnel driving. Fréjus was the inspired work of an engineering genius; Gotthard, on the other hand, proved too much for the technical resources of the time. That venture hovered throughout on the brink of catastrophe; the job was done, but at too high a price in human life and personal tragedy. Simplon, of which more anon, set a record for tunnelling performance, which still stands despite everything that has happened in underground developments since 1945.

The Arlberg tunnel forms a bridge between Gotthard and Simplon. It was advanced partly with the machines used in Gotthard, partly with equipment subsequently employed in Simplon. Considered on its own virtues, Arlberg was a neat operation carried out without dramatic incidents in a crisp, efficient manner. It was finished 420 days ahead of time, whereby the contractors gained a premium of $163,000.

The Arlberg tunnel was quickly decided upon, as a political stroke by the Austrian government to counter the German action of imposing a tariff detrimental to Austrian interests. A new railway was to be built from Innsbruck joining up with the Swiss system via Landeck–St. Anton–Bludenz, a distance of 85 miles. It was a friendly gesture towards the Swiss, a potential threat to German traffic, and the section would form a link in a Paris–Constantinople through-line. The cost of the railway, much of which runs through mountainous country, was estimated at $9.4 million, not including the tunnels. On a section of this line, from St. Anton to Langen, lies the Arlberg range rising to a height of 5,910 ft., and this mountain had to be pierced at an estimated cost of $7.9 million.

No time was lost. On 15th May 1880 the Austrian government gave the order for the work. On 24th June a Swiss contractor working from the west and an Austrian from the east began operations, at first with manual drilling. On 13th November machines were working on both headings.

Power for the rock-drilling machines was obtained by damming the Rosanna torrent three miles above the east portal and conducting the water to turbines developing 1,500 h.p. At the western portal, the Alfenz torrent was tapped at three points and carried to turbines developing the same amount of power. A saving of $1.4 mil. in coal and freights was made by utilizing local sources of water power instead of erecting steam plants at both ends, as first planned.

There was from the beginning keen rivalry between the two contractors, each of them eager to show that his choice of equipment was the better one. And, seen in the light of subsequent developments, this is the most interesting feature of the Arlberg advance.

At St. Anton, the Austrian contractor followed the Fréjus-Gotthard line. He had installed a number of improved Sommeiller water-spout compressors run at 50 r.p.m. (as against 12–15 r.p.m. at Fréjus) delivering 530 cu. ft. of air per second at 6 atm. In his 9 × 8·2 ft. heading he had six Ferroux perforators, as used in the Gotthard.

At the Swiss end, however, something new was being tried. Instead of compressors, the three turbines installed drove three groups of four double-acting pumps. Each pump delivered 3½ pts. of water per second at a pressure of 100 atm. (1,420 p.s.i.). The pressure water was conducted to the heading to drive two hydraulic drills of the Brandt type. This new machine, here tried on a major scale for the first time, held a drill steel provided with a crown bit against the rock with a pressure of 12,000 kg. (nearly 12 tons) while it slowly revolved with a speed of 3 to 4 r.p.m., thereby crushing and grinding a hole in the hard rock.

The inventor of the hydraulic rock drill was Alfred Brandt, a German engineer from Hamburg. While employed as a junior engineer with the Gotthard Railway he had been sent to the Airolo end to look into the trouble experienced with the hydraulic installations. Brandt returned from this assignment impressed by the inane waste of power inherent in the compression of air, whereby some 80 per cent of the input was lost in useless heat. The trouble at the southern end of Gotthard, according to his view, was because so much of the available water power obtained at great expense and never in adequate supply, was wasted in worthless compression heat, while men in the tunnel were gasping for air and the advance was slowed down owing to reduced pressure.

On his return to Zürich, Brandt recommended utilizing the hydraulic power of the water directly, thereby saving the compression losses. His suggestion was approved and he set about developing an entirely new type of rock drill. His first machine was of the impacting type and did not work. The second one was designed on entirely new lines, and became a tremendous success. With this machine he left the railway company and set himself up in the tunnelling business.

This, then, was the machine used on the Swiss side of the Arlberg.

In the Arlberg contract was a clause stipulating that a minimum of 150 cu. m. (5,296 cu. ft.) of air per minute, or 50 per cent more than in the Gotthard, should be supplied to the workings. Here again there was a difference between the two ends. The east installation consisted of piston machines which compressed air in a 45-in. cylinder with a stroke of one metre (3.28 ft.). The capacity of these machines was 6,350 cu. ft. per minute. With a supply pipe of large diameter (15·75 in.), air was conducted a distance of 3½ miles into the tunnel. At the western end, 5 ft. 3-in. fans were employed, arranged in two series of three fans each. With all six fans in action the plant was capable of producing 5,300 cu. ft. of air per minute to a heading 2½ miles distant.

The 75 sq. ft. pilot gallery was advanced according to the Austrian method, i.e. by bottom heading. In the east heading twenty-five to thirty holes of 1·18 in. gauge were drilled per round, as against eight to twelve holes with a gauge of 2·76 in. in the west heading where the Brandt machines were employed. A Brandt round required 17 to 26 lb. of dynamite as against 42 to 44 lb. on the Ferroux heading.

Some 828 ft. in the rear of the headings the roof of the pilot gallery was broken out, with a raise to the crown of the finished tunnel. From this new point of attack a top heading was advanced in both directions and broken out to full width. The raises, at intervals of from 72 to 197 ft., were used as loading chutes for the broken rock which was dumped into cars on the bottom gallery. The cars were hauled away by a steam locomotive provided with a large water boiler and stoked to 15 atm. pressure, whereby the engine emitted no smoke while in the tunnel.

The race between the contractors gave the following results:

	Ferroux	Brandt
Advance per day, in metres	5·44	5·43
Number of machines	8	4
Number of miners	12	7
Number of muckers	7	7
Mechanics[1]	—	1
Total advance, in metres	5,290	4,535

The Brandt hydraulic rock drill proved its capability in the Arlberg tunnel. It was somewhat slower than the Ferroux, but it saved five men, required less maintenance, reduced the explosives consumption and in general gained a reputation as a reliable and economic machine.

To sum up, the Arlberg tunnel was a solid success from beginning to end. The breakthrough occurred three years to the day after the machines were put to work, and the tunnel was opened for traffic in 1884 one year and fifty-five days ahead of the time estimated.

The Arlberg set the stage for the big push through the Alps—the Simplon tunnel.

[1] The Ferroux machines were taken out of service and overhauled every four days. The Brandt machines were repaired on the spot.

Chapter 9

THE SIMPLON TUNNEL

THE Simplon tunnel linking up the Swiss and Italian railway systems under Monte Leone was officially opened for traffic on 1st July
1906 after six years and ten months of difficult work. With a length
of 12·06 miles Simplon is still the longest tunnel in the world and is
likely to remain so for many years to come.

The auspices for the Simplon tunnel were not too good. The railways linked up by the tunnel had a chequered history of mismanage-
ment, swindles, intrigues and litigation that would have impressed
contemporary railway pirates in other countries had they known
about it. What ended with the mighty Simplon began with a modest
swindle by a French journalist and promoter who succeeded in getting a concession for a railway through the upper Rhône valley, from
St. Gingolph to Sion in Switzerland, and from Arona to Domodossola
in Italy, on the other side of Monte Leone.

A railway company with a long and impressive name but locally
known as Ligne d'Italia was formed, and some 25 million francs were
raised in France. A line was actually built on the north side and 9·3
miles of track were laid on the Italian side, then the company went
bankrupt. A new company was formed, by the old management,
which paid 2½ million francs for the assets and managed to keep
alive until 1868 when that company too went broke. The whole railway, such as there was of it, was bought at auction by a Swiss finance
syndicate for 10,100 francs. The new owners formed a third company, Chemin de fer du Simplon, which extended the line and some
years later merged with a company operating railways in western
Switzerland to form a fourth company, Chemin de fer de la Suisse

Occidentale-Simplon, for the purpose of building the tunnel. The chief engineer of the company, Jean Meyer, began seriously to investigate the possibility of tunnelling through Monte Leone in 1881.

He had numerous schemes to choose from. From 1860 onwards there had been nine different plans for tunnelling through the mountain by means of a base tunnel, summit tunnel and tunnels half-way down the slope. There were to be several more before a final scheme was agreed upon. A conference with the Italians in Berne in 1889 fixed the southern portal at Iselle, and the plans had to be revised again. Since the financing of the tunnel proved beyond the capacity of the Swiss railway company, a new and larger company was formed. The new company which took the responsibility of building the tunnel reflected in its name the succession of mergers that had proved necessary in order to obtain the scale needed for the Simplon venture—The Jura-Bern-Luzern-Bahn. It operated a 620-mile network of track extending over ten cantons and converging on the northern slope of Monte Leone. The final scheme worked out by Dumur, technical director of the new company, incorporated the Meyer plan of 1881 with an older plan from 1864. This modified Lommel-Meyer scheme was approved by the Simplon canton in 1891.

That, of course, was not the end of it. For one thing, where was the money to come from? Political trouble in Italy kept the government from committing itself to the scheme, and the Simplon project was still hanging in mid-air when on 20th September 1893 the railway company concluded a contract with the construction firm of Brandt, Brandau & Co. which had allied itself with the firms of Gebrüder Sulzer of Winterthur, and Locher & Cia of Zürich, as well as with the Bank von Winterthur.

The contract signed by the Simplon consortium was, like so many nineteenth-century tunnelling agreements, nothing better than a suicide pact. Why anyone of sound mind should willingly enter into such an agreement can only be explained by the uninhibited optimism of the nineteenth-century entrepreneurs and their naïve faith in science. The scheme was approved and backed by a geological commission, and the geological profile, on which the success or failure of the entire Simplon scheme rested, was accepted without question: after all, the members were professors and renowned geologists and could do no wrong. Their forecast promised good rock all the way, with little or no water except for a few calcareous strokes at the southern end which were regarded as not particularly difficult and well within the capacity of the builders to master.

Under the contract the Simplon consortium undertook the excavation and building of two 12-mile tunnels from a northern portal at Brig in Switzerland to a southern portal at Iselle in Italy for a total price of 69·5 million francs ($13.5 million). One of the two parallel pilot tunnels was to be expanded and lined, whereas the second one was to be left as a pilot gallery, to be finished at a future date when the volume of traffic warranted a double-track railway through the mountain.

The breakdown costs were as follows:

Portal installations	7·0 million francs
Excavation of two pilot tunnels	47·5 million francs
Lining and completion of one tunnel	15·0 million francs

The first tunnel was to be completed five and a half years after the commencement of the work and the second tunnel in four years. As a guarantee of this, the contractors were to deposit one million francs in caution money and 7½ per cent of the part payments were to be retained until the sum reached 5 million francs. After finishing the first tunnel, 2 million francs were to be withheld for two years. After three years, 500,000 francs were to be retained and used as caution money for the second tunnel. While driving the second, 7½ per cent of the payments were to be withheld until the caution money reached 1½ million francs. Not until two years after the completion of the second tunnel was the railway company to release the final 500,000 francs used as caution money. For every day the contractor exceeded the completion date he was to be fined 5,000 francs; for every day gained he was to be paid the same sum as a premium. Finally, the contract stated that if the consortium should be dissolved or fail to complete the work within one year of the contracted date the caution money would be forfeited.

But this was not all. The Gotthard debacle had not been lost on the railway lawyers who thought they had the answer to that one. The Simplon contract therefore contained an extra clause dealing with unforeseen developments. It was to be clearly understood that the prices given included full compensation for any difficulties encountered during the work, whether due to water, high rock temperature, poor rock or any other conceivable reason, except war in which Switzerland and Italy were involved, epidemics, or a general strike.

Among other details, also inspired by the Gotthard experience, the contract stipulated that at least 1,765 cu. ft./sec. of air should be supplied at each end, the air in the tunnel should be cooled to 25° C., detritus should be removed from the tunnel, fresh drinking-water should be supplied to all workings and these should, if possible, be electrically lighted;[1] the workers should be provided with free baths and drying facilities for their clothes, as well as proper lodgings and good food. A benefit fund was to be set up for the widows and children of men killed during the construction, and injured workers should be given medical attention.

The total price per linear metre (3·28 ft.) of the finished tunnel, including the parallel pilot tunnel, was determined at 2,210 francs ($425) for the first kilometre from the portals, with increments for the farther advance.

The contract was approved by the Bundesrat, but with the ugly memories of Gotthard still haunting the members, the assembly decided to request the opinion of an international commission of tunnelling experts about the feasibility of the project.

The technical Commission, consisting of Professor Giuseppe Colombo of Milan, Sir Francis Fox, builder of the Mersey tunnel, and Karl Johann Wagner, inspector of the Austrian State Railways and engineer-in-charge of the Arlberg tunnel, reported in July 1894. They approved every detail of the scheme and did not envisage any particular difficulties. However, the Commission recommended the use of electric traction, and included in its report some views on the safety and welfare of the workers. For one thing, the Commission insisted on strict medical control. No man should be hired who did not possess the physical stamina required for underground work; all miners, and particularly those in the deep workings, should be subjected to continuous medical supervision, tests were to be made to find the most suitable food and refreshments for consumption in the tunnel. Most important of all, the Commission stressed the need for strict inspection of the lodgings and for each man to have his own bed. These views, as well as the welfare measures included in the contract, are of special interest because this is probably the first expression in modern times of formal concern for the welfare of underground workers. Simplon marks a definite break from the ruthless exploitation of labour that was taken for granted in the past, although the initiative shown seems largely to have been lost on the construction industry elsewhere. The social amenities and welfare features formalized in the Simplon contract still remain to be adopted on many modern construction sites.

At the Swiss end everything was in readiness, the rest was up to Italy. At long last a conference was arranged in Berne where the Swiss and Italian governments agreed to subsidize the building of the Simplon tunnel and its approaches. The Swiss government was to

[1] Electricity had never been used before in a major Alpine tunnel.

pay 16·26 million francs, the Italian government 4 million and the
Jura–Simplon Railway 50 million francs—70·26 million francs in all.
The Italians were to build the line connecting the portal at Iselle
down to the town of Domodossola, and the Swiss the 1¼-mile
approach to the northern portal.

The financial agreement was concluded on 2nd February 1896,
but there was still no green signal given to go ahead with the tunnel.
Now followed lengthy negotiations with the Swiss cantons to share
the financing. In the early part of 1898 proposals were raised to
nationalize the Swiss railways, which further confounded the Simplon issue. Finally, on 28th July 1898, the ratified Simplon agreements were exchanged between the two governments, and on 13th
August the Jura-Simplon Railway declared the five-year-old contract
to have come into force. After thirty-eight years of talk the hour of
action was at hand.

Portal Installations

Actually, the contractor had jumped the gun. Work had started
on the northern heading on 1st August, and on 16th August hand
drilling began at the southern portal. On the northern heading an
advance of 5·47 ft. per day was made and by the time mechanical
drilling began on 22nd November a total advance of 623 ft. had
been gained. In the south the rate of advance was much slower from
the beginning, and only 1·54 ft. per day for a total length of 193·5 ft.
had been achieved when on 23rd December mechanical drilling
began also at that end. The primary power was obtained from steam
locomotives stationed outside the portals. By the end of the year the
contractor had 1,052 men at work at both ends. Of these, 660 were
occupied with the portal installations.

As was usual on nineteenth-century tunnel developments, the contractor's first concern was to get water power to the site. At the
northern portal water for the turbines was obtained from the Rhône.
Sluice gates were installed on the river bank and water was conducted to a storage dam. A 2-mile canal, of which 730 ft. consisted
of a rock tunnel, carried the water to a 262-ft. penstock through
which a 5 cu. m./sec. (176·55 cu. ft.) flow with a head of 171·5 ft.
impacted on four Pelton wheels developing altogether 2,239 h.p. At
the southern end, the Diveria torrent was impounded 7,540 ft. above
the village of Iselle and conducted through a pressure pipe and penstocks to Pelton wheels working under a head of 577 ft. The installed
capacity was 1,950 h.p.

The turbines on both sides were coupled by means of pinion and gear to six high-pressure pumps which delivered water at a pressure of 120 atm. (1,700 p.s.i.) to a high-pressure supply line extended to the face of the heading. Other turbines drove an air compressor used for charging the compressed-air tunnel locomotives as well as delivering power to the machine tools in the repair-shops. One turbine on each side drove an electric generator which delivered energy for lighting the tunnel.

The ventilation plant at each portal consisted of two turbine-driven horizontal fan-wheels, each one delivering 25 cu. m./sec. (882·75 cu. ft.) air at a pressure of 738 ft. water at 350 r.p.m. The fans could be operated in different combinations, for blowing and suction; when working in tandem they had a rated capacity of 50 cu. m./sec. (1,765·5 cu. ft.). The air was blown into tunnel No. 2 and was evacuated through tunnel No. 1.

Outside the portal were erected office buildings, numerous repair-shops, a foundry, family houses, a bath and dressing room, canteens, houses for engineers, clerks and foremen, waterworks, shops, a hospital, a district heating plant, stores for materials, etc. The workers' camp formed a village of its own at both ends. The railway track serving the portal installations totalled nearly 5 miles.

The portal installations were built to the same scale at both ends, although great difficulties and delays were experienced keeping the southern end supplied, since every item, from heavy machines to building materials and food, had to be hauled over a steep and narrow 12-mile summit road over Monte Leone which had been built by Napoleon in 1805.

What in the end proved to be the most vital portal installation was the bath and dressing room immediately outside each portal. It was a 118 × 39 ft. building fronting the railway leading into the tunnel. When a shift of some 200 men came off work they had to pass through the building and were not checked out until they had showered and left their tunnel clothes to dry hanging on hooks pulled up under the ceiling. The contractor provided the working-clothes and kept them washed and in repair. When leaving the building washed and dressed in their regular clothes the men surrendered mining lamps and tallies. Similarly, when beginning a shift they changed into their dry tunnel clothes, hung their regular garments on the ceiling hook and upon entraining were given their lamps and tallies. They rode six men to a car and detrained 3,930 ft. in the rear of the face. Heading miners and foremen continued farther in and were ready to put the rest of the men to work when they arrived on foot.

This, in brief, was the organization which worked so satisfactorily in the Simplon tunnel. Although there were numerous deaths and casualties, the Simplon operation was a model from the point of view of health. Apart from a small typhus epidemic involving forty men and quickly brought under control, the hygienic arrangements more than paid for themselves in good health. Simplon entirely escaped the horrors of Gotthard because of the sanitary installations inside and outside the tunnel and, of course, the excellent ventilation. Otherwise, with the hot springs and high temperatures subsequently encountered, the slaughter of men would without a doubt have become more excessive than in Gotthard.

But Simplon, unlike Gotthard, was dogged by strikes, and a large number of working days were lost owing to labour unrest at both ends. The improved social conditions brought new social problems in their train.

The Advance

The Simplon tunnel has its northern portal to the east of the village of Brig at an elevation of 2,249 ft. above sea-level. The tunnel enters the mountain on a 1,213·6-ft. radius curve for a distance of 530 ft., after which it goes on a straight line under Monte Leone for a distance of 12 miles and ends with a 402·4-ft. curve (R = 1,312 ft.). The total length of the tunnel is 12 miles, 845 ft.

The southern portal is situated in the Diveria valley about 2,624 ft. below the village of Iselle and has an elevation of 2,078·58 ft.

From Brig the tunnel rises on a 2:1,000 gradient to a point 30,110 ft. up, after which follows a horizontal section 1,640 ft. long at an elevation of 2,309·4 ft., whereupon it slopes with a 7:1,000 gradient towards the southern portal.

To facilitate axis alignment, the pilot headings were driven in a straight line from adits at both ends. With these adits the pilot tunnel had a length of 12 miles 1,438 ft.

The tunnelling scheme used in Simplon was radically different from anything hitherto attempted. The previous Alpine tunnels had been made double-track, but for a number of reasons, principally the excessive rock pressure expected and the difficulty of ventilating such long headings, the Simplon scheme involved the driving of two parallel pilot headings 55·2 ft. apart. At every 656 ft. an oblique cross-heading united the two pilot tunnels.

The major advantage of the two-heading scheme was, of course, the ventilation; fresh air was forced into Tunnel 2 and then admitted into Tunnel 1 through the cross-headings. By providing the latter with weather doors the air supply could be directed as needed to the workings. The main drainage trench was sunk in Tunnel 2, which also relieved the transport congestion in Tunnel 1. Not least important, with two interconnected pilot tunnels the chances of escape in case of dangerous falls were much improved.

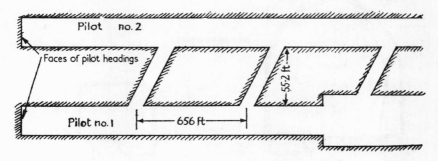

Fig 90. The single-line Simplon tunnels are situated 55·2 ft. apart, separated by a rock partition. The left tunnel was completed in 1906 while the second one was left in the pilot stage. It was not completed until 1920.

The size of the pilot headings varied in width from 8·2 to 10·49 ft. and in height from 6·56 to 8·2 ft., i.e. the cross-section area was 53·8 to 75·3 sq. ft. depending on the nature of the rock. Four Brandt hydraulic rock drills were used in the heading. Each machine drove a heavy hollow drill provided with a three-pronged crown into the rock with a pressure of 15,000 kg. (33,000 lb.) and turned it 4 to 6 r.p.m. In this manner a hole was milled out of the rock at a rate of 1·31 to 2·62 ft. per hour. In hard rock, twelve to fifteen holes were drilled to a length of 4 ft. and placed to a simple pattern using a three-hole centre cut, the rest of the holes being relievers and trimmers.

From various scraps of information, monthly and quarterly reports issued by the railway management, and subsequent technical inquests, an attempt has been made to sum up the performance during the first quarter of 1900 in the following table. These bare figures convey a fair idea of the output in underground work when at its best at the beginning of this century.

The figures below reveal that because of the tension of rock presenting only one face to the miners, as in the pilot tunnel, it required 42 to 45 man-hours and the expenditure of more than 8·8 lb. of dynamite to break out one cubic metre of rock. However, once the pilot tunnel had been excavated the work of expanding the tunnel to full area was greatly facilitated. This work was accomplished by

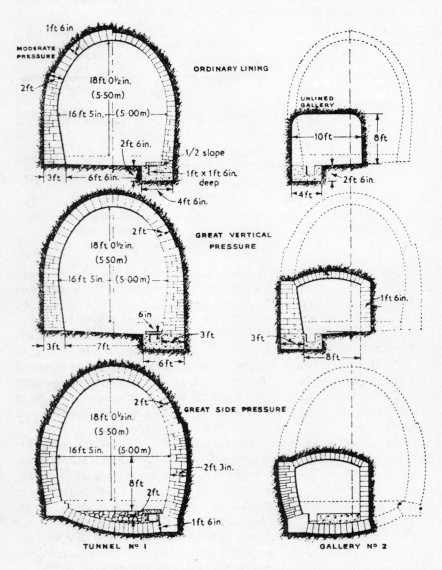

Fig 91. The lining of Simplon 1 varied with the rock pressure encountered.

manual drilling, whereby the removal of one cubic metre of rock was achieved with only 3·81 man-hours and an expenditure of 1·36 lb. of dynamite. One item worth noting is the excessive consumption of drill steel. The figures given are averages, the maximum consumption reached ninety-eight steels per round.

Analysis of one round in the Simplon tunnel
Averages for January–March 1900

Type of rock	North heading Mica gneiss	South heading Gneiss
Area of tunnel, in sq. m.	5·4	5·3
Number of machines	2·8 Brandt	3·0 Brandt
Number of holes per round	7·3	10·4
Gauge of holes, mm.	70·0	70·0
Total length of hole per round, in m.	1·85	1·27
Drills used per round	70	52
Dynamite per hole, in kg.	5·51	3·81
Dynamite per round, in kg.	40·5	39·5
Advance per round, in m.	1·84	1·22
Rock pulled per round, in cu. m.	10·0	6·5
Number of rounds per 24 hrs.	3·3	4·5
Dynamite required for 1 cu. m., in kg.	4·72	4·29
Accidents per m. of advance	0·2	0·4
Man-hours required		
for drilling 1 m. of hole, hrs.	28·59	19·42
for drilling 1 cu. m. of rock, hrs.	45·35	42·18
for charging, blasting, mucking 1 cu. m. of rock	93·40	38·40
for excavating 1 cu. m. of rock	138·75	111·30
Total time for 1 m. advance, hrs.	3·83	4·64
Men at the face	13–14	18–19

The four headings were driven continuously with three eight-hour shifts throughout the year, except for Christmas and St. Barbara's Day, 4th December—St. Barbara being the patron saint of miners and men handling explosives.

The number of men working in the tunnel varied from 392 at the end of 1898 to a maximum of some 2,000 a few years later, or about 1,000 at each end. However, since Tunnel 2 was not broken out to full size, 800–900 men were crowded into Tunnel 1. The mining team advancing the pilot gallery consisted of a foreman and fourteen men. About 328 ft. in the rear of the face came the hand-drilling teams, at a distance of 164 ft. from each other. At these points they began by driving a raise up to the crown of the finished tunnel from which they drove a top heading in both directions. Other manual teams broke out the arch of the tunnel down to the shoulders. The rock excavated was dumped through the raises into cars loading 53 to 70 cu. ft. Finally, the two remaining benches along both sides of the bottom heading were drilled and blasted. This concluded the mining operations. Farther in the rear, large numbers of masons lined the tunnel. In the arch, brick was used, the sides and invert were lined with ashlar or cement blocks.

This was the normal routine method of advancing the tunnel. But conditions were not always normal in the Simplon tunnel. On 29th November 1898, at a time when the gigantic undertaking was in its critical development stage, the leader and guiding technical genius of the contracting consortium, Alfred Brandt, died suddenly from a stroke. Like all the great nineteenth-century engineers he died in his early fifties—at fifty-three—and like them he had worked himself to death. Before he was struck down he had been working twenty-four hours a day, with brief snatches of sleep, for several months. However, what apparently broke this giant was the tremendous death roll in a Spanish tunnel that his firm drove simultaneously with Simplon.

Brandt's place as chief engineer on the northern end was taken by the Swiss Colonel Edward Locher-Freuler, who remained in command until the end. The southern end was from the beginning in charge of Karl Brandau, partner in the contracting firm of Brandt, Brandau & Co.

These, then, were the two men who carried the responsibility of piercing Monte Leone in face of all the difficulties that the mountain could put in their way. They were also responsible for overcoming these difficulties within the time-limit stipulated. Although no troubles worth mentioning developed until well into the new century, the rate of progress was not quite according to plan almost from the beginning. At the end of one year, 1,510 ft. of adits and 6,232 ft. of pilot tunnels were to be driven, or 7,742 ft. altogether. The total advance actually recorded during the first year was 7,547 ft. The small difference was no cause for worry by itself; more serious in the long run was the deficiency in the daily rate of advance which reached an average of 19·22 ft. at the north heading and only 15 ft. at the southern, as against the daily average of 19·18 ft. required to complete the work within the terms of the contract. This was the first indication that there was trouble brewing at the southern end.

According to the plan, the portal installations, including the permanent ventilation plant, were to be completed after the second year, which they were—or nearly so. At the northern end, the tunnelling team ran into numerous hot springs with a temperature varying from 45° to 55·4° C. The air temperature in the tunnel rose to 28° C., but by injecting cold water spray into the air line supplying the heading, the temperature could be considerably reduced. At the end of the second year, the two headings had been advanced altogether 18,512 ft.; the total length of the lined tunnel was 10,532 ft. The advance was now somewhat ahead of schedule, although the southern heading, still in dry rock, was running 45 per cent behind the northern owing to drilling difficulties in the horizontally layered gneiss (4 ft. per round as against a planned 6 ft. per round).

The horizontal gneiss at the southern end had begun to give rise to peculiar pressure phenomena; the lateral pressure bent up the floor in both tunnels and lifted the rails. To compensate for the pressure, the invert had to be ballasted with heavy stone construction over large distances, and the cross-headings also had to be ballasted to withstand the pressure.

Then on 30th September 1901, at 14,530 ft., serious trouble developed in the southern heading. In No. 1 tunnel, the mining team struck a spring which flooded the heading with 33 gals./sec. and necessitated abandoning the drilling machines. In order to get rid of the water, a cross-heading was driven 3 yds. in the rear, where another spring was struck and poured a further 44 gals./sec. into the heading. In the No. 2 pilot tunnel, a third spring was encountered that produced 102 gals./sec. An underground basin had obviously been tapped, and the miners were astounded to see 60° C. hot water rising, while a few feet away a column of 15° C. water was descending. They were probably the first human beings to watch the hydraulic forces actually at work shaping the earth's crust. Together, the three springs poured out 12° C. water at a rate of 179 gals./sec., flooding the 1·2 × 1·6 ft. drainage trench in Tunnel 2 and rising 11 in. above the floor.

After two months of fighting the waters in the calcareous fissures, the major heading entered at 14,596 ft. a zone consisting of micaceous limestone shot through with gypsum. It was too weak for machine drilling, but since the section was dry it did not seem particularly difficult at the outset. However, after an advance of 20 ft. water was struck and the firm rock turned into a doughy mess which began to exert tremendous pressure from all directions. In Tunnel 2 the zone was struck at 14,652 ft. and the heading was lost.

This was the famous 'pressure zone' in the Simplon tunnel which presented the miners with one of the ugliest problems encountered

in the history of tunnelling. All the conventional methods were tried
in vain to overcome this zone of decomposed calcareous mica-schist.
To begin with, timbering was tried, but 2-ft. larch logs placed
side by side snapped like matchsticks under the uneven pressure.
They were replaced by 16 × 16 in. oak timbers in a small 5 × 6 ft.
heading, but the oak timbers also broke under the shifting loads.
Monte Leone, after giving ample warning by throwing increasingly difficult obstacles in the way of the miners, turned on its

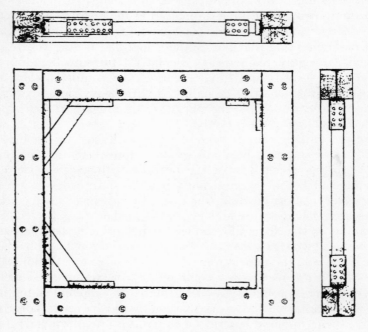

Fig 92. The steel frames used in
bridging the pressure zone in Simplon.
The window opening was 2·5 × 2·8 m.

really ugly side and for a while it looked as if the mountain would
win. For a number of weeks it seemed beyond human capability to
master this running rock which squeezed the miners in its lethal folds.

But in the end the heading was recovered; it simply had to be. The
crush zone was literally bridged by the use of rectangular steel frames
with a window opening of 2·5 × 2·8 m. Each frame was made of
14-in. girders heavily braced with 20 × 20 in. pitch pine timbers
bolted to the steel. The first of this series of frames was firmly anchored to the sound rock in the rear of the crush zone, and the

remainder were slowly and laboriously planted one by one, side by side, and tied together with longitudinal 70 cm. steel beams placed over the caps and screwed to each frame.

The work of placing these heavy frames began on 19th January 1902. One by one, gaining a distance of 20 in. at a time, the frames were put in position and screwed together until in the end a distance of 137 ft. had been bridged by seventy-four frames. It took until 20th May, or six whole months, to bridge 137 ft. at a cost of one million francs. These feet played havoc with the time schedule, and from that day the Simplon contractors faced the same situation as did Favre in St. Gotthard. The gamble had been lost between 14,596 and 14,733 ft. and there still remained 17,623 ft. to advance before meeting the northern heading.

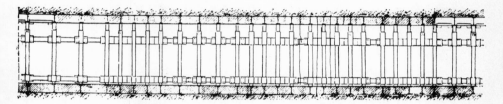

Fig 93. It required 74 steel frames joined together into a bridge to cross the 137-ft. pressure zone. The cantilever bridge was anchored in the sound rock at the left and extended, frame by frame, through the fluid decomposed rock.

There also remained the seemingly impossible task of breaking out and lining this steel-enclosed pilot tunnel to full tunnel area, but that was something Colonel Locher had to put off as a problem for the future. What mattered at the moment was to keep advancing the pilot heading. Fortunately, after the crush zone followed a bank of firm gypsum through which the advance was exceptionally rapid. A daily average of 26·4 ft. was obtained during the ensuing months; one day the teams made 36·7 ft., the record advance in Simplon.

Meanwhile, the north heading had run into numerous hot springs and ever higher rock temperatures. Accidents occurred almost daily, men were killed although less frequently. The air temperature in the tunnel reached 32° C. despite all attempts to reduce it. More hot springs were tapped, some of them with 55° C. water, but these difficulties were dealt with as they arose and the advance proceeded at an average rate of 19 ft. per day, or exactly according to plan.

But the operation taken as a whole was now hopelessly in arrears. According to plan the two pilot headings should have advanced

46,904 ft. by the end of the fourth year and 39,360 ft. of tunnel should have been finished. Actually, the pilots had only reached 43,456 ft., and 38,484 ft. of the tunnel had been lined. Owing to the trouble in the crush zone an annual advance of 10,295 ft. had been made, as against a planned gain of 15,088 ft. during the fourth year.

The fifth year was the best of all with an average gain of 20·33 ft. per day. The rock temperature in the northern heading kept rising from 40° C. at 20,795 ft. to 52° C. at 23,944 ft., until it reached 56° C. at 29,848 ft., the highest recorded in the Simplon tunnel. Rock bursts were common and the walls had to be lined to protect the workers from being wounded or even killed by sharp rock flakes flying off the walls owing to local tension in the rock. More hot springs were struck, one of them giving 40° C. water.

On 19th July 1903 the northern heading passed the culmination point and continued towards the southern portal. At 28,889 ft. Tunnel 1 was expanded to a width of 50 ft. and a height of 27 ft. to provide space for the northern end of the siding in Tunnel 2, to permit trains to pass in the tunnel.

On 1st August 1903, the fifth year had come to an end when, according to the contract, 63,620 ft. of headings and 57,400 ft. of lined tunnel were to have been completed. Actually, only 56,498 ft. had been excavated and 40,338 ft. of tunnel lined. Ruin faced the contractors. They were saved by the nationalization of the Swiss railways. The new owner could not allow the enterprise to end in financial catastrophe and the Simplon contract was revised. The date of completion was moved ahead to 30th April 1905, and the fine for exceeding the date reduced to 4,000 francs per day. The contract price was raised by 8·5 million francs to 78 million francs. In this manner the contractors, relieved of the most pressing anxieties, were able to continue the work.

The northern heading, having passed the southern end of the summit level at 31,399 ft., should now have been driven on a downward gradient of 7:1,000 which of course would have been against good tunnelling practice, since water would accumulate in the workings and have to be pumped out. In contemporary accounts in the technical press it was taken for granted that the heading was driven in this manner in order to meet the heading from the south that was being advanced on this gradient.

What actually happened was altogether different and is shown in Fig. 94. Instead of descending, the miners continued the northern heading on a 1:666 gradient which eventually would have struck the roof of the finished tunnel. The heading was advanced for a further 1,391 ft. on this gradient when a number of small springs were

struck which emitted altogether 115 gals. of hot water per minute.
The heat in the tunnel rose to what would have been an unbearable
temperature but for the simple and ingenius method used to cool the
ventilating air. Pressure water at 72–78 atm., used to operate the
rock drills, was bled at intervals and injected as a fine spray into the
ventilating pipe, whereby the air was cooled to 25° C. or less.

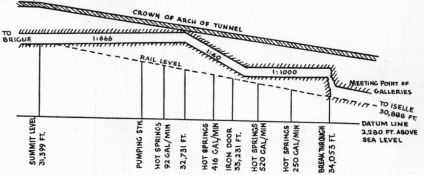

Fig 94. Owing to the danger of flooding the southern heading
with hot water, a unique method of breakthrough was chosen
for Simplon 1. The northern heading was continued from the
summit level on a slightly inclined gradient until it approached
the crown of the finished tunnel, from where it was driven on
a sharp incline towards the rail level. A sump and a pumping
station were installed at the low point to deal with the water
accumulating there. A heavy bulkhead door was also put in
before the heading was advanced on a slightly rising grade
for 763 ft. Here it was abandoned when power from the
northern portal became insufficient to carry on the advance.
The door was closed and the sealed-off appendix was left to
become filled with hot water. The breakthrough was planned
in such a fashion that the water-filled northern heading would
drain through the breach blown in the floor, at the junction
of the two headings.

At 32,731 ft., when approaching the roof of the tunnel, the direction of the heading was changed once more and driven on a sloping
1:48 gradient for a distance of 500 ft. where it hit the rail level
on the sloping grade towards Iselle. On this downward grade the
miners had the misfortune to strike springs emitting 400 gals. of hot
water per minute, which flowed into the heading. A sump and a
number of turbine pumps were installed at the low point to drain
the workings. A water-tight bulkhead door was installed at this point
(see Fig. 94) and the mining team struck out on a rising grade of
1:1,000.

Almost immediately a large spring was struck which poured
570 gals. of water per minute into the heading. The advance continued for a total distance of 763 ft. A further number of hot springs
were encountered which kept adding 250 gals. of 43° C. water per
minute to the previous flow. Then, in the spring of 1904, a landslide
at the water intake on the Rhône cut off the water supply to the
portal installations. The pumps stopped, the ventilation plant ceased
to function, and so did the refrigeration scheme. Inside the tunnel
the temperature rose to above 50° C.; water filled Tunnel 1 and
flooded Tunnel 2 for a distance of 1,148 ft.

This was the end of the advance from the north. Although the
hydraulic power capacity was restored it proved inadequate to keep
the forward heading dry and ventilated. It had to be abandoned.
The door was shut and caulked tight. When abandoned, the northern
heading had reached 34,053 ft., and when the miners left it they
could hear faintly the rumble of the machines in the south through
the 3,280 ft. of rock separating the two headings. Hot water from
the subterranean springs filled the sealed-off appendix, but in the rear
of the closed door work went on as before, breaking out and lining
the tunnel.

Meanwhile, the work of advancing the southern headings proceeded rapidly in dry rock and at the end of August only 882 ft.
remained. A breakthrough was confidently expected by the end of
October. Then, on 8th September, the heading crossed a fault which
flooded both pilot tunnels for a distance of 2,624 ft. The air temperature rose to 38° C. The advance was stopped for seven weeks and all
the men were put to work enlarging the drainage trench in Pilot 2 to
accommodate the flow. From the cold springs 16,400 ft. in the rear,
water was piped under a natural head of 6 atm. to the face to cool
both the hot water and the tunnel air.

With working conditions once more restored to what could be
endured by the miners the advance was resumed, but owing to more
hot springs, rock falls and badly decayed rock which required extensive timbering, progress was slow. At the end of the year, 554 ft.
remained to be excavated. At that time the water discharge through
the southern drainage trench was 200 gals./sec.

On 17th February the rock separating the two headings had been
reduced to 105 ft., and two days later the hot water pouring out of
some long drill-holes was thought to derive from the sealed-off northern heading because the gauge pressure as measured at the door
dropped by 0·5 atm. The southern heading was then 30,783 ft. from
the portal and the northern one 34,053 ft. The last 1,131·5 ft. had
taken nearly six months.

The peculiar manipulations with grade at the end of the northern heading, previously described, began to make sense now when at long last the breakthrough was at hand. Owing to the hot springs at the end of the northern heading, it would have been lethal to permit the two headings to meet in the conventional manner, i.e. face to face. Instead, it was planned to blow a breach in the roof of the southern heading which, hitting the floor of the northern pilot, would permit the hot water filling the appendix to be drained off slowly into the southern heading and carried off through the enlarged trench in the floor. Any lethal gases filling the sealed-off gallery would also be evacuated through the breach.

This was the plan carried through at 7.20 a.m. on 24th February 1905. Both the southern headings had been evacuated when the final rock partition was blasted, leaving a 6·5-ft. breach in the top of the heading. After the hot water had escaped, cold water was sprayed on the rock to reduce the temperature.

The precautions proved necessary. After the news of the break-through had spread through the Iselle camp a crowd of people ignored the rules and went into the tunnel. A few ventured too close to the hot face and two of them, an office employee of the contractor and an Italian railway inspector, were overcome by the fumes and died later of carbon monoxide asphyxiation. After these fatalities the headings were closed for a few days with the ventilation system working at full capacity.

The first to enter the tunnel again was a small survey party which detrained 2,296 ft. from the break. The heat in the heading was still unbearable and nobody could remain at the breakthrough for longer than one minute at a time. Some quick measurements could nevertheless be made which proved that the tunnel was 5 ft. 3 in. shorter than calculated. The difference in levels appeared to be 0·98 ft. One wall was in alignment, but because of irregular crags remaining on the opposite wall the alignment on that side could not be determined.

The worst was over, but much remained to be done. For one thing, the breakthrough had to be celebrated as custom demanded, but conditions in the tunnel did not invite ceremonies for a number of months. However, on 2nd April two trains carrying dignitaries, lay and clerical, pulled up on each side of the sealed door. On the stroke of noon the door was broken open and the two parties met and exchanged such pleasantries as could be mustered under the circumstances, since the heading was still hot. Then followed the banquet, which could be held in a relaxed atmosphere for the contractors had been informed that the Swiss railways had relieved them of the obligation to finish the tunnel by 30th April.

There still remained some 2,952 ft. to be advanced in Tunnel 2, but by using a number of adits a breakthrough was achieved by 6th July. However, owing to some hot springs and poor rock, the lining of the second pilot gallery was not completed until the end of the year. The second heading was not expanded and lined until after the 1914–18 war.

Fig 95. This is the way a contempor-ary artist visualized the breakthrough in the Simplon. In actual fact the tunnel was evacuated when the last partition was blasted. The picture is yet another useful reminder that any 'artistic' representation, pictorial or literary, bears little relation to reality.

Tunnel 1 was completed by 18th October under indescribable difficulties due to decomposed rock, shifting pressures and the ubiquitous hot water pouring out from innumerable fissures. Breaking out to full tunnel area and lining the 137-ft. steel-enclosed section through the crush zone between 14,596 and 14,733 ft. at the southern end presented, to begin with, insuperable obstacles. This section was bridged with steel for its entire length and was safe as long as the steel frames remained in place. The method ultimately adopted and the manner in which it was carried out are shown in Fig. 96.

Briefly, the method involved dividing the section into fifteen sub-sections, each 9 ft. long. Somewhere in each of these sub-sections a small opening was made through the steel frame large enough for a man to squeeze through. Temporary timbering and lagging were placed against the exposed ground as the miner carefully scooped out a few feet outside the steel lining, whereupon he sank a shaft 8 to 10 ft. below the floor of the finished tunnel. The shaft was widened to the length of one sub-section, or for a linear distance of 9 ft.

The space excavated under the pilot tunnel was filled with dimensional stone laid in cement up to the grade of the invert (tunnel floor) which thus obtained a thickness varying from 8 to 10 ft. Having placed this tremendous foundation under the pilot heading, the wings of the invert were excavated to beyond the sides of the finished tunnel and the invert extended to full width. This terribly difficult work, carried out under crowded and hazardous conditions in the slushy rock, took one year. However, once the heavy invert was in place the work of breaking out the tunnel to full width and lining it with stone was greatly facilitated. The crown of the tunnel down to the shoulders was excavated by means of an overhead pilot supported with steel beams and subsequently also with steel arches resting on the walls. The stone vault was laid on the temporary steel arches which, when the entire section had been expanded and lined, were removed by blasting. Putting in the roof took six months.

After the tunnel had been lined, the rest was easy. The ballast and track laying took little time. Since the line was to be electrified, 68 miles of cable were laid and connected in ten days, and on 25th January 1906 the first train, consisting of a steam locomotive and one coach carrying Swiss railway officials, passed through the tunnel and emerged at the Iselle portal. The world's longest tunnel was at long last completed.

Then followed the inquest. The geological Commission absolved itself of all errors. The geological forecast had, after all, been correct up to the fifth kilometre on the northern end and for the first kilometre on the southern, but as for the rest, where it was badly off the mark—so much, in fact, that the Simplon tunnel would not have been undertaken had the actual conditions been known beforehand —as for that, the Commission exonerated itself in a lengthy brief. The crush zone at the southern end could not have been foreseen. 'When

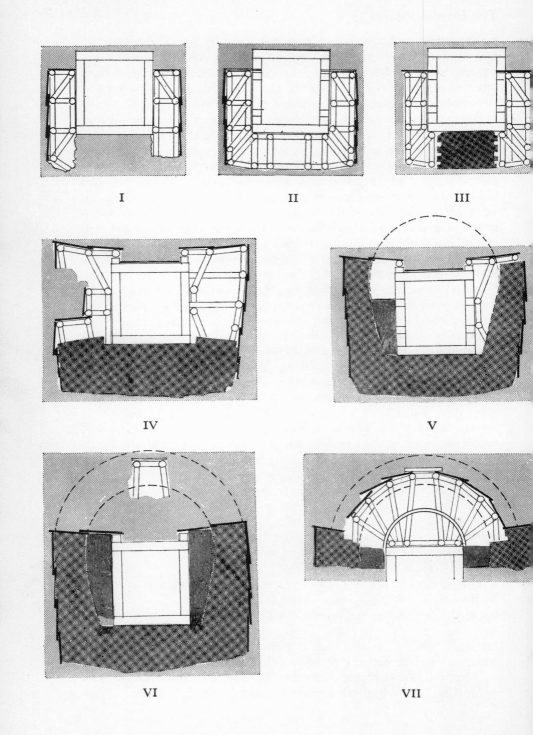

I

II

III

IV

V

VI

VII

passing through large mountain massifs one must always expect to run into decomposed rock that will exert pressure, but it will probably never be possible to determine such zones in advance.' Furthermore, the geological forecast of the Simplon tunnel was never meant to be taken literally; it was a matter of likelihoods and probabilities and certainly not of assertions. Having uttered these words of comfort to the Simplon miners, the members of the Commission went back to marking students' papers.

Other professors hailed the Simplon tunnel as an outstanding technical achievement. The method of advancing two parallel pilot headings was touted as the only one to be used on long mountain-tunnels. The Brandt rock-drilling machine was never likely to be surpassed, since it was perfect for rock tunnelling. The medium used for its operation, i.e. high-pressure water, could be used also for operating pumps, ventilation and refrigeration, as was proved in the Simplon tunnel.

None of the professors of civil engineering appear to have noticed a small one-line item in the quarterly March report issued in 1902 mentioning the testing of one Ingersoll machine in one of the cross-headings. As it turned out, no Brandt machine was ever used after Simplon, since all subsequent rock tunnels have been advanced by

---

Fig 96. Breaking out of and expanding the steel-enclosed pilot through the pressure zone in the Simplon Tunnel is one of the classical feats of tunnelling. The sequence opposite shows how it was accomplished.

I. A small opening, large enough for a miner to crawl through, was made in the steel frame. A heavily timbered shaft was sunk to below the tunnel floor.

II. The ground below the steel frame was excavated and timbered.

III. The excavated space below the steel frame was filled in with stone masonry to a height varying from 2·50 to 3·10 metres.

IV. Having laid a solid stone base below and on both sides of the tunnel floor, the excavation was carried up to the shoulders of the tunnel.

V. The stonework was extended up to the shoulders.

VI. A top heading was driven above the crown of the tunnel.

VII. Heavy timbering resting on the steel frame carried the roof prior to placing the arch.

compressed-air drills, mostly by the Leyner type of machines manufactured by Ingersoll-Rand. The parallel heading scheme used for
the first time in Simplon was, it is true, resorted to in some Rocky
Mountain tunnels, such as the Moffat, Rogers Pass and Cascade
tunnels, but apart from these instances it remains an historical oddity.

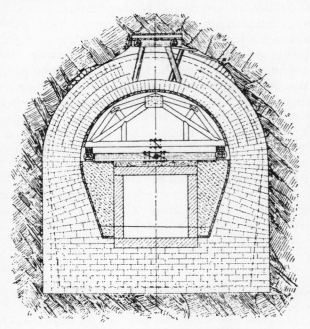

Fig 97. After the heavy lining through
the pressure zone was in place, including the fill between the intrados and
the steel frame, the construction inside
the finish line of the tunnel was removed by blasting.

The advances of the engineering sciences and the availability of
electric power on the sites have made the two-heading scheme as
obsolete as the high-pressure water used to drive the Brandt rock
drills.

The human sacrifice in Simplon was on a much lower scale than
in St. Gotthard. Only thirty-nine men lost their lives, in addition to
Rudolph Brandt and two railway directors who died from overwork,
as well as the two sightseers who ventured too close to the breakthrough heading. The number of reported casualties was about 5,500,
of which 133 were permanently disabled.

The length of the Simplon Pilot 1 was finally determined at 12·3 miles and the deflection of the axis 7·8 in. The difference in levels was 3·3 in. The total cost of the finished tunnel and the second pilot gallery came to 78 million francs ($15.2 million), or 3,940 francs per linear metre. The exact cost of advancing Pilot I was 316·8 francs per metre, whereas Pilot 2 cost 318·8 francs. The total cost of excavating one cubic metre of rock came to 50 francs, or $9.50. Disregarding the inflation that has taken place during the ensuing sixty years, that is just about what it costs now to remove one cubic metre of rock from the bowels of the earth. This is but one of the many reasons why the Simplon tunnel is still hailed as one of the outstanding tunnelling performances in history.

Chapter 10

SUBAQUEOUS TUNNELLING

*'Even the waters forgotten of the
foote: they are dryed up, they are
gone away from men.'*

FROM the point of view of technical efficiency, economy and sheer
beauty of performance, no human tunnelling can of course be compared with the burrowings of the mole and teredo. Both of these
creatures possess the ability to evaluate a burrowing job; they know
what can and cannot be done with the equipment at hand. And
when indications are positive they go to work in a peerless and highly
conscientious fashion until they have achieved their aim.

It is quite obvious that two such superior burrowers would attract
the attention of their two-legged colleagues. In Russia, the mole has
inspired the design of a tunnelling machine which burrows through
soft ground in the manner of a mole and takes out the entire area of
a circular tunnel measuring some 10 ft. in diameter. No details of this
machine are available and it is not possible to evaluate the design
in comparison with western 'mole type' machines, which hitherto
have proved disappointing in practice.

The burrowing method and mechanics of the teredo, the dreaded
ship-worm, attracted the attention of an engineer some 150 years
ago, and from his observations he evolved a superior machine and
tunnelling method suitable for subaqueous work in silt, mud, running
sand, and gravel, where previously such work was altogether impossible.

The Brunel Shield

The original inventor of the tunnelling shield, inspired by the teredo's shell-plates which protect the mollusc when rasping its way through wood, was a young French emigré to England, Marc Isambard Brunel. The inventive son of yeoman farmers in Normandy, he had remained royalist like the rest of the Norman farmers during the French Revolution. At the height of the Jacobin purge of the insurgents in Normandy and Brittany in 1793, Brunel imprudently addressed his dog as 'Citoyen' in front of a patriot and became listed as a candidate for the guillotine. He managed to escape to New York, whence he sailed to England in 1798. In his new country he introduced in succession a mechanized method of making blocks which appears to be the first line production ever set up, a new type of saw-mill incorporating his circular saw, and, to his ruin, a method of mass-producing boots for the army. Having set himself up with a capacity equal to the annual requirements of the British Army, he was caught by Waterloo and the ensuing peace with 80,000 pairs of boots which the Government refused to take off his hands. His bankruptcy put him in the King's Bench prison for a few months in 1821.

London was growing and the streets were getting clogged with traffic. From Wapping 3,700 passengers were being conveyed daily across the river to Rotherhithe by 350 watermen, while wagons and carts were forced to add two miles to their journey on a roundabout route via London Bridge. The idea of a tunnel under the Thames had been broached by Dodd at the end of the previous century, and in 1817 Richard Trevithick had started driving a pilot tunnel under the river on behalf of the promoters, the Thames Archway Company. After five years of fruitless effort, the first attempt at tunnelling under the river was abandoned, but a prize of £500 was offered for a viable scheme. The offer attracted forty-nine plans, but after reviewing them the two-man technical committee declared that, without presuming to put a limit to human ingenuity, the members were nevertheless inclined to believe the idea of a river tunnel to be impracticable.

By the time this pronouncement was made a British patent had been issued to Brunel (in 1818) for a device which he described as 'a casing or cell to be forced forward before the timbering which is generally employed to secure the work.' Brunel had hit upon the idea of the tunnel shield after picking up a piece of teredo-riddled oak timber in the Chatham Yard and noticing the pair of strong shell-plates protecting the mollusc when gnawing its way through wood.

As eventually constructed, the Brunel shield consisted of an 80-ton cast-iron structure 38 ft. wide and 22 ft. 6 in. high. It was made up of twelve parallel frames, each one having a width of 3 ft and being divided into three floors, or cells. When assembled the shield contained thirty-six cells, each measuring 3 × 6 ft., for miners to work in. To facilitate moving the shield it was divided vertically into three parts which could be moved ahead by means of large screw jacks

Fig 98. The Brunel shield consisted of twelve 3-ft.-wide cast-iron frames joined together to form a 38-ft.-wide structure containing thirty-six 3 × 6ft. working cells, each one holding a miner.

bearing on the lining in the rear. Behind the shield was a movable working stage on which the miners threw the rubble and which was also used by the masons putting in the lining.

After presenting his scheme to the Institution of Civil Engineers, which received it with acclaim, Brunel got backing for his tunnel venture. A company with a share capital of £160,000 was formed in 1824 and Brunel was retained as the engineer of the tunnelling project with a salary of £1,000 per year. He was also to get £5,000 for his patent and a bonus of £5,000 upon completion of the tunnel. The duration of the job was conservatively estimated at three years.

The work of the Rotherhithe–Wapping tunnel got started on 2nd March 1825 with the ceremonial laying, to the peal of church bells, of the first brick of the shaft lining, followed by a 'sumptuous collation' when 200 guests with speeches and toasts committed themselves to the success of the magnificent enterprise thus begun.

Borings had been carried out across the river, and upon the advice of the geologists, who predicted strong blue clay all the way across, Brunel decided on a 37 ft. 6 in. × 22 ft. 4 in. double-road tunnel to be driven at a depth of 14 ft. below the river bed. It was given a gradient of 2 ft. 3 in. in 300 ft., where, under the middle of the river, the bottom of the tunnel was calculated to be 76 ft. below high-water level. At the Rotherhithe end he erected upon an iron curb a circular tower of brick, 42 ft. high, with walls 3 ft. thick. By excavating the ground enclosed by the tower (or shaft lining), he sank it a few inches a day, and by August the shaft had been sunk to grade 50 ft. below the surface. On 28th November the shield had been assembled at the bottom of the shaft and tunnelling could begin.

Seldom has a construction development attracted such attention, national and international, as the Thames tunnel. It was being discussed the world over, and ambassadors to the Court of St. James were ordered to keep reporting on its progress. British travellers in distant lands had to be prepared to give detailed accounts of the construction when received in audience by the high and mighty. In a monastery on a sun-scorched mountain-top in Calabria a British visitor was kept up all night answering questions about the tunnel put to him by the Prior and his Brothers.[1] The workings became a fashionable visiting place for the leading personages in Britain.

But workers took a different view and Brunel ran into considerable trouble getting miners and masons for his tunnel. At long last he

[1] Celia Brunel Noble: *The Brunels, Father and Son*, Cobden-Sanderson, London (1938).

succeeded in assembling a labour force by paying 4*s*. per day for masons, 3*s*. for miners and 5*s*. for foremen.

Once started, the work proceeded uninterruptedly in three shifts and by the end of December 7 ft. of tunnel had been excavated and lined. The tunnelling method worked as planned. It proved not particularly difficult moving the heavy shield ahead with the screw

Fig 99. Advancing the first Thames Tunnel in 1826. The Brunel shield is shown at the right.

jacks; for each shove an advance of 18 in. was gained and immediately bricked in with a double-arched lining. But there was trouble ahead; in fact, Brunel must already have been aware of it when sinking the shaft. Instead of striking the clay as predicted, he had found pockets of gravel in the shaft which did not promise well for the enterprise. The first trouble was encountered early in January, and on the 26th—when 14 ft. of lining had been completed—water broke through the crown and flooded 12 ft. of the shaft. The workers panicked and the portal engines running the pumps stopped working.

The crisis was mastered and the damage repaired, and when water broke into the heading a month later the mining crew took it in its stride. The shield and the organization worked to satisfaction in the blue clay, but at times the miners struck pockets of gravel and silt which let in water and caused much trouble. Having advanced in this fashion about 300 ft. by February 1827, the directors of the company were tempted by the public interest to collect revenue by admitting visitors to the tunnel at one shilling per head. The shield was then advancing through gravelly ground, but despite Brunel's anxiety lest there should be some mishap hundreds of sightseers were admitted each day to gaze at the tunnel. At the end of April the number exceeded 700 per day. A concert was held in the finished portion, while at the front the shield was being pushed through slushy ground and the workers were catching mysterious sicknesses, including temporary loss of sight, from the sewer water seeping through the loose gravel.

On the evening of 18th May Lady Raffles and a large party of sightseers were brought to the shield by an engineer sick with apprehension over what might happen if the green Irish mining crew then at work should suddenly panic upon striking water.

A few hours later came disaster. The tide in the river rose fast and ripped a hole in the crown. A flood of mud and water swept everything before it, extinguishing the lamps as it rose, and in the darkness men fought for their lives in the roaring waters. Strangely enough, a roll call in the shaft revealed that nobody had been lost. The damage was eventually repaired by filling the hole with bags of clay lowered from a barge on the river, the standard practice still used when a hole is blown through the roof of a subaqueous tunnel. Then followed the dreary job of pumping out, by hand, the water in the tunnel and cleaning up the mess, which was interrupted by a new break. By 27th June the younger Brunel succeeded in advancing to the shield in a boat. He found it intact, and after further pumping the tunnel was drained by the end of July, two months after the disaster. But it was not until November that the damage had been fully repaired.

The occasion of the renewed advance was celebrated by a dinner for fifty guests held in the tunnel, with music provided by the band of the Coldstream Guards. In the adjoining archway 120 miners were also treated to food and drink. There was a great deal of heady talk about defeating the river in the manner of Admiral Codrington's victory over the Turks at Navarino, the news of which was announced at the dinner.

For a few months everything went well with the Thames tunnel, but on 12th January 1828 the river had its little joke. At six o'clock in the morning when the men were picking away at the face in the top cells, the ground suddenly swelled and gave way before a powerful jet of water that could not be stanched. By the time the

Fig 100. Sketches from Brunel's diary illustrating the break in the crown of the tunnel. (1) The younger Brunel with company is shown approaching the shield in a boat after the hole had been plugged with clay. (2) Slushy ground is shown breaking through the breast-boards. (3) The younger Brunel is inspecting the damage to the crown in a diving bell. (4) Water pouring through the breast-boards in front of the shield. (5) The younger Brunel and Beamish inspecting the damage to the shield after having crawled up to it on top of the silt deposited in the tunnel. The hole in the crown has been stopped by clay dumped from above.

shield crew had been ordered to retire, water reached up to the men's waists and kept rising. The rush of air extinguished the lamps and by the time the men reached the safety of the shaft, the tunnel was filled with water. This time six men drowned in the stinking sewer water.

Once more the leak in the river bottom was stanched by throwing down 4,500 bags of clay, but it proved less easy to stanch the drain on the company's finances. The capital, inadequate to begin with, had been dissipated by the two disasters, and since an attempt to raise more money failed, there was nothing to do but to stop the work. After the tunnel had been drained once more the shield was bricked up, the two arches were stuccoed and a large mirror was placed at the farther end to make the interior look more impressive. Brilliantly lighted, the Thames tunnel became a popular destination for sight-seers. One wit of the day suggested that it would make a lovely wine-cellar.

However, at the end of 1834 after a stoppage of seven years, through the efforts of the Duke of Wellington and Lord Althorp, Chancellor of the Exchequer, the tunnel company was granted a Treasury loan of £246,000. The old shield was taken out and a new one weighing 140 tons was assembled in situ from some 9,000 parts. The advance could proceed again.

The new heavy shield succeeded where the old one had failed and, despite five breaks, steady progress was made through cavities in the river bed. The lesson of the previous disasters had been learned and the weak points were strengthened by dumping clay in the river bottom ahead of the advance. Everything was not well, however. The farther the miners advanced under the river the worse became the hygienic conditions. Fire-damp burst into sheets of flame enveloping the shield. The noxious black mud caused serious sickness among foremen, engineers and miners. They were knocked unconscious by the foul air, some were suddenly blinded by the gases, everyone in the tunnel suffered from diarrhoea and violent headaches. Miners died, bricklayers in the rear lost consciousness while standing on the scaffold and fell to the floor. But some 900 visitors per week kept streaming into the tunnel during the six years needed to complete the work.

Finally, the shield reached the Wapping shore at 2 p.m. on 12th August 1841. To accomplish 'the subaqueous structure'—1,200 ft. in length—had required sixteen years and two months, at a cost of £433 per linear foot, and the broken health of the engineer. Seven lives had been lost in accidents and numerous workers had had their health impaired for life.

The tunnel was officially opened on 25th March 1843 with a great to-do, and 50,000 persons passed through it during the first twenty-four hours. To the public and the world at large it was the wonder of the age, but to Brunel and the tunnel company it was a ruinous failure. The Treasury loan was consumed, and there was no money available to complete the tunnel so that it could perform its function as a traffic artery for wheeled traffic. The approaches could not be developed and nothing came of Brunel's idea of installing 'hoisting apparatus' at either end. The exhaustion of the funds prevented the company from honouring its obligation to pay Brunel's bonus of £5,000 upon the completion of the work, and the best the directors could do was to offer him £1,700. Brunel felt cheated, and his grievance soured his remaining days and brought on the stroke which turned him into an invalid.

The only person who seems to have made any success out of the Rotherhithe–Wapping Tunnel was one of the stall-keepers selling souvenirs to sightseers. When on 26th July 1843 Queen Victoria and Prince Albert visited the tunnel he spread his entire stock of souvenir silk handkerchiefs on the ground for the Royal party to walk on. Before being trodden on, the handkerchiefs had sold at 3*s.* 6*d.*; after being soiled by the royal feet they fetched half a guinea each.

The first subaqueous tunnel in the world since the 3,045-ft. tunnel under the Euphrates, connecting the royal palace of Babylon with the temple of Jupiter Belos, became nothing more than a pedestrian pathway and a favourite shelter of the numerous homeless generated by the Victorian Age, who by paying a toll of 1*d.* could take refuge from the weather and spend a night there. When the East London Railway purchased the tunnel in 1869 the 'Hades Hotel' went out of business and Marc Isambard Brunel's masterpiece of subaqueous construction could at long last begin its useful life. Except for a sheet-iron lining for the roof nothing was needed to accommodate the tunnel to the railway age.

The Second Thames Tunnel

The ill-fated Wapping tunnel discouraged for twenty-five years any further attempt to advance a bore through clay and silt under a river. The next attempt, in 1869, which also involved tunnelling through the clay under the Thames, was altogether successful and inaugurated a new era in tunnelling.

When driving the Tower Hill tunnel, a distance of 1,320 ft. from Tower Hill to the Vine Street end of Tooley Street, an entirely new shield patented by P. W. Barlow in 1865 was used. But instead

A View of the Western Archway of the Thames Tunnel

Fig 101. A contemporary sketch of the western archway of the
Thames Tunnel before it had deteriorated to a night shelter
for London's homeless.

of a conventional lining of masonry, the new system employed a sectionalized cast-iron lining that was erected as the shield advanced.

The shield used on the second Thames tunnel resembled a large cartwheel, with the rim made of cast iron and strengthened with six short wrought-iron spokes extending half-way to the centre and joined by plates so as to form a large hexagonal opening in the centre. From the reinforced face of the shield a slightly tapered cylinder nearly 3 ft. in length extended towards the rear; this provided protection for the miners. At the inner face, where the spokes joined the rim, were six screw jacks abutting against the end of the finished lining. The front of the shield was about 8 ft. in diameter and the entire structure weighed 2½ tons. After each shove, a cast-iron ring, 18 in. long and made up of three segments, was erected and bolted to the finished lining.

The tunnel was driven from a 60-ft. shaft sunk on Tower Hill, through which the shield was lowered to grade. The shield was advanced through stiff London clay by three miners, at the rate of 9 ft. per twenty-four hours. The three men, protected by the steel cylinder, excavated enough clay through the hexagonal opening in the centre to permit one man to enter the cavity in front of the shield. He enlarged the opening so that the second man would have room to work; later the third man also joined in the excavation in front of the shield. When the clay ahead had been cleared away, the shield was pushed ahead about 2 ft. by the six jacks, which brought about 60 tons of pressure to bear against the finished lining. Actually, only one screw proved necessary to move the shield under normal conditions. Having advanced the shield, a 1⅞-in. flanged and segmented cast-iron ring was bolted to the finished lining and a new working cycle started.

The tunnel was completed without incident in less than a year at a cost of under £20,000.

When advancing such a cast-iron-lined tunnel the outside diameter of the circular lining will be somewhat less than the bore made by the shield, since the cast-iron segments will have to be erected inside the shield. Therefore, when the shield is jacked ahead after erecting a ring, a concentric space is formed around the lining which is liable to cause a run building up dangerous local pressure on the lining. This danger was realized from the outset, and the annular cavity was filled with lime mixed with water put in place by means of a hand syringe.

The engineer in charge of driving this prototype of all subaqueous shield tunnels was a twenty-five-year-old South African, J. H. Greathead, of whom the world was to hear a good deal before the century was over.

Greathead was born and educated in the Cape Colony and, arriving in London in 1864, he entered the office of Peter W. Barlow from whom he learned the new tricks of subaqueous tunnelling.

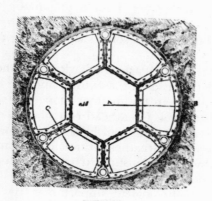

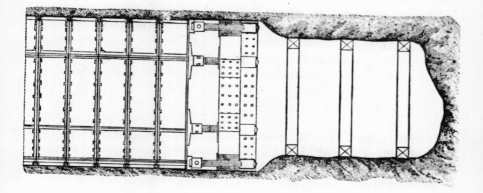

Fig 102. Cross-section and longitudinal view of the Barlow shield used to excavate the second Thames Tunnel, the pedestrian tube from Tower Hill to Toley Street. The tunnel was finished in 1870.

When Barlow engineered the Tower tunnel five years later the memories of the Brunel tragedy were still haunting the trade and no contractor was found willing to bid on the tunnel. In the end, the Barlow firm undertook the work and the gifted apprentice was put in charge of the advance which he concluded in such an admirable fashion.

While Greathead was driving the first subaqueous shield tunnel in London, A. S. Beach, editor of *The Scientific American*, successfully drove a short 8-ft. tunnel under Broadway in New York City, between Warren and Murray Streets, by means of a shield constructed from boiler plate. He used hydraulic rams to advance the shield. The idea of the tunnel was to use it for a pneumatic railway, but the public did not take kindly to it and the venture was abortive. The Beach shield was later used in some short tunnels in Cincinnati and Cleveland.

These two shields, particularly the Barlow one and the lining used with it, contained the seed of the future, and all subsequent river-tunnels have been built in the manner pioneered with such success in the Tower Hill tunnel. Greathead contributed notable improvements to the early method, as will be shown below, and before the turn of the century the Greathead tunnelling system had emerged as the most technically sophisticated ever developed. Nothing of significance has been added to it since.

But, despite its technological importance, the second Thames tunnel was insignificant from the point of view of size compared with the subaqueous work then going on in the Great Lakes area in the United States, without benefit of sophisticated engineering, and indeed without any tunnelling experience at all. For sheer impudent daring there is nothing comparable with the Chicago Lake tunnel begun a few years before the invention of the tunnelling shield.

The Chesbrough Idea

By 1861, the city of Chicago was in dire need of additional supplies of water. The city had up to that time obtained its water from Lake Michigan, but with the growth of the population the lake shore supply had become badly polluted and a suggestion was made to lay a 5-ft. pipe one mile out in the lake to obtain water beyond the reach of the shore contaminations.

The engineer of the newly created Board of Public Works, E. S. Chesbrough, had another idea. He proposed to drive a tunnel under the bottom of Lake Michigan sufficiently far out so as to tap clear water. As eventually carried out, a 5 ft. × 5 ft. 2 in. masonry-lined tunnel was extended for 10,567 ft. out into the lake to a large crib sunk to the bottom of the lake. Inside the crib, and protected from the buffeting of the storms and ice, a shaft was sunk from the surface down to the bottom and into the clay to join the tunnel from the shore. The capacity of the tunnel was estimated at 50 million gallons of water per day.

The work of sinking a 9-ft. cast-iron-lined shaft on the shore down to tunnel grade was begun on 17th March 1864, and the tunnel advance started on 26th May. No trouble was experienced with the stiff Chicago clay that stood unsupported for thirty-six hours, or long enough to line the heading with masonry. Occasionally, local pockets of quicksand were encountered but they gave no serious trouble.

The most unpleasant part of the job consisted of the sound effects which when first experienced caused panic among the workers. Ice churning against a breakwater 60 ft. above the tunnel produced loud noises, as if the ice was crunching against the crown of the lining. Log rafts passing over the tunnel also created a series of frightening sounds; there were the puffing of the steam-engine, the churning noise of the paddle wheels, the rubbing and striking of the logs, the grating of the chains holding the raft together—all this miscellany of eerie sounds could be clearly heard in the tunnel. Indeed, when work was stopped for the benefit of the survey party, even the rain-drops striking the surface of the lake could be clearly distinguished.

The most dangerous element of the job was the gas which was encountered from the outset and continued to the end of the advance. When the inexperienced men ran into the first gas explosion they were singed and badly scared, but they soon learned how to detect gas pockets by the hollow sound produced when they were struck with picks. When a pocket was detected the miners bored a small hole into it and ignited the gas as it escaped. They threw themselves on the floor and let the flames pass over them.

In this manner the work proceeded in three eight-hour shifts, with four miners and three muckers per shift, followed by four masons with six helpers. The average advance was 12 ft. per day. Every 1,000 ft. the tunnel was expanded to double its width to permit marshalling of the cars pulled by mules. An 8-in. sheet-iron pipe supplied ventilating air from a fan blower on the shore, that is, when the pipe was not knocked down by the mules.

To get alignment of the tunnel and for placing the lake shaft, a 6-in. tube was sunk from the lake surface down through the clay and the masonry crown of the tunnel, at a distance 280 ft. from the shore shaft. By plumbing down the shaft, the axis of the tunnel was orien-tated towards the lake shaft during the advance.

The timber crib sunk into the lake was pentagonal in shape, each side measuring 58 ft. Its total height was 40 ft. The crib was built on shore and towed to its place on 24th July 1865. It was sunk to the bottom by filling the 25-ft. space between the inside and outside wall with rock.

In the 22-ft. well of the crib, a 9-ft. cast-iron cylinder, made of

9-ft. sections having a thickness of 2¼ in., was assembled to a total length of 64 ft. and sunk to the bottom. Since the heavy cast-iron cylinder was supplied with a false bottom of wood it obtained buoyancy when sunk to a depth of 30 ft., which made it relatively easy to handle. When placed on line the heavy iron cylinder sank by its own weight 3 ft. into the clay until stopped by the false bottom. A hole was then drilled through it, whereupon the cylinder sank several more feet into the clay.

After two more sections, including one containing the water-gates,

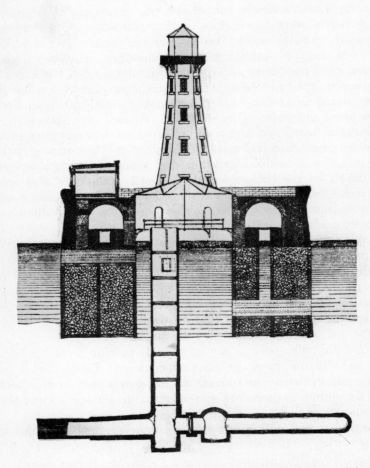

Fig 103. The lighthouse marking the crib enclosing the lake shaft leading to the first Chicago water tunnel conducting Lake Michigan water to the city.

had been bolted to the top of the cylinder the false bottom was knocked out and the clay inside it excavated. As the excavation proceeded the cylinder continued to sink to 23 ft. below the bottom of the lake. The remainder of the shaft was sunk to tunnel grade without protection, but since no water was met with there was no need to line the bottom part of the shaft.

From the bottom of the lake shaft a tunnelling team advanced westwards, at the rate of 9½ ft. per day. After driving 2,290 ft. without incident and lining the heading, the work was stopped 100 ft. from the opposite heading. Since some doubts were felt about the alignment, the remaining 100 ft. were driven as a small, timbered drift. When the breakthrough was accomplished on 30th November 1866 it was found that the masonry lining in the east face was 7⅓ in. out of line and the total distance only 3 in. longer than calculated.

The tunnel was lined and the meeting-places filled in. The work was completed on 24th March 1867, three years almost to a day after sinking the shore shaft. The total cost came to $457,815, as against an estimated $307,522.

For this insignificant sum Chicago obtained approximately 3 million gals. of excellent lake water per day. A few years later a parallel 7 ft. × 7 ft. 2 in. tunnel was advanced in the same manner about 50 ft. from the first and into a second shaft sunk into the crib. This tunnel was extended under the city for a distance of 20,680 ft. The capacity of the second tunnel was 100 million gals. per day, although the pumping capacity restricted the daily supply to 6 million gals. The cost of the second lake tunnel was $414,719, against an estimated $400,000.

After such an intelligent civic performance it was not surprising that the city fathers decided to enclose the crib in masonry and erect a lighthouse on top of it, as a guide to shipping as well as to the other cities in need of water around the Great Lakes.[2]

Tragedy in Cleveland

All around this vast inland sea the rapidly growing towns lacked water since they had already succeeded in contaminating the water

[2] Chicago's systems of lake tunnels have been continuously expanded since the original Chesbrough ones, although not always with the same success. When another lake tunnel was driven in 1909, the crib caught fire and of the one hundred men working on it 7,500 ft. out in the lake, sixty lost their lives, most of them in the fire or in the water. A great many who had taken refuge in the unfinished tunnel that had been advanced from the crib shaft were found suffocated.

close to the shores. In the end some 30 miles of masonry-lined tunnels were built to bring water in prodigious supply to the Great Lakes communities. But for a while it looked as if Chesbrough had consumed the supply of luck needed to burrow under water in such a simple, even primitive manner. When the city of Cleveland ventured to repeat the performance by extending a water tunnel 6,606 ft. out under Lake Erie the enterprise was haunted by trouble and tragedy from the outset.

The Cleveland Water Board obtained permission to go ahead with the tunnel without going through the normal procedure of calling for bids. It hired local talent to sink the shore shaft and employed a foreman who had learned mining in English coal-mines. The work began on 23rd August 1869, and by the time the shaft had been sunk 63 ft. and only 4 ft. remained to tunnel grade the miners struck gas and the foreman went down with a miner to investigate. When the bucket was about half-way down, this old-time coal miner did something quite unexpected. He struck a match. That was the end of him and his companion in the bucket. The explosion and fire also severely burned two men leaning over the opening of the shaft. But St. Barbara, patron saint of miners, was nevertheless in a playful mood that day. One man standing on a plank laid across the top of the shaft was blown 12 ft. into the air, and so was the plank. When he descended, the plank had fallen back into place a fraction of a second earlier and was there to receive him. He was the only one round the shaft to be unhurt by the explosion.

From this ugly beginning the Cleveland tunnel was cursed by gas. The 5 × 5 ft. tunnel was driven 35 ft. below the lake bottom through clay and quicksand, gas pockets and springs. Each time a storm raised the waves, gas and water became worse. When 1,300 ft. had been gained, gas, water and quicksand broke into the lined tunnel and filled it with sand and silt. Since no further progress could be made on the straight line, the tunnel axis was turned 20° and when run 40 ft. from the original line angled back to the original course.

After slogging it out with gas and water to a point 4,000 ft. from the shore, the miners on the night shift of 29th April 1871 heard a loud noise in their rear. They panicked and ran towards the shore, leaving everything behind. About 600 ft. in the rear water was pouring through the masonry in innumerable jets for a distance of 150 ft. The water piercing the lining filled the tunnel beyond the capacity of the pumps, and the heading had to be abandoned.

A new heading was now established from the intake crib out in Lake Erie and advanced towards the abandoned one. After 380 ft.

from the lake shaft, however, soft clay was encountered which flowed into the heading faster than it could be removed. Having heard of Beach's shield the management borrowed it from New York and made an attempt to force it through the soft clay; but as they were inexperienced with the shield method, more trouble developed. The shield could not be kept on line, it got stuck on boulders and finally cracked. All the same, by the time the broken shield was removed, the heading had actually passed through the running clay. Thereafter, the heading continued through firm clay and the advance proceeded without trouble to within 20 ft. of the face of the abandoned shore tunnel. Then the face exploded and blew soft clay, gas and water into the lake heading, which filled with water and had to be abandoned.

That was just about the end of Cleveland's attempt to fetch water from Lake Erie. Several years of work, the expenditure of several hundred thousands of dollars and the lives of nineteen men had resulted in two headings filled with water and muck, and separated by 20 ft. of running clay. But then, quite unexpectedly, something strange happened. When pumping took place in the shore shaft it was noticed that the water level sank in the lake shaft. The two headings were obviously fed with water from a common source. By increasing the pump capacity the two sections were finally drained. But the gas remained. The miners entering the lake section with lamps in their caps crouched under sheets of gas which kept exploding and filling the space under the crown with flame. But beyond singeing the hair of the miners the fire-damp did not cause any injuries. After clearing 50 ft. of the lake heading of sand and clay, the miners continued the advance and on the second day the team broke into the shore heading and found the tools, clothing and lunch boxes left by the escaping miners two and a half years earlier. The headings had been recovered.

However, that was by no means the end of the work. As the miners proceeded in triumph towards the shore they found the shore tunnel filled with sand where water had broken through. Farther along, the entire lining had sunk 5 ft. into the mud. An attempt was made to restore the lining, but the new masonry cracked as soon as it was put in. Since there was no hope of saving the collapsed section of the shore heading, it was decided to seal it off with a bulkhead. Towards the shore, about half a mile from the shaft, they found the tunnel filled with sand, and began to clear up the clogged section. But, again, it was of no use, as the sand kept flowing in faster than it could be removed. Another bulkhead was erected, and the 832 ft. of the tunnel between the two bulkheads were abandoned. From behind the bulkheads two new headings were struck at an angle and advanced 73 ft. westwards, whereupon the axis was turned so that the headings ran parallel to the old line. Here the clay proved much better and there was no trouble joining up the two headings.

All the deviations forced on the miners by the bad ground caused a great deal of anxiety about the survey. Originally, it had been intended to sink a pipe Chicago-fashion from the lake surface to the crown of the tunnel at a distance of 300 ft. from the shore, as an aid to keeping the tunnel on line. But before this could be done the first deviation had become necessary. After that, the entire tunnel advance from the shore shaft, or 3,592 ft., had to be directed from two wires hung in the shore shaft. The two points guiding the alignment of the shore headings were only 7 ft. apart.

The lake heading was advanced from two points plumbed down the 110-ft. shaft and 13 ft. apart. From this backsight 2,700 ft. of tunnel were built. Under these conditions, the anxiety whether the two headings would meet at all is not surprising; but in the end, it was found that they were only 7 ft. 7 in. out of line. However, since the junction was made at an angle the error was of no practical importance.

The Cleveland tunnel was finished on 2nd March 1874, after four and a half years of work and at a cost of $320,351·72. A beacon was also erected atop the Cleveland crib, whether to guide the ore traffic or whether in memory of the miners who died so that the mining magnates in Cleveland could get water for their newfangled bathtubs is lost in the mists of mid-Western history.[3]

The Watery Severn

While tunnelling through the stiff clay under the Great Lakes was nearing completion, another ambitious scheme got under way in England. The directors of the Great Western Railway, after ten years of procrastination, finally decided to go ahead with a 4½-mile tunnel under the Severn to link up its lines on both sides of the estuary. This tunnel would do away with the trouble and expense of ferrying the trains across the ugly waters beset by 50-ft. tides, sudden fogs, shifting sandbanks, and treacherous currents. A tunnel under the

---

[3] Tunnelling in Cleveland has always had its points. When extending a similar water tunnel in 1915 through gassy ground the miners hit upon using canaries to warn them of the gas. The birds were brought down into the tunnel for half an hour altogether each day, but the practice had to be abandoned owing to the public outcry against this cruelty to animals.

Severn would reduce the travel time from London to Cardiff by nearly an hour.

The idea of a tunnel under the estuary had occurred to Charles Richardson, engineer of the Great Western (who, as a pupil of the elder Brunel, had been blooded in the first Thames tunnel), when supervising the building of the company's shore installations in 1862. He had then noticed the remarkably level rock and marl beds uncovered at low tide, which suggested excellent conditions for driving a tunnel.

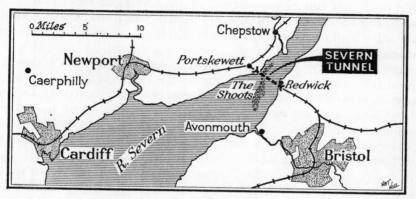

Fig 104. The 4½-mile Severn Tunnel on the Great Western Railway was driven 1877–86.

Plans for the Severn tunnel were deposited with Parliament in 1864, but lack of funds, and doubts about the feasibility of carrying through such an immense undertaking, postponed the scheme until 1872 when an Act of Parliament was passed authorizing the work. Preliminary surveys were carried out which bore out Richardson's conception. The critical part of the crossing was a deep ¼-mile channel close by the Welsh shore known as The Shoots, and it was decided to drive a small pilot tunnel to see whether it would be possible to cross under it.

The work of advancing the 7 × 7-ft. heading began in March 1873 from a 200-ft. shaft situated on the Welsh side, about half a mile from The Shoots. The shaft was sunk through sandstone and marl, as predicted by surface indications and test borings. The bottom of the shaft was reached in December 1874 and the miners then struck out towards the English shore, using McKean drills and dynamite. Working in eight-hour shifts an advance of 14 to 18 yds. was gained per week. The heading was driven with a gradient of 1:480 towards the lowest point under The Shoots, about 800 yds. distant.

The idea was to use the exploratory tunnel as a permanent drainage trench for the final tunnel. In July 1877, when the heading had been advanced 1,600 yds. without incident through safe rock, the railway called for bids on the final double-track tunnel. When the tenders were opened they proved to be from £200,000 to £500,000 in excess of the estimate and were rejected. The Great Western decided to go ahead with the tunnel to prove to the contractors that the hazards were not as great as they thought.

A number of new shafts were sunk and the advance of a new 8 × 8-ft. pilot tunnel was begun. The old McKean drills had been worn out in 1875 and an improved design was introduced whereby the advance in the exploratory tunnel was raised from 6 to 8 ft. per twenty-four hours. In the new heading a record advance of 9 ft. was made in 1877. The new rock drills, designed by John J. Geach, were bar-mounted, with two units on the carriage. The method of operation was as follows: the drill carriage was moved up to the front from a siding at 11.30 a.m., set up by 11.41 a.m. and after drilling twenty holes in 1 hr. 6 min. it was run back to its protective siding and the holes were charged with dynamite. Total time for drilling and charging came to 1 hr. 19 min. The drill set used was 2 ft. 6 in. to 6 ft. 6 in. In the Pennant sandstone the drills lasted 10 ft. between re-forgings. While drilling, a jet of water with a 180-ft. head was injected into the holes to bind the dust.

The rock drills worked at 60 p.s.i. pressure delivered by a single-acting 12 × 15-in. compressor with water-jacketed cylinder; the air was further cooled by water injection. The new 200-ft. pumping shaft was provided with an 18-in. by 9-ft.-stroke plunger pump, driven by a 40-in. Cornish beam engine. Steam for the engine was raised by three 5 ft. 9 in. × 28-ft. boilers with a working pressure of 50 p.s.i. The capacity of the pumping plant was 100,000 gals. per hour.

There was certainly nothing amateurish about the Severn operation. By the end of the year two shafts had been sunk on the Gloucestershire side and the heading from the Monmouthshire side had reached 7,600 ft. without incident. The directors of the railway company were confident that the two headings would meet within a few months. Then, in October 1879, the smooth operation ran into serious trouble. While the pilot tunnel was being extended inland from the shore shaft on the Welsh side, a spring was struck at the junction between the millstone grit and the carboniferous limestone, and 360,000 gals. of water per hour poured into the tunnel and flooded the workings. At that time, there remained only 130 yds. between the two headings under the Severn.

This was the end. The not inconsiderable pumping capacity which at the time of the tragedy had been increased to 262,000 gals./hr. in the shore shaft and 46,000 gals./hr. in the inland shaft proved inadequate to cope with the flood, and the tunnel advance came to a full stop. In their predicament the directors of the Great Western requested Sir John Hawkshaw, consulting engineer on the tunnel, to take charge of the operations. He accepted the offer upon the condition that Thomas H. Walker, one of the bidders on the contract, was put on as contractor on the basis of his original tender of £948,959 submitted two years previously.

Walker moved in with his men and began the salvaging work by sinking three new shafts in an attempt to drain the workings. New pumping engines were ordered whereby the pumping capacity was raised to 460,000 gals./hr. One of the pumps installed was 38 in. in diameter, with a 9-ft. stroke, driven by a large Cornish engine. It was the largest and most modern pump in England, which at that time was synonymous with the world. It was started in early July 1880, but in their eagerness to drain the shaft Walker's pump engineers overstressed the pump and the barrel fractured after ten days. It took three months to get the giant pump into service again.

By 14th October, water in the shore shaft had been reduced from 170 to 30 ft. Progress was painfully slow, since in addition to the original 360,000 gals./hr. still gushing out from the shore spring, another flood of 150,000 gals./hr. poured into the subaqueous part of the tunnel. It was then recalled that there was an iron door in the heading about 1,000 ft. from the shore shaft. This door had been left open in 1879 when the miners ran for their lives through the rising flood. It was decided to try to close the door to shut off this supply in excess of the installed pumping capacity.

With the contractor's attempt to close the door in the flooded tunnel the British newspaper readers of the day acquired a hero more worthy of admiration than the idols of the tabloids a century later. Walker sent his chief diver Lambert, accompanied by two assistant divers, into the darkness of the water-filled tunnel littered with broken timbers and other debris. But the length and other difficulties with their trailing air hoses prevented the divers from reaching the door. On a second attempt, Lambert was provided with a self-contained diving apparatus, recently invented by H. A. Fleuss, which permitted him to advance without being encumbered by the hose. Lambert reached the door and managed to rip up one of the rails passing through the opening, but by that time he had had enough of his gruesome labour and returned leaving the door still open.

Lambert made a third attempt on 10th November. He managed to pull up the second rail so that the door could be shut. Noting a valve on the far side of the door he closed that, after which he shut the door tight. Before returning, he also noticed a sluice valve on the near side of the door and decided to shut off that valve also. After having turned the spindle as far as it would go, he returned in triumph to be acclaimed as the first successful self-contained diver.

On Lambert's return, water stood 20 ft. in the shore shaft and it was expected that the workings would be drained without delay. Instead, the pumping proceeded very slowly, a few inches were gained each day, some days the level did not drop at all. Finally, on 13th December, the tunnel was pumped dry, and an inspection party was able to enter it as far as the notorious door. It was then found that instead of closing the sluice valve as he had thought, Lambert had actually opened it, since for some unknown reason the spindle worked counter clockwise instead of clockwise. Although the door was shut, the water-filled tunnel under the estuary kept discharging into the shore section. By closing the valve the water was shut off and the workings could be kept dry without effort, with one pump in reserve.

The spring was now walled in, and the undiminished flow deviated from the workings. The door closed by Lambert was opened and the gallery under the estuary inspected. In the Pennant rock the tunnel was found to be intact but in the marl towards the Gloucestershire shore a 20-ft. conical cavity had been formed and there was great risk that the river would break through. For this and other reasons Hawkshaw decided to lower the tunnel by 15 ft. The gradient on the English side was retained at 1:100 whereas on the Welsh side of The Shoots it was sharpened to 1:90.

From January 1881, the excavation of the tunnel continued with a considerably increased labour force. When Walker moved in, the parish of Portskewett had 260 inhabitants. By 1882, the population had grown to over 2,000 and had to be provided with housing and simple social amenities. On the Gloucestershire side a community with 1,000 inhabitants also had to be established in a hurry. When the Severn operation culminated in 1884 the contractor had 5,000 men employed.

The breakthrough in the Severn tunnel took place at 10 p.m. on 26th September 1881, at a point 3,370 yds. from the Welsh side and 678 yds. from the English shore. The time required to advance the pilot tunnel was four years and ten months, not including the eighteen months' stoppage caused by the flooding of the works. The total length of the subaqueous headings was 4,048 yds. The two faces met 'exactly', i.e. the errors in alignment and levels were insignificant from a practical point of view.

Now followed two years of rapid progress. The tunnel was expanded and lined without incident, and by August 1873 about 3,900 yds. had been completed. The cost had grown to £1,250,000 and it was confidently expected that the entire tunnel would be completed within two more years. The Board of the Great Western was to be called upon to express its confidence about the pending completion of its costly tunnel several times in the ensuing years. The troubles were by no means over.

On 10th October 1883—four years less a week after the great flood —the miners struck the same spring on the new gradient 15 ft. below the original one. This time it spouted in earnest, and the old conservative measuring standards proved too cumbersome; instead of measuring in gallons per hour it became more convenient to measure in gallons per minute. The spring poured out 27,000 gals./min. against an installed pumping capacity of 11,000 gals./min. After ten days the water stood 70 ft. in the main shaft. With the wisdom gained from previous evils the contractor had installed water doors where water hazards were indicated. Divers were once more sent into the messy gallery to feel their way towards the doors. Once again they succeeded in closing them and the pumping plant began to master the second flood.

But there was much more in store for Walker and his harassed men. Three days later the largest pump broke down, and the inshore shaft became filled with water. Before the week was over a gigantic tidal wave passed up the Bristol Channel and flooded the low-lying country between Cardiff and Newport, submerging everything in its way. It swept through the construction camps along the shores, doused the fires in the boilers of the engines working the pumps and poured into the open shafts, filling them up to the rim. This triple catastrophe was eventually mastered, and in a surprisingly short time. The fires under the boilers were lit anew, and the pumps put to work once more. Within three weeks the workings were dry, and the spring was again walled in. Additional pumps were installed and the work of expanding and lining the tunnel continued unabated during 1884. On 24th October that year, the Chairman and Managing Director of the railway were able to walk through the length of their troublesome tunnel. They confidently expected to have it opened by the Prince of Wales on 1st August 1885.

However, nothing came of that. For one thing, the Board of Trade insisted that a ventilating plant be installed midway between the shores. For another, water kept pouring into the tunnel. The floods

were finally mastered in August 1885, and on 15th September the
railway sent its first train through the Severn tunnel, again confident
about its completion.

But the end was not yet in sight. On 24th October, the walled-in
spring began to rise through the ground exerting a pressure of
54 p.s.i. on the lining. The bricks were ejected with cracks like pistol
shots, and powerful jets of water began to fill the finished tunnel for
the third time. The pressure continued to grow and Hawkshaw declared the tunnel unsafe. A new shaft was sunk outside the tunnel
to relieve the pressure. Eventually, this crisis too was overcome, and
on 15th January 1886 the first coal train passed through the tunnel.
Passenger traffic began on 1st December. By that time the Severn
tunnel had cost the Great Western Railway £1·67 million, or £209
per yd. About 700,000 cu.yds. of rock and earth had been excavated,
eleven shafts had been sunk, and 75 million bricks put in place.
Added to which, with the draining of the Great Spring, the city of
Bristol had lost its major source of water. The time of travel from
Cardiff to Bristol had been reduced from two and a half to one and
a half hours.

The men responsible for the tunnel and carrying the heavy burden
during thirteen long years were suitably rewarded. Sir Daniel Gooch,
Chairman of the Great Western, was made a peer and his general
manager Grierson was knighted. As for T. H. Walker, he struck his
camps on the Severn shores with the firm determination that never
again would he undertake such work. 'One subaqueous tunnel is
enough in a lifetime for any one man,' was his epitaph over the
Severn tunnel.

The Perfection of the Greathead Method

Thus, within a few decades the impossible feat of tunnelling under
water was undertaken with varying success both in England and
America. But there was a decided difference between the five tunnels
discussed above. Brunel's Thames tunnel was a daring attempt by
an inspired engineer that ended in economic failure but nevertheless
contained the seed that after several decades of germination was to
grow into the most sophisticated tunnelling method hitherto developed. The Great Lakes tunnels depended too much on luck for their
successful completion; the primitive method worked in Chicago, but
when repeated in Cleveland without the benefit of luck the cost in
lives was high.

Severn, finally, was a rock tunnel driven under water in conventional fashion. The miners struck water in the firm ground on the

Welsh shore, which turned the tunnel into a disappointing and costly undertaking. Sir John Hawkshaw's decision to put the final heading 15 ft. below the original one was severely criticized at the time, and no doubt rightly so, because it added to the cost and time by striking the Great Spring twice. Otherwise, the method of advance was beyond reproach.

Barlow's Tower Hill tunnel was an altogether different operation. It inaugurated a technical revolution in subaqueous tunnelling; it was radical in concept, and every detail of the method was capable of infinite development. Not only did the Barlow shield permit tunnelling through heavy ground—in silt, sand, mud and clay, as visualized by Brunel but commonly regarded as impossible—but the equipment and method were sound from the outset. As originally devised, the shield and its operation were planned for manual work: the shield was fitted with screw jacks, the segmented lining rings were erected and tightened by hand, the grouting of the annular space outside the lining was injected with a hand syringe. All that was needed to perfect the method was to mechanize these manual elements and to introduce compressed air at the front in order to hold back water.

The mechanization of the Barlow shield was Greathead's great contribution to tunnelling. After completing the Tower Hill tunnel in 1870 Greathead struck out for himself as a consulting engineer. For many years he was chiefly occupied with railway work, but he also found time to develop his ideas for improving the Barlow shield and its associated cast-iron lining. The improved Greathead method of subaqueous tunnelling, including the use of air pressure to hold back water from the face, was fully developed by 1876. The plant for driving the Woolwich tunnel was constructed and delivered to the site, but the contractor ran into trouble elsewhere and was forced to give up the Woolwich work. T. A. Walker, who some years later was to get his fill of subaqueous tunnelling under the Severn, took over the Woolwich contract and drove the tunnel at a lower level, through solid chalk, and had therefore no reason to use the Greathead plant. Greathead's advanced ideas had to rest another ten years before the time was ripe to put them into practice.

The Plenum Process

Before proceeding any further it may be useful to dwell for a moment on the compressed-air method introduced by Greathead and combined with his shield. It had been known for centuries that air holds back water; it had been applied, for example, in the diving-bell. There was indeed an old patent granted to Lord Cochrane in 1830 which provided for all the major features needed to introduce compressed air into subterranean excavations and '. . . to allow workmen to carry out their ordinary operations of excavating, sinking and mining . . . and also allow them to pass to and from the enclosed space into the open air . . .' As eventually applied, the Plenum Process, as it came to be known, was based on the physical fact that 0·43 p.s.i. air pressure will balance a head of water of 1 ft. A cavity underground subjected to a 20-ft. head of water would therefore be kept dry if the air pressure inside the cavity could be raised to 8·6 p.s.i.

However, to apply this principle in practice presents a serious problem of how to seal the cavity so as to be able to build up and maintain the pressure. Greathead chose to do it at the face, using the front of the shield as an airtight bulkhead. Subsequently, the entire length of the tunnel came to be sealed off by a bulkhead placed near the tunnel exit. Such a bulkhead is usually made of concrete and designed to resist tremendous pressure. For example, a 20-ft. diameter bulkhead in a tunnel driven under 30 p.s.i. pressure must be built to stand up to a pressure of 678 tons, which requires it to be keyed into the lining to prevent slipping. The thickness of the bulkhead is usually made one-third of the tunnel diameter. This means that all piping for some twenty different services plus spares must be placed during the construction of the bulkhead, because once it has been built nothing can be added as an afterthought.

Then comes the problem of getting men and materials through the solid structure. This is accomplished by building in two airlocks in the bulkhead, one for men and the other for materials. The locks are airtight steel cylinders provided with a door at each end opening towards the heading. The man lock is long enough to provide seating room for all persons liable to be in the tunnel at any one time. The material lock is much longer and will admit an entire train.

An airlock is worked in the manner of a canal lock. One door is always kept shut. The men enter the lock through the open door and take their seats, whereupon the lock-keeper shuts the door behind them. If they enter the tunnel, the air pressure is gradually raised until it reaches the gauge pressure inside the tunnel and the opposite door is opened to let the men in. When leaving the tunnel, the procedure is reversed. The men enter the lock, the door of which is always kept open as long as there is somebody in the tunnel. The air pressure is gradually reduced until it reaches atmospheric pressure, and the outside door is then opened to let them out. When the working pressure exceeds 30 p.s.i. the men are decompressed at the rate of

1 lb. per minute. The material lock is worked in a similar manner, except that compression and decompression are carried out much faster.

Now, how much pressure can be applied? An old rule of thumb states that one foot of head requires ¼ lb. of air. An air pressure of 15 p.s.i. produces no problems whatever, which means that water with a hydrostatic head of 60 ft. can be balanced and the workings kept dry. Most wet jobs require no higher pressure than that. But some New York tunnels have been driven with 50 p.s.i. pressure—often with lasting ill-effects on the workers.

Henry Greathead appears to have included the plenum process in his shield method around 1875. Two years earlier he had devised a hydraulic erector to facilitate the handling of the heavy cast-iron segments making up the lining rings, and a pneumatic grouting-pan for use when backfilling the annular cavity left by the shield. The jacks required to push the shield ahead he also made hydraulic. The tunnelling machine on which so much inventive effort had been spent was thus available for the Woolwich tunnel one year later, where the work was in soft ground, the most difficult and treacherous material for tunnelling. No such machine has as yet been developed for work in rock: it awaits the arrival of a Barlow or a Greathead.

The air method was first applied with complete success in a small tunnel in Antwerp in 1879. That year a major attempt to drive a railway tunnel under the Hudson River, between Hoboken in New Jersey and Morton Street in Manhattan, also got under way. It was driven by a wealthy Californian, De Witt Haskins, who on a journey to New York had been impressed by the ease with which a caisson in Omaha had been sunk with the aid of compressed air. While watching the work he got the idea, apparently independently of Lord Cochrane fifty years previously, of applying the method for tunnel-driving in wet ground.

Haskins eventually succeeded in getting the contract for a railway tunnel under the Hudson River, which involved driving two parallel 16 × 18-ft. headings. His tragedy was that he thought it could be done with air alone. In July 1880, after he had progressed 360 ft. under the river, the 35 p.s.i. pressure used blew a hole through the soft silt in the roof of the heading. The miners took refuge in a faulty airlock and twenty men were drowned. The catastrophe also spelt financial ruin for the contractor, and after being suspended for two years the first attempt to tunnel under the Hudson River was definitely abandoned in 1882. A British company revived the scheme in 1889, using Sir Benjamin Baker and Henry Greathead as consulting engineers. This time the tunnel was driven with shield and air according to the fully developed Greathead method, but this second attempt also failed. When by the middle of 1891 the northern tube had reached 3,700 ft. from the Jersey shaft—with only 1,600 ft. remaining—money gave out. About $3 million had been spent and only $650,000 was needed to conclude the work. But no money was forthcoming and in June 1899 the tunnel company's assets were foreclosed and sold. The assets, including the silted tunnel, were bought for $400,000 by a new company formed by William McAdoo. The new company completed the crossing of the Hudson through the silted river bed under the direction of the English tunnelling expert Charles M. Jacobs.

Work on another Hudson tube (to the south of the existing one) began in 1904. This time the advance did not succeed too well. When jacking forward the shield at one time a column of silt shot through the open door in the shield and buried one man. The rest of the tunnelling crew fled and took refuge in the airlock. Compressed air shot up through the river bottom and carried silt with it for a height of 40 ft. above the surface. The hole in the bottom was stanched by dumping clay into it and the work was brought to its successful conclusion.[4]

Although the second attempt to tunnel the Hudson failed for financial reasons, a considerable improvement was made in the plenum process by eliminating its lethal feature. Prior to 1889, the method had been hard on the 'sandhogs', as New York tunnelling workers came to be called. About 25 per cent of the work force died from the 'bends'—also known as 'diver's palsy' or 'caisson disease'—arising from failure to get rid of the supersaturated nitrogen in the blood when returning to atmospheric pressure. Of the forty to fifty men working under pressure in the Hudson tunnel one man died from the bends each month. To stop this frightful toll E. E. Muir, one of the site engineers, devised a so-called hospital lock, an air lock above ground, to which men showing symptoms of the disease, usually an excruciating pain in the elbows and knees, could be rushed. Upon entering the high-pressure compartment of the lock, the pres-

---

[4] The following year a similar blowout took place in the Rapid Transit tunnel being advanced under the East River about 200 ft. from Joralemon Street in Brooklyn. There were at the time eight men in the shield when compressed air blew a hole through the river bottom, which at that place was only 5 ft. above the crown of the tunnel. When attempting to stop the leak with a bale of hay a sandhog by the name of Richard Creegan was blown into the hole. For a moment he got stuck in the silt, with only his legs showing below. Eventually the air pressure shot him through the silt and hurled him upwards through 15 ft. of water to the surface of the river. There he was rescued unharmed by a number of highly amazed longshoremen.

sure was rapidly increased to that used in the tunnel, after which the patient was decompressed at half the rate used in the regular lock.

Owing to the danger to health and even life, work under pressure is now strictly regulated by law. The New York code, for example, stipulates that no man may work more than four hours without a break in pressures up to 18 p.s.i. When the pressure reaches 43 p.s.i. a man cannot be worked more than half an hour, after which he must rest a minimum of six hours in free air, followed by half an hour of work, or altogether one hour per day. But such tight working-rules belong to the middle of the present century. When compressed air was introduced into tunnelling by Greathead no one was aware of the dangers, and since the early tunnels were advanced with modest pressures no great harm was done.

The First Subway

Henry Greathead's hour struck in 1886 with the start of the work on the City and Southwark Subway. After many years his great dream of providing London with a 'scientific system of communication' had won public recognition by the passing of the Subway Act of 1884. Two years later work began on the 3½-mile subway extending from the City to Stockwell, and on 5th March 1890 the first run was made by a train consisting of two carriages 'in perfect comfort and pure atmosphere'. The world had obtained its first subway and Henry Greathead was its engineer.

However, before considering this historic tunnelling job it may be well to look back briefly and consider some of the major difficulties in the way of providing London with an underground transport system. The passing of the Subway Act was the culmination of a forty-year debate on the London transport services.

The concern with the transport problem may be said to have originated in 1845 when nineteen Bills for railways in the London district were deposited in Parliament. At that time the Railway Committee treated them as applications for extending existing railway services into the heart of London. The railway was still being considered the successor to the stage coach, and the idea that it could also fill the function of the hackney carriage and omnibus was not yet recognized.

By 1864, when the population had grown to 2·94 million, the Great Western had built a feeder line through a tunnel from Paddington to Charing Cross. The Metropolitan Railway, as it was called, ran a twenty-minute service through the smoke-filled and unhealthy tunnel, but despite the unpleasant mode of travel the

Metropolitan carried 42 million passengers through the tunnel in 1864. The General Omnibus Company carried 11 million. That year, Bills for building 174 miles of railway in London at a cost of £44 million were thrown out by the House of Lords Committee. The Committee expressed as its opinion that the best way to relieve the traffic congestion of the rapidly growing metropolis would be the building of subways, or tunnels.

By 1874 the District Railway had been added, and London's 3·42 million inhabitants made 155 million journeys, or forty-five per head each year, on the wholly inadequate Metropolitan transport system. From this time on, Greathead became a familiar figure before the Parliamentary Committees, arguing the virtues of a subway system to be built below the London substructure—below the foundation of buildings, below water mains and sewers, with the platform level from 45 to 60 ft. below the surface.

Greathead's radical proposal to relieve the surface congestion was well received by the Parliamentary Committees but fell foul of the concepts of property rights. The possession of a piece of property in the centre of London, the lawyers argued, included everything above and below the surface plot, from the centre of the earth to zenith in the heavens. Accordingly, a property owner had the right to claim compensation for the circular space excavated through the clay 60 ft. below his living-room. As the talk of subways became more urgent, property owners became more pressing in their demands for compensation, until in the end the idea of underground transport foundered on the impossibility of financing the leave-way.

There were also the streets. Who owned the streets of London and the ground below them? Eventually, this legal conundrum was resolved by the Subway Act of 1884 whereby the streets and, more to the point, the ground below them were declared public property and the building of underground transport lanes would not require any payment for leave-way so long as they confined themselves to the virgin ground beneath the public highways. The legal base was laid for London's underground transport and the first line could be built. It was long overdue. London's population had grown to 4 million people who made 308 million journeys per year on the public conveyances. In twenty years the population had grown by 36 per cent and travelling by not less than 500 per cent.

As engineered by Greathead, the world's first subway line consisted of two 10 ft. 6 in. circular cast-iron-lined tunnels, or 'tubes', running 5 ft. apart and, in order to reduce the width and cost of the stations, one below the other. The line had five stations; from the City end they were: King William Street, Great Dover Street, The

Elephant and Castle, Oval, and Stockwell, the terminus at Clapham Road. The total length of the line was 3½ miles. The stations were situated with the platform level 45 to 60 ft. below the street surface. The City station had a diameter of 28 ft. and the intermediate ones 20 ft. 2 in. The shaft leading to the surface was 25 ft. and cast-iron-lined. In the shaft were two hydraulic lifts capable of bringing up fifty passengers in fifteen seconds. A circular stairway also provided access to the street. The tunnels ran almost level except under the Thames and at the City station, where the 'up' line had a gradient of 1:30 and the 'down' line one of 1:15. At the point of going under the river at Swan Lane the cover of the top tunnel was only 15 ft.

As originally planned, a power station near the Elephant and Castle was to provide both traction and hydraulic power for the lifts. The trains, consisting of three carriages each with altogether 100 passengers, were to be pulled by endless wire ropes travelling at a speed of 10 miles per hour. One rope made a loop through the 'up' and 'down' tubes to the City, the other made a similar circuit to Stockwell. No ventilation fans were to be installed since it was expected that the trains would act as a series of pistons pushing the air ahead of them, thus creating the necessary air circulation through the deep tubes. Total costs were estimated at £550,000.

Driving the Tubes

The building history of the City and Southwark subway is one of the most pleasant and admirable on record. The tools were well adapted to the job, the methods of applying them fully developed in advance, and fortune smiled on the operation from beginning to end. The tubes, altogether 7 miles in length, were driven without a single fatal accident.

The main shaft was sunk behind the Old Swan Pier down through the river-bed to grade. The 13-ft. shaft was lined with cast-iron rings 1⅛ in. thick except for the somewhat thicker bottom ring that was provided with a cutting edge. It was sunk by excavating the material inside it with a grab, and as the cutting ring descended other rings were added until the shaft reached the crown level of the top tunnel. The remainder of the shaft, descending to the invert of the bottom tunnel, was lined with brick.

On the stage built atop the Swan shaft was erected a crane which lifted the skeps loaded with clay on to a tramway leading to barges which removed the clay for use as fill along the river. The shaft installation also included a small steam-engine which drove an air compressor, a ventilating fan, and pumps. Close by was a small site-office. That was the entire installation.

The Greathead shield, here used for the first time, had an outside diameter of 11 ft. 4½ in. It was 6 ft. long and provided with an adjustable cutting edge. To the rear of the cutting edge was a bulkhead with a door through which the miners could be admitted to the face. When working in firm clay, the miners excavated a circular cavity about 2 ft. deep in front of the shield. First the clay was mucked out into skips run on rails up to the shield, which was then pushed forward a distance of about 2 ft. with six hydraulic jacks worked by two hand pumps. When jacked forward the cutting edge trimmed the cylinder cut in the clay. After each gain, a cast-iron ring 19 in. long and consisting of six segments was erected at the rear end of the shield and bolted to the fore end of the existing iron lining with ¾-in. bolts. The inside diameter of the lining was 10 ft. 6 in. Since the lining was erected inside the shield it did not quite fill the circular cavity cut by the advancing shield. The annular space outside the lining, measuring about one inch, had to be grouted to prevent the development of local pressure on the lining, as well as to make the ground airtight. The space was filled with the aid of another Greathead invention, the pneumatic grouting-pan. It consisted of an airtight vessel filled with a grouting made of blue lias lime and water which was kept thoroughly stirred by paddles worked from the outside. Compressed air was admitted to the vessel and the grouting was applied by means of a hose ending in a nozzle inserted into holes in the lining ring. In this manner the entire annular space outside the lining was filled, whereupon the grouting holes were plugged. Working in this manner the shield was advanced at the rate of 10 to 16 ft. per twenty-four hours. In 1888, when the tubes were advanced on altogether eight working faces, a total of 2¼ miles of tubes was completed.

When passing through soft ground, the heading was mined by hydraulic action. Water was pumped from the river and conducted under pressure through a pipe extending to the upper part of the face. A return pipe from the lower part of the face collected the slurry and deposited it in a barge close by the main shaft. When using hydraulic mining in this fashion the door through the shield bulkhead was closed and the entire operation controlled from inside the shield. At other times, and particularly at the Stockwell end where the tubes were pushed through water-logged sand, the face was held back by means of 15 p.s.i. air pressure. The miners entered the heading through an airlock built into the shield. Something like 200 yds. were driven under pressure to offset a 35-ft. head of water. This short stretch provided basic experience with one of the major difficulties in compressed-air tunnelling, that of striking the right balance between the lower head at the top of the tunnel and the higher one at the bottom. Accommodating the pressure to the top head will cause water to break out at the bottom; compensating for the bottom head invites danger of a 'blow' at the top.

While the two tubes were being advanced the original plan of using a rope drive was abandoned in favour of electric traction. A power station with a 1,000-h.p. boiler plant was built at Stockwell and 500-volt DC 'generating dynamos', delivered by Edison-Hopkins, were installed. Fourteen electric locomotives, with 25-h.p. traction motors mounted on the wheel axles, were used to pull five-car trains accommodating 160 passengers at a speed of 25 miles per hour.

The first train passed along the 'up' tube on 5th March 1890, at which time there still remained 70 yds. to be driven at the Stockwell end of the 'down' line. By the end of the year the subway was in regular service with trains running on a three-minute schedule.

Greathead's City and Southwark (later South London) Railway was an altogether satisfactory pioneering venture which triggered a boom in subway construction. By 1892, a joint committee of both Houses reported favourably on electric traction and deep tunnels, and authorized the building of five more lines, of which the Central London Railway was begun in 1897. It ran from Shepherd's Bush under Oxford Street, and to the Bank—a total length of 10,163 yds. The line had twelve stations, with the platforms situated 65 ft. below street level. It was planned from the outset for a 2½-minute service, with trains of seven carriages accommodating 336 passengers. On this basis the annual capacity of the line was estimated at 100 million passengers.

With the Central London Railway the era of underground mass transportation set in. During the following decades London's underground transport lanes kept expanding until the lines reached a total length of more than 90 miles. Other large cities followed London's example and found the solution to surface congestion by going underground. In Paris the first underground line between Porte Maillot and Porte de Vincennes was begun in 1898; in New York the first rapid transit tunnel from the Battery in Manhattan to Joralemon Street in Brooklyn was started in 1902.

But Greathead saw nothing of this vast underground construction under the metropolitan centres of the world, nearly all of it conducted with the use of his machines and methods. He died in 1895 while engaged on the engineering of the Central London Railway.

He had reached fifty-two, a good average age for an old-time tunneller. Underground working stresses men and machines, and the pioneers, always working close to and frequently beyond the limits of their resources, had to give their lives to make up the balance.

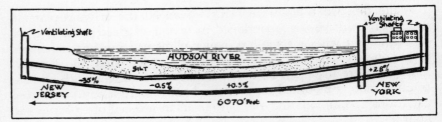

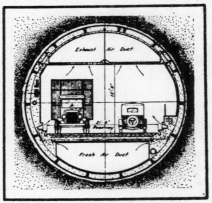

Fig 105. Sections of the Lincoln Tunnel under the Hudson River, built in 1939. The details are similar to the Holland Tunnel, the first motor tunnel under the river, opened for traffic in 1927.

In London, the birthplace of the subway and the Greathead method of shield tunnelling, no tube through the central parts has been driven since 1907 and none whatever since 1940. Elsewhere, prior to the war a number of large motor tunnels, such as the Mersey, Holland and Lincoln tunnels, have been built according to the Greathead system. Although greatly improved, the method used on all these large subaqueous tunnels retained all the characteristic features of the original, spadework at the front, bolted cast-iron linings, and grouting of the annular space between the lining and the soft ground.

With the new Victoria Line and other projected extensions of the London underground system in the offing, London Transport engineers began trying out a modernized method of tunnel building in 1960. The old method had become prohibitively costly, and a wealth of experience had been accumulated in respect of the stresses acting on the tunnel linings in the stiff London clay.

The new method developed by London Transport incorporates a new tunnelling machine called a 'drum digger shield' consisting of two concentric drums. For driving a 14-ft. tube the stationary outside drum, i.e. the equivalent of the Greathead shield, has an outside diameter of 14 ft. and is provided with a bevelled cutting edge. Inside it is a 5½-ft. rotating drum mounting six arms, each one provided with eight removable cutting teeth, which removes the clay in the concentric space between the shield and the drum. The clay in front of the rotary drum is cut by teeth mounted on a diagonal arm also fitted with teeth. The rotating drum is driven by six hydraulic motors at a speed of 4 r.p.m., and the forward movement of the 9-ft.-long shield is given by fourteen hydraulic motors acting with a pressure of 2,000 p.s.i. on the last completed tunnel ring. The clay excavated is deposited on a belt conveyor and charged into skips.

Two types of linings are being tried out. One is made of 1-in. cast iron with shallow flanges and provided with knuckle joints. The other is of 4½- to 9-in. pre-cast concrete with the same kind of a joint. Regardless of the lining used, the method of placing the lining is the same. After a segmented cast-iron ring has been put in place it is expanded against the outside clay by means of hydraulic jacks exerting a pressure of 15 tons per jack. This produces a small gap between the invert and the sides which is filled with shaped knuckle-pieces and two pairs of tapered packings.

The cast-iron ring, which is 2 ft. long, is made up of six segments and the concrete one of fourteen. The concrete ring has a 7-in. gap at the top which is filled with a pair of concrete wedges which expand the ring and hold it in its final position. By expanding the lining rings in this manner no annular space is left between the outside lining and the clay, thereby eliminating the slow and costly grouting.

Two experimental lengths of twin tunnels were driven by the improved shield method in 1961. One section from Finsbury Park to Manor House is concrete lined and the second one from Netherton Road to Manor House is cast-iron lined. The driving of a 934-ft. section of the latter tunnel was done in two weeks, an average advance of 3½ ft. per working hour. This is about twice as fast as the record previously set with the conventional shield. It is also

much faster than any progress recorded in modern hard rock tunnelling, where the greatest post-war records have been made.

There is no doubt but that the new method pioneered by London
Transport will save millions of pounds on the new 10½-mile
Victoria line. The circle is closed.

Chapter 11

TUNNEL SURVEYING

*'For he looketh to the ends of the
earth, and seeth under the whole
heaven.'*

WHEN about 700 B.C. the engineers in the service of Hezekiah,
twelfth King of Judah, found themselves in the embarrassing situation of not knowing where they were in the Siloam tunnel linking the
water of the Virgin's Spring with the pool of Siloam, what did they
do? Nothing could be simpler; they spent a few months driving a
rise to the surface to have a look.

The Siloam tunnel was not a unique undertaking, every walled
town in Palestine and in the Fertile Crescent obtained its water by
means of a tunnel connecting the spring outside the citadel with a
pool at the bottom of a stepped shaft sunk to grade inside the wall.
The Jerusalem tunnel was made famous by the difficulties encountered in driving it, as described in Chapter 3. The tablet commemorating the meeting of the two tunnelling teams is more remarkable
than the tunnel itself, since the inscription on it is one of the earliest
cursives of the Phoenician alphabet to be preserved. There was a
similar accident when tunnelling teams failed to meet underground,
in the Samos tunnel, also driven from both ends. Here, the teams
missed each other by 5½ yds., which necessitated linking up the
headings with a curve. This should not have presented any difficulties since the two teams were close enough to hear each other. There
may have been other cases of the teams failing to meet when driving

tunnels in pre-Roman times, but probably not many. The reason why such failures must have been uncommon was simply due to the ancient practice of sinking shafts along the axis of the tunnel at intervals of about 50 yds. Northern miners with their more primitive methods 2,000 years later were able to drive a straight heading for about 50 fathoms, but beyond that distance they got lost.

The *qanaat* builders, still active in Iran, placed their shafts about 50 yds. from each other and excavated the subterranean aqueducts in a straight line between adjacent shafts without difficulty. Vitruvius recommended as good Roman practice that the shafts be sunk one *actus* (120 ft.) from each other and that the gradient be less than 6 in. in 100 ft. or 1:200.

This ancient practice was resorted to by the early railway tunnellers, who always sank a number of shafts along the line, between which the tunnel was advanced. The early American tunnels were driven between double shafts, one on each side of the tunnel and tangent to its sides. When, in 1871, an 8-ft. tunnel was driven by means of Beach's shield under the streets of Cincinnati, Ohio, some 20 ft. below street level, the exact position of the shield was determined in the manner of Hezekiah's engineers, except that the Cincinnati tunnellers drove a pipe through the tunnel linking up to the street surface.

However, there is an important point to consider in this context. By driving shafts close enough for the tunnelling teams to hear each other, alignment can be maintained, but there is also the matter of grade. A water tunnel—and all ancient tunnels were driven for conducting water—needs a smooth gradient from the spring to the pool or well in the town to be supplied. To establish this gradient the line must be levelled, so that one would know with reasonable accuracy how far down a shaft should be sunk to intercept the tunnel. It is not hard to devise a means of establishing level. California gold-miners used whisky bottles nearly filled with water to determine the gradient of their water chutes. The Romans used a so-called *chorobate*, a 20-ft.-long board provided with cross-pieces at both ends marked with lines perpendicular to the board. By adjusting the lines to a plumb-line the board could be levelled up. The board also had a 5-ft. groove in the top surface that could be filled with water, whereby the chorobate was levelled when a strong wind disturbed the plummet. Working with a chorobate, Roman engineers were able to establish a 1:2,000 gradient, which was a higher degree of accuracy than is required for any tunnelling project.

During the second half of the first century, Roman surveyors should have had at their disposal a sophisticated surveying instrument, the so-called *dioptra*, invented by Hero of Alexandria. The dioptra combined the functions of a modern theodolite and level; i.e. by means of this instrument alignment could be given, angles turned and read and, by exchanging the theodolite for a level attachment, the difference in elevation between the two points could be

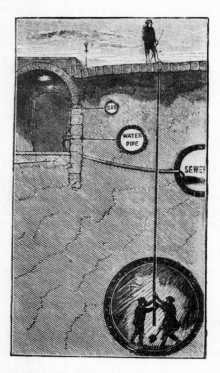

Fig 106. A variation of the classical method of determining the exact position underground was used in Cincinnati, Ohio, when driving a tunnel in the 1870's.

determined. With Hero's dioptra anything could be accomplished in the way of regular surveying, as well as guiding tunnel advance. Although Hero's own manuscript describing the instrument is still extant, except for eight pages, there is nevertheless some doubt as to whether his instrument was ever built. The reason for the doubt is that the instrument was supplied with two levelling screws at right angles to each other, and the cutting of such screws, some experts claim, was beyond the capacity of Roman artisans. The doubts cast on Hero's dioptra are unfortunate because if it had been in common use there would have been no essential difference between the methods used by modern civil engineers and by their Roman predecessors.

To build a tunnel to grade, *distance* must also be known with reasonable accuracy. This presented no problem, since the Egyptians and other ancient engineers had good measuring-rods and chains for measuring distance. A complete set of compasses and other drafting instruments in bronze, similar to conventional types, have been found in Pompeii. All this suggests that a Roman tunnel or aqueduct

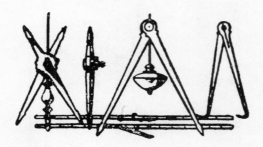

Fig 107. Bronze drafting instruments used by Roman engineers, found in Pompeii.

was laid out and measured, whereupon maps and profiles were drawn, very much in the same manner as today. A school for surveyors was established in Rome where the art of mensuration, inherited from the Etruscan priests, was taught to both civil and military engineers.

The art of surveying was of course lost in the Dark Ages, like so many other good things from the ancient world. However, the need for mine surveying did not arise for some 800 years, by which time Saxon mining had become established legally and technically. There arose, for one thing, the problem of marking and recording the claims in a mining range. But more important for the development of mining surveying were the transport and drainage tunnels driven into the deposits. The advance of these headings was undertaken by different persons from those mining the claims, and according to common practice the tunnelling enterprise was given the right to whatever ore was encountered when the tunnel was being advanced. Similarly, the claim owners had the right to the ore found when sinking the shaft.

In brief, there developed a conflict of interest between the tunnellers and the miners. This conflict turned into a race between the shaft-sinkers and the tunnellers, because the team that first reached the grade given for the shaft gained the right to the ore contained in the excavated rock.

Thus arose the need for a surveyor. The shaft-sinking claim owner had to know just how deep he was to sink his shaft; the tunnelling company needed to know the gradient of the tunnel and the distance to the shaft. Moreover, the boundaries of the different claims in a range had to be fixed below ground, so as to correspond with the boundaries originally set by the Bergmeister above ground. The surveyor held a position of trust, although it is not known whether he was an official subordinate to the Bergmeister or whether he held an independent office. He had at his disposal an instrument resembling a compass dial for reading horizontal angles; another graduated semicircle was used for measuring vertical angles.

The principal method employed in medieval mines, however, was that of measuring with analogous triangles. The method becomes apparent by reference to Fig. 108 by Agricola. A cord (F) has been stretched from point (H)—in the extended axis of the shaft—to the portal of the tunnel (G). The distance (F) is measured. By constructing the plumb-line (KL) the surveyor obtained a small triangle with the sides (P), (N) and (O). Measuring the side (P) and relating that to the known side (F)—the hypotenuse of the large triangle—he could calculate the depth of the shaft and the length of the tunnel. The medieval surveyor constructed a small triangle to a known scale and applied the known elements to a large triangle with two unknown sides, very much in the manner of an analogue computer.

This was the simplest case: the Saxon mine surveyor in fact operated with altogether seven different triangles in this manner. The triangle measured at the mine was laid out to full scale on a 'surveyor's field', a plot of flat land, on which the figure was described using cords pulled tight between stakes driven in the ground. Since the cords stretched, they were checked for correct length by a 'calibrated' cord made of linden bark and assumed to be accurate. The results were given with ridiculous accuracy. The length of a tunnel or depth of a shaft was reported to a fraction of a digit (0·703 in.). In some examples supplied by Agricola the length of a 60-fathom (360-ft.) tunnel is measured to within one-thousandth of an inch. This is of course sheer nonsense, as no such accuracy could be obtained with the measuring tools at the disposal of the medieval surveyor. But it did no harm as long as everybody believed in it, and the real accuracy obtained was more than good enough for the purpose: the tunnellers and shaft sinkers met where the surveyor predicted they would meet.

Fig 108. Medieval method of mine
surveying employing the principle of
analogous triangles.

Strangely enough, no maps were drawn, either of the ground or of the underground workings. Egyptians mapped their mining centres; the oldest such map known is dated *c.* 1300 B.C. and represents the gold-mines in Wadi Hammamat, between the Nile and the Red Sea. However, the principal purpose of this particular map is to show the route by which a gold idol was carried through the mining centre in connection with some ceremony.

Although Agricola does not mention it, the first surface mine map began to be plotted when he was busy writing his *De re metallica*. The first known mine map is a plot of a Tyrolean mine made about 1530.

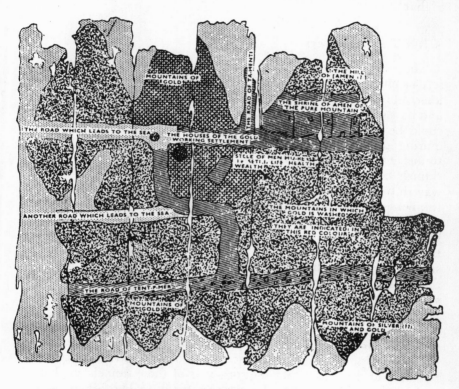

Fig 109. Egyptian map drawn *c.* 1300 B C of the gold-mining range of Wadi Hammamat in the Egyptian desert. This is the oldest map on record.

The Grakofel gold-mine in Carinthia and the Sowitz silver mountain in Silesia were mapped in 1577. The first true mining map, showing the different levels, seems to be one made in Sweden in 1629. By that time the art of surveying had been immeasurably improved by the invention of the plane-table, Thomas Digges's *theodolitus*, Edmund Gunter's chain of 100 links and, not least, by newly published trigonometric and logarithmic tables. A survey method of the utmost importance for the measuring of long tunnels, *triangulation*, had been invented in 1533 by Gemma Frisius, professor of mathematics at Louvain University. Hence, when the canal-building epoch set in with the construction of the Languedoc Canal in 1679, the art of surveying was fully matured; as a matter of fact, the levelling of that canal and the summit supply is one of the finest on record up to that time.

Alpine Tunnel Surveys

The grand Alpine tunnels, as well as the Hoosac, presented a serious challenge to surveyor and engineer alike. These tunnels were long, all of them in excess of 7 miles. They were driven under rough and partly inaccessible mountain ranges where no intermediate shafts could be sunk. They were in themselves very hazardous work, requiring tremendous investments. For these and other reasons the tunnels had to be driven from both ends. To drain the workings, the tunnels had to possess a gradient rising to a summit at about halfway through the tunnel. If such a long tunnel had been driven only from one end it would have been impossible to ventilate the workings.

But two tunnelling teams working towards each other through the bowels of a mountain had to be guided, to be kept on line so that they would eventually meet, after some twenty years. To make the survey work more interesting, the portals of these long tunnels were always fixed in advance. The topography of the country on both sides of the obstacle that necessitated the tunnel also determined the positioning of the railway and hence where the line was to enter and leave the mountain. The problem, in short, resolved itself into striking a line from point A to point B which were separated from each other by a more or less inaccessible mountain chain. It should be noted at the outset that the surveyors of these tunnels conducted their difficult and responsible work in an admirable fashion. If the actual tunnel advance had been performed with the accuracy characterizing the survey work, many lives and much money would have been saved. This difference in performance can be explained by the fact that the art of measuring and the mathematical theory on which it is based were much further advanced than the mechanical means for driving a long railway tunnel: rock drills, the most important machines for rock tunnelling, were in their infancy, the ventilation plant was poor, and transport facilities were undeveloped.

The model for subsequent tunnel surveys was devised on the Fréjus. As mentioned elsewhere, work on the Fréjus was started on 18th August 1857, according to a twelve-year-old and rather sketchy survey. The two portals were fixed by railway considerations. Two engineers, Borelli and Capello, were commissioned to carry out a detailed survey for the purpose (1) of determining and fixing the axis of the projected tunnel, (2) of determining the exact length of the tunnel, and (3) of finding the exact difference in elevation between the portals, in order to establish the gradient.

They began the field work in September 1857 by running a trial line from the northern portal across the massif to Bardonnèche, the southern terminal. This line missed the point fixed for the southern centre and, after correcting the angular error, a second line was run which came close to the point aimed at. Correcting once more for the small error, they succeeded in their third attempt, just before the autumn storms began to pile up snow and put a stop to the work. But by that time some important signals had been erected along the axis and fixed against damage.

With the thaw the following spring the line was firmly secured at fifteen points across the range. On the highest point, Gran Vallon, an observatory was built strong enough to stand up to the buffeting of the mountain storms. From this main observatory a point was set 9,840 yards away at Les Sapins on a hill beyond the northern portal, and at Beauvois, beyond the southern. A number of subsidiary stations were fixed between the observatory and these points in order to get good reference sights for the two observatories B and T, placed across the valleys from the two portals. It was from these two observatories that the axis of the tunnel was projected during the advance. From the optical and mechanical characteristics of the instrument used, and from the manner in which the survey had been conducted, the largest error in alignment was calculated to less than 10 in., which over the distance covered would be equivalent to 11·42 in. in error. Such a deviation of the axis would not matter in a double-track tunnel.

Now followed the more time-consuming and difficult measuring task, to determine the length of the tunnel between the two observatories outside the portals. This was done by triangulation—by measuring the angles in a train of triangles extending across the massif and calculating the sides by trigonometry. In order to carry out such a chain of calculations, one needs to know the length of one side of the first triangle measured. In this particular case the surveyors were lucky because the Fréjus had already been included in a primary triangulation net, and a point, which by measurement proved to be 465·97 ft. distant from the observatory on Gran Vallon, was included in this geodetic survey. The distance from this point and the neighbouring peak Jafferau had been determined by the primary triangulation to 28,544·93 ft. This known line, then, was

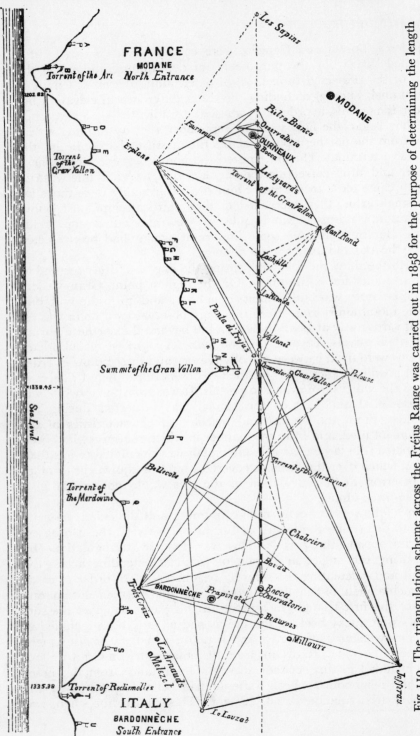

Fig 110. The triangulation scheme across the Fréjus Range was carried out in 1858 for the purpose of determining the length of the tunnel between the two observatories, one situated at Fourneaux outside the northern portal and the other at Bocca, beyond the southern portal.

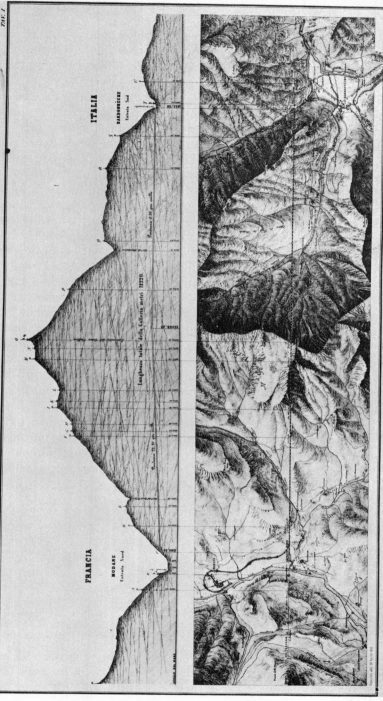

Fig 111. This beautiful topographical map and profile of the Fréjus Range was included in a book presented to King Victor Emanuel at the opening of the Fréjus Tunnel. The copy is now in the Turin technical museum. For the pertinent details see Figure 110.

used as a base and two systems of triangles, one extending to the north and the other to the south of the base line, were constructed and the angles measured, all known precautions being applied to avoid errors.

The two nets contained twenty-eight triangles and eighty-six angles. The measuring of one angle was repeated ten times, important ones twenty times, and the critical ones sixty times. After numerous calculations, the length of the tunnel axis between portals was determined at 40,093·8 ft. The probable error was 14 to 18 ft., which was regarded as insignificant for determining grade.

On the Fréjus was established a practice which has been followed on all subsequent tunnels of any length. The survey, and hence the tunnel, was projected as a straight line between two adits, one at each end. The actual railway tunnel has curved approaches at both ends, but owing to the fear of errors in alignment being introduced because of the curves, the pilot tunnel was driven as a straight line between the two pilot adits. Once the two headings had met, the curved portions of the railway tunnel itself were excavated. The measurements used in driving the Fréjus and subsequent Alpine tunnels therefore differ materially from the final railway length of the tunnel. This practice also explains why it is virtually impossible to obtain accurate information on such a seemingly simple matter as the length of a tunnel from available reference works, and why the source information on a given tunnel is altogether different from that obtained from modern data on the same tunnel.

The levelling across the massif was done three times in 1857 and 1858 whereby the error in elevation between the two portal observatories was reduced to 1·574 in., well within the requirements for establishing grade. The results of the triangulation and levelling can be summed up as follows:

Elevation above sea-level at Bardonnèche	1,335·28 m.
Rising gradient of 1 : 2,036	3·15
Summit level	1,338·43
Elevation above sea-level at Fourneaux	1,202·82 m.
Rising gradient of 1 : 45	135·61
Summit grade	1,338·43
Length of tunnel as determined by triangulation	12,220·00 m.

These, then, were the basic figures guiding the advance of the Fréjus. Twelve years later, after the breakthrough on 25th December 1870, it became possible to check the work. Although reality proved to be somewhat different from mathematical theory, the difference did not greatly matter from a practical point of view. The error in alignment proved to be about 'half a yard' and the measured length 40,138·28 ft., or 44·5 ft. longer than calculated.

However, of the total tunnel tangent of 40,138 ft. only 38,184·8 ft. were actually used, to which were added the approach curves at both ends whereby the total railway length of Fréjus came to 42,137·62 ft.

The Hoosac Tunnel

The Hoosac tunnel was surveyed in much the same manner as Fréjus, except that no triangulation was used. The rough country was slope-measured with a 100-ft. steel tape and the horizontal distances calculated. Two large and heavy transits were made specially for the work and used in tracing the axis above ground. On the highest points 10-ft. stone houses with peaked roofs were erected and provided with a 3-in. pipe projected through the roof to mark the line.

However, the tricky part of the Hoosac survey was to project the axis down through the 1,030-ft. central shaft to allow a west and east heading to be advanced from the bottom of the shaft. The shaft was 23 ft. in diameter and contained sixty-four floors. It was crowded with hoisting and pumping gear which jarred and shook the head frame.

The engineers, notably Philbrick, had to devise a measuring method by trial and error. This is how this forbidding measuring task was carried out in the end: two masonry piers, placed roughly on the tunnel axis and on each side of the shaft, were built and insulated from the jars of the head frame. On each of the two piers was bolted an adjustable cast-iron block provided with a ⅛-in vertical slit. The slits could be adjusted and aligned with a transit so that the plane of the tunnel axis passed through them.

But aligning the two rough slits was not as easy as it would appear. The air rising out of the shaft caused such a disturbance that no alignment could in fact be made despite the short distance between the piers. A horizontal wooden flue had to be built across the head frame in order to exclude the air currents. The sights were made through the flue. After repeated observations, the two slits were ultimately lined up, whereupon two piano wires were tensed by ratchet devices so that they touched the edges of the slits.

Now came the really difficult part of the job: to project the axis down to the bottom of the 1,030-ft. shaft. It proved impossible to drop the wire through the shaft owing to the disturbances, and in

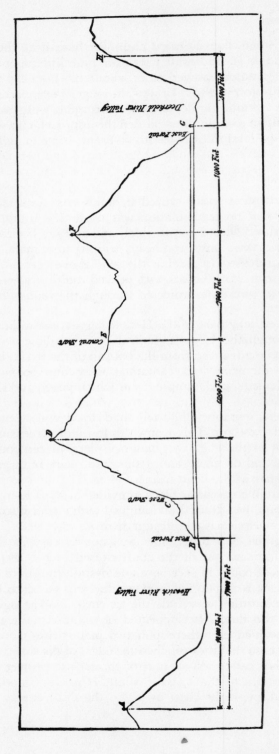

Fig 112. Profile of the Hoosac Range showing the signal stations used for determining the tunnel axis.

the end two 6 × 6-in. flues of wood had to be built from the bottom to the top of the shaft. Platforms were raised at opposite ends of the shaft opening extending above the horizontal axis flue. A wire drum with a screw adjustment was mounted above each vertical flue and a thin copper wire provided with a 15-lb. plummet was sunk through the flue to the bottom of the shaft. The wires were adjusted by eye so that they bisected the ⅛-in. distance between the tensed horizontal wires which marked the tunnel axis as determined above ground. At the bottom of the shafts the plummets hung in basins of water.

These two vertical copper wires, then, constituted physical projections of the plane of the tunnel axis down to the tunnel grade at the bottom of the shaft. But although damped by water the two wires were never still; they kept oscillating all the time with a swing totalling about one-hundredth of an inch. A scale was therefore placed at each end of the shaft and several hundred observations were made of the amplitudes before their mean was finally taken as the line point. Two fine wires were now hung from the mean points marked on the two scales and their plummets damped in water.

These two vertical wires, placed 23 ft. apart, were regarded as marking the tunnel axis and used as guides to advance the two headings driven from the shaft. As the headings advanced, wooden plugs were placed in the roof of the tunnel from which a plummet line was set by means of back sights to the original axis points. As the advance proceeded, the sights became longer, in excess of 1,000 ft. when the air was not disturbed by the workings. Numerous test runs were made to correct the original short sights, the mean of six or eight observations being used.

By the time the two headings east of the main shaft met on 12th December 1872, it was found that the axis extended from the east portal differed from the one projected from the shaft by five-sixteenths of an inch. The difference in grade was a few hundredths of a foot. The distance advanced from the portal was 11,274 ft. and that from the shaft 1,563 ft. The two west headings met at a point 10,138 ft. from the west portal and 2,056 ft. from the shaft with an error of nine-sixteenths of an inch in alignment and 0·134 ft. in level.

Considering the endless trouble, stoppages, frequent change of contractors and all the other difficulties besetting this classic American tunnel, the accuracy achieved is remarkable. It was a record performance that was never beaten in driving any of the long tunnels that followed.

The Simplon Survey

The great classic of the Alpine tunnel surveys is, of course, the Simplon triangulation, with subsequent projection of the tunnel axis, carried out by Max Rosenmund who, owing to his excellent work, was appointed Professor of Geodesy at the Polytechnic University in Zürich. The work is remarkable for the accuracy attained under enormous difficulties and treacherous conditions, such as the gravitational effects of the mountain masses which distorted the instrument readings, and numerous optical illusions caused by the difference in refraction of the air inside the tunnel and near the portals.

The original survey of the Simplon was carried out in 1876 for the purpose of planning and estimating the cost of the work, but although it established the two portals of the tunnel it was not good enough for advancing it.

Rosenmund was retained by the contractors in 1898 to determine the axis and gradients of the tunnel. As in the previous Alpine tunnels, the pilot headings were laid out as a straight line, although the finished tunnel required two approach curves. The following brief outline of the survey work refers to the pilot tunnel through the Monte Leone range. The rugged mountain country prevented the axis from being traced on the ground, as in Fréjus and Hoosac, and the length and direction had to be calculated by triangulation. In triangulation, the plan of the work is about as important as its accurate performance. The prerequisites of the Simplon survey, as determined beforehand, were (1) that the end points of the tunnel axis should be observed from at least three points in the net; (2) the net should consist of two lateral trains of triangles linked by at least four lines; (3) that to determine the length of the tunnel the net should include the Wasenhorn–Faulhorn line of the Swiss geodetic survey.

The triangle net is shown in Fig. 113 and consists of eleven points, of which Monte Leone, the highest peak of the range, has a height of 11,670 ft. On each of these points a permanent station was built of stone, in the centre of which was cast an iron pipe. A sheet-iron cone was placed on the cemented rock pillar. When it was used as a sight a wooden rod was extended through the top of the cone; when used as an instrument station the cone was removed and a templet marked with an engraved cross was placed over the iron pipe. A heavy Kern theodolite was positioned over the pipe so that its vertical axis passed through the cross. The signals were built in June and July 1898 and the actual observations were carried out from 14th August to 4th

September. Each angle was measured forty-eight times, with four to six series of observations. The measured angles were included in a train of twenty-seven triangles constituting the net.

As every schoolboy knows, the sum of the three angles in a triangle is 180°. But that is not necessarily the case when adding three *measured* angles in a triangle. As a matter of fact, should the three angles add up to exactly 180° a surveyor has reason to be suspicious, because then he has made a mistake somewhere. No instrument can

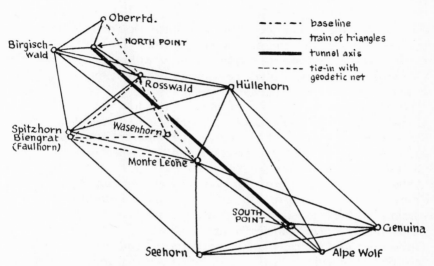

Fig 113. From the Simplon triangulation was determined the length and direction of the tunnel.

measure as accurately as that, and if such an instrument existed the human eye is incapable of making such accurate readings.

The sum of the three measured angles of a geodetic triangle is always 180° plus some fraction which includes the spherical excess due to the shape of the earth. For the Simplon survey this would be small, not more than 0·25″. But when checking the Simplon observations it was found that the average error of the triangles was much larger than that, or 3·1″; the maximum error was 8·5″. This was far in excess of what could be expected on theoretical grounds, and the entire measuring procedure was repeated during the latter half of September and the first weeks in October. The total number of field days thereby rose to forty-one. Repeating the observations gave no better results, and the surveyor began to suspect that some extraneous forces were at work, particularly on the steep sights where the observation errors reached a maximum. Ultimately, it was discovered that the local mountain masses created an attraction on the plumb-line, and since the instrument is adjusted with the use of the plumb-line, the readings had been taken with an instrument improperly set up. This phenomenon had been noticed earlier, in Switzerland and more particularly in the Himalayas, and there were methods for correcting the gravitational effects. By applying the corrections, the mean closing error of the triangles was finally reduced to $\pm 1\cdot 7''$.

If no consideration had been taken of the gravitational effects on the readings, the tunnel axis from the north would have deviated $1\cdot 55''$ to the left and the one advanced from the south $3\cdot 66''$ to the left, which would have resulted in a difference of $0\cdot 26$ m. The error in length would have been insignificant, or merely $0\cdot 03$ m.

The corrected survey gave a mean error for one direction of $\pm 0\cdot 91''$, and a probable error of $\pm 0\cdot 61''$. This meant that the linear error at the point of breakthrough would amount to $0\cdot 05$ m., which would grow with the errors committed when extending the line through the mountain.

The calculated length of the pilot tunnel was $19{,}728\cdot 7$ m., with a mean error of $\pm 0\cdot 14$ m. However, since the base used in the calculations also possessed some errors, the mean error was put at $\pm 0\cdot 83$ m., and the probable error at $\pm 0\cdot 56$ m.

In order to fix the calculated axis on the ground, two steel frames were placed outside each portal as far as possible from each other and firmly bedded into the rock. In each frame was mounted a screw-adjusted sight consisting of a narrow slit provided with opaque glass which could be illuminated at night. These two slits were to be lined up so that they would serve as backsights when projecting the tunnel axis. In the previous surveys the axis had been traced on the ground and the important backsights placed by projecting the line of the axis to some accessible points beyond the portals. In the Simplon survey the two backsights outside each portal were set by turning angles calculated from the triangulation survey, an extremely difficult job. To place and accurately align the two sets of backsights, 482 angular readings were made at the north end and 384 on the south end. The mean error of the angle readings was calculated to $\pm 0\cdot 1''$.

With the backsights permanently fixed in the rock away from the disturbance of the tunnel work and the construction activities outside the portals, an observatory was built at each end. It consisted of a round house in the centre of which a heavy pier was sunk to solid rock to prevent it from being shaken by disturbances in the ground. On the top of the pier was fixed a metal plate with a fine cross set by observations to the distant backsights. This cross marked the tunnel axis. It proved very difficult to find suitable sites for the two portal observatories owing to the restricted space outside the portals, and for this reason the one at the north end was placed at a considerable distance from the portal and only 31 m. (102 ft.) from the nearest backsight. The southern observatory was placed 22 m. (72 ft.) from the nearest sight. The reason for the permanent observatories was of course to protect the instruments and the observers from wind, rain and sudden changes of the weather, as well as to shield the observation work from the construction activities.

The tunnel axis was set out by the instrument inside the observatory, after having been accurately centred with the aid of the permanent backsights. Inside the tunnel the axis was fixed by setting permanent marks in the floor 200 m. (656 ft.) apart. These fixed points were sunk into the rock and protected by cast-iron hoods. The distance between two points was determined by 5-m. (16·4 ft.) measuring rods laid with the ends spaced a little apart and along a string pulled taut in the axis of the tunnel. The gap between the ends of two rods was measured by micrometer. This was the manner in which the early points were set. Each point was determined as a mean of eight observations, and over a distance of one kilometre each of the five points had to fall within 10 mm. to be accepted.

However, as the tunnel advanced the alignment problems grew. After 4 kilometres, the curvature of the earth grows by one metre, which prevented accurate settings from the portal observatory. The instrument had to be moved into the tunnel in order to advance the line. Now the hazards began in earnest, the work of advancing the pilot heading could not be interrupted and there was always the risk that the sights and measurements would contain excessive errors. For this reason, the tunnel alignment was accurately checked twice a year. This axis control took from twenty-four to forty-eight hours, during which the work in the tunnel was stopped. After work ceased it took six hours before the dust settled in the tunnel to make it possible to see one mile ahead. When the ventilation plant was installed the air was cleared within two hours by sending a current of fresh air through Pilot 2 and directing it, by means of weather doors, into Pilot 1, in which the axis control was being performed. When this procedure began to be used, the tunnel had advanced beyond the observatory limit and the instrument had to be set up inside the tunnel, using a lamp placed on the pier in the observatory as a backsight.

On such a six months' control carried out on St. Barbara's Day, 4th December, 1901, the instrument was set up on a point situated 17,384 ft. from the observatory. The lamp could not be seen by the naked eye from this distance, but through the telescope it appeared just above the floor of the tunnel, the earth curvature and refraction having depressed it by 6·23 ft. However, on the first control sight over this distance, the longest taken up to that time, a peculiar phenomenon was observed. The observer saw not one but two lights, one above the other. The top light was taken as being the correct one and the work proceeded, checking the intermediate points which proved to be out of alignment. With the arrival of the grey winter's dawn, the tunnel opening became visible. The section of the tunnel was in reality nearly square, but owing to the curvature of the earth only a horizontal rectangle, i.e. the upper half of the tunnel area, with the light shining just above the lower edge, should have shown. Instead, the tunnel opening appeared as a vertical rectangle, with the height about two and a half times the width. The figure was also bent over to the right. The beam of light from the lamp in the observatory emerged clearly. As had been the case during the night it showed two images, one on top and one below, but like the tunnel opening the top one was bent to the right. The angle distended by the two images was 45″, i.e. a linear deviation of 3·9 ft. over the 17,384 ft. distance. Another sight 11,152 ft. from the observatory gave similar results. Persons passing the tunnel opening also appeared bent over to the right.

The observations made during this night of 4th December 1901, i.e. more than three years after the work began, proved that all the points previously set with the instrument inside the tunnel were seriously wrong owing to this phenomenon not hitherto observed. Theoretical analysis revealed the causes of these major errors. The ventilation air had become heated by the warm rock and increased in density from the periphery towards the centre of the tunnel. Cold air entering through the portal also became denser. Owing to the difference in refraction of the cold and warm air the beam of light was bent in the manner observed.

A new set of observation rules had to be laid down. No observations could be carried out when the temperature of the outside air was below 0° C. The ventilation air must not possess too high velocity. Long sights from inside the tunnel could not be made. The first 100 m. (328 ft.) from the portal were to be regarded as particularly hazardous, and here only short sights were permitted. After the danger zone had been passed and a backsight placed inside the tunnel, longer sights could be made.

This routine was followed on the next axis control carried out the following Easter. A door was placed in the tunnel portal after a back-sight had been set 80 m. (260 ft.) from the portal, at a distance of 430 m. (1,400 ft.) from the observatory. Farther along, 600 m. (1,970 ft.) from this backsight, an instrument point was set, and the axis projected via a number of points at distances of 1,000–2,000 m. (3,300–6,600 ft.) from each other. By a series of careful observations the differences at seven stations, from 200 to 5,900 m. (656–19,350 ft.) inside the tunnel, were found to vary from 1·68 in. to 2·58 in. The mean of the differences was taken and used for the farther projection of the tunnel axis from the north end.

On the south end no such refraction difficulties were encountered. Here an accurate point could be set at 3,300 m. (10,824 ft.) from the portal and used as the instrument station for the continued advance of the tunnel axis.

This somewhat detailed account of the Simplon survey, although by no means adequate for the specialist, has been given in order to show the high skill needed to guide a long tunnel advance. As mentioned in passing, the work was conducted by one of the leading survey specialists in Europe, and despite his experience, theoretical learning and highly developed measuring skill it was only by chance that a serious error was avoided. Had the refraction error not been discovered in time the two headings would have missed each other by about 1·64 ft., which would have necessitated a wholly unwarranted curve at the junction between the two headings and would have needlessly increased the cost of the tunnel advance.

As mentioned in the Simplon chapter, the breakthrough of the two headings took place at 7.20 a.m. on 24th February 1905, about seven years after Rosenmund had begun his work. Owing to the heat and hot water discharged by the sealed appendix at the northern end, no accurate measurements could be carried out immediately upon the breakthrough. All that could be done at that time was to check to see how the headings had met. A quick dash into the hot section revealed that the two west walls were in good alignment but remaining abutments on the opposite side prevented ocular observations. A quick run with a steel tape to the nearest station point suggested an error in length of − 5·24 ft. It was not until the following August that the work was stopped for two days to enable the surveyors to make a final control. It was then found that the deviation of the axis was 7·87 in.; the southern heading had deviated towards the east and the northern to the west.

The difference in levels, as measured from the north and south portals in metres, was also slight:

Level at breakthrough, as measured from the north   698·768 m.
    ,,   ,,   ,,   south   698·855

                                    Difference   0·087 m.

The length of the tunnel also agreed with the calculations:
Final length between portals, as measured   19,755·52 m.
Length as calculated from triangulation   19,756·31

                                  Difference   0·79 m.

The equivalent differences in length were in St. Gotthard 7·6 m. and in the Arlberg tunnel 3·0 m. In the Gotthard, the total axis deviation was 0·3 m. and the difference in elevation 0·05 m. In the Fréjus, the length proved to be 15·55 m. longer than calculated, according to one source. Others give much larger errors.

*

In some such manner as that outlined for the classic railway tunnels, the surveys of all other tunnels and sub-surface structures have been conducted. In principle there have been no changes, although the measuring instruments have been improved. Errors have been made, particularly in the treacherous job of projecting the axis through a narrow shaft and using the two wires suspended in plummets a few feet apart as backsights on which the advance of the entire tunnel has to be guided. Sometimes an instrument-man when laying out a curve has set off a small angle to the right instead of to the left, and the slight error prolonged has thrown the heading some 50 ft. out of line at the point of breakthrough, to the great embarrassment of all concerned. But in the overwhelming number of cases the accuracy of the survey is such that the headings meet without perceptible error. In Sweden, visitors invited to a breakthrough never fail to be impressed by the simple trick of drilling a hole from both sides through the remaining rock partition so that the drills meet and the bits scrape against each other. In America, the headings meet on a dime; if the tunnel is not too long a skilled instrument-man will hit the dime's edge.

Electronic Measuring Instruments

But it now looks as if such traditional survey skills are becoming redundant. In South Africa, an electronic microwave system has been developed which will measure lines in a fraction of the time and effort required by the conventional triangulation survey. This electronic tellurometer will measure, by means of microwaves, distances up to 35 miles with a probable error of 3 parts in a million, or ±2 in. The system does not even require visibility between the two points being measured, but since the speed of the microwaves is determined by, among other factors, the moisture of the air—which can hardly be measured with any accuracy over a distance of 35 miles—there appears to be some uncertainty in applying the meteorological corrections. The tellurometer has not yet been employed on any tunnel surveys, but the method holds great promise in simplifying the triangulation work of long tunnels.

In Sweden an electronic-optic instrument has been developed along different lines. The geodimeter, as the instrument has been called since its introduction in 1949, sends out a modulated light-beam to a station that may be located some 150,000 ft. distant. Here the beam is reflected back to the instrument by means of prisms. When picked up by the instrument, the light-beam is converted into an electronic wave by a photo-cell and the phase relation between the transmitted and the reflected beams is measured. From this reading the distance between the two points can be computed. The advantage of the geodimeter is that distant stations need not be manned after the reflector has been placed.

The accuracy claimed for the instrument varies in the three models available. The lightest model, with a range of from 250 m. (750 ft.) to 10,000 m. (32,800 ft.) has an 'instrument error' of 10 mm. and measures with an accuracy of 1 : 25,000 at 250 m. and 1:170,000 at 10,000 m. The heaviest unit has an accuracy of 1 : 90,000 at 1,000 m. (3,280 ft.) and 1 : 850,000 at 50,000 m. (164,000 ft.). The base of a first order triangulation, the distance most accurately measured on the face of the earth, requires a probable error of one in a million. Such a base will take several months to establish, whereas the time consumed in using the geodimeter is 45 minutes. Using the small model over the range given, the distance is measured in 5 minutes.

The trouble with these electronic survey instruments is their great weight. The smallest geodimeter model weighs 79 lb., the largest 202 lb. To this weight should be added that of the electrical power equipment, which for the large model consists of a 140-W. generator driven by a petrol engine. The small model can, if necessary, be run on a storage battery, which is not the most convenient item to carry on one's back up a steep mountainside.

Geological Surveys

Both old-time tunnellers and modern engineers tend to be sceptical about geological surveys. 'It is only when you open up the ground
that you know for sure what the rock is like,' is a phrase recurrent
in all languages. The geologist on the job has to put up with a lot
of rough jokes. On the other hand, the diamond core drillers sell
their services with the slogan 'You pay for your borings whether
you get them or not.' It is now inconceivable to start any large-scale
underground development without a preliminary geological survey
showing with greater or less precision and detail the condition of the
ground through which a tunnel is to be advanced.

There are many ways of conducting a geological survey, from
banging punch rods into the soft ground down to some 40 ft. and
taking up soil samples with a spoon, via churn drilling and wash
drilling, to core drilling using diamond bits. With the latter method,
continuous core samples are taken up for study from bore holes many
hundreds or thousands of feet deep. Naturally, it is also possible to
drill ahead from a heading to determine in advance the conditions to
be met with. If the English Channel tunnel is ever undertaken, it
will probably be necessary to probe thousands of feet in advance
to detect fissures, infilled valleys, and other dangerous features not
previously detected by bore holes from barges anchored in the open
sea.

It is interesting to note in this context that the Mont Blanc tunnel
was driven without access to a detailed geological survey determined on the basis of borings, for the simple reason that nobody has as
yet devised a method of taking borings extending some 5,000 ft. into
rock from nearly vertical rock walls or through glaciers hundreds of
feet thick and at heights of thousands of feet, in sub-zero storms. The
Mont Blanc, as well as the other Alpine tunnels, was driven with the
hope that the body of geological knowledge accumulated from previous tunnelling operations in the region would prove accurate also
in detail. In general, it is possible to forecast exactly what rock conditions will be encountered, but a few feet of unexpected bad rock
conditions may prove lethal, if not necessarily to the men encountering it, at any rate to the profits of the contractor advancing the
tunnel.

In less precipitous regions than the Alps, a preliminary air survey
usually lays the foundation for the cadastral and geological surveys.
From an air map the ground can be studied in great detail—the
nature of the rock, the presence of subterranean water, shear zones,
and a wealth of other important information. This can be culled

from the map in the office, and a suitable line chosen for a tunnel or the location of an underground power house without a visit to the site even being necessary.

Nevertheless, core drillings will have to be made, although a good preliminary survey can reduce the number of test bores required to sound the bowels of the rock. But such are the problems presented by nature that no matter how carefully a job is surveyed nobody knows for sure what the conditions are underground until the ground is opened up. The geologists can do a great deal to reduce the gamble underground, but the margin of error, however thin, is still wide enough to leave ample scope for tragedy.

Geophysics

Science is a matter of measuring. Anything that cannot be measured cannot be made the object of scientific study.

Geophysics is the science of measuring the physical properties of the earth. By measuring magnetism, density, electrical conductivity, and elasticity by various means from the surface of the earth the geophysicist can form a fairly accurate idea of the sub-structure. Whereas the geologist maps what he can see, the geophysicist explores the hidden geology and forms his opinion from the way it reacts to electric and seismic probes. Geophysical methods have been applied in oil and mineral prospecting for about forty years with excellent results, and all new oil fields and mining ranges developed in recent decades have been discovered and defined by geophysical prospecting. The advantage of the geophysical methods is the speed and economy whereby an area can be explored and the sub-surface geology charted.

Geophysics, then, is a scientific prospecting tool, which only recently has been applied to civil engineering and tunnelling; but the possibilities offered for utilizing the technique for the purpose of discovering faults, fissures, and water-bearing strokes should be attractive to the tunneller. By sending an electric current between two electrodes driven into the ground, the resistivity can be measured and the profile obtained. Any anomalies in the profile will signify variations in the sub-surface geology, particularly water-bearing formations. By the exploding of charges placed in the ground and measuring of the seismic waves, the depth to a consolidated layer or bedrock can be determined with great accuracy. By the use of a gravity-meter the location of massive ore deposits and other structural conditions can be determined at small cost. Since most rocks possess magnetic properties, igneous rock being more strongly magnetic than sedimentary rock, much useful information may also be obtained from magnetic measurements.

By a combination of some or all of these geophysical measurements, the sub-surface conditions for an underground power house or the line of a tunnel can be mapped rapidly and cheaply, whereby the diamond drilling programme can be materially reduced by placing the bore holes only where suggested by the geophysical profile. But such tidy procedures belong, unfortunately, only to the textbook world. In a power development, for example, the site of the dam and near-by access to fill may, owing to the great cost of the dam, be of overriding importance. In such a case the tunnellers will have to take whatever rock there is—and make the best of it.

Chapter 12

THE STRANGE STORY OF EXPLOSIVES

ROCK can be mined hot or cold, to speak in the manner of medieval miners. Given time and patience, a hole can be driven through any rock, no matter how hard, with simple tools—hammers, gads, wedges, drills. Hard rock can be excavated with stone tools slightly harder than the rock worked. The Egyptians were masters of quarrying and dressing basalt monoliths with dolerite balls. With patience and know-how, now largely forgotten, anything could be done in rock.

Strange as it may at first appear, 'cold mining' is without a doubt the most humane and civilized way of excavating hard ground. An underground working advanced with hammer, wedge and bar is a healthy place of work. The temperature is uniformly pleasant, there is ample room at the face for men to operate. The dust raised by gad or pick is not enough to matter, and the air is clean. With some exceptions the working postures are natural and do not induce deformities of back or limbs. It is quiet work, and in medieval tunnels the miners sang, singly or in chorus, during their six-hour shifts. It was also skilled work; the Saxon miner was a recognized member of a mining society at its technical peak.

With 'hot mining' the output in hard rock is materially improved. By *hot* in this context is meant the use of fire to fracture and spall hard rock. Tremendous pyres of timber were built on a ledge and left to burn for several hours, whereupon the rock was doused with water or, perhaps more commonly, left to cool. By exposure to the heat the rock expanded and, being tensed, spalled off in flat chunks an inch or more in thickness. In a recent experiment, 0·4 tons of sulphide ore were produced by a fire-setting consisting of one cubic metre (35·31 cu. ft.) of pine cordwood.

Fig 114. Contemporary sketch showing fire-setting in a German mine at the end of the seventeenth century. To the left is a burning pyre in a drift, to the right a stope where other phases of fire-setting are indicated, i.e. raising the pyre, scaling the walls of spalled rock and mucking out the ore by means of a batea.

Fire-setting was discouraged in the Saxon mines, and when used the rock was never doused with water owing to the noxious fumes arising from sulphide ores. To mine with fire, permission had to be obtained from the neighbouring mines as well as from the Bergmeister of the range. When fires were used they were often co-ordinated in a number of adjoining workings and lit at the end of the Friday shift so that the stopes could be adequately ventilated by the time the miners entered the workings the following Monday. These civilized conditions stand in contrast to the barbaric practice in the contemporary Swedish mines where fire-setting was exclusively used from the beginning of hard-rock mining at the end of the thirteenth century until the eighteenth century and, in isolated instances, up to the end of the last century. In the Falu copper mine, for example, some hundred cubic metres of wood (about 30 cords) were piled up against the hard pyrites and lighted at six p.m. Six hours later, at midnight, the mining churls went into the stopes and doused the fires. The hot rock emitted sulphurous fumes which forced the men to throw themselves on the floor and cover their faces with wet rags. But this primitive gas mask did not help much. A Swedish mine churl did not live long.

Fire-setting naturally entailed a frightening waste of timber. The annual consumption of firewood in the Falu mine was about 70,000 cords, and since several times as much was consumed for roasting the ore and in the making of charcoal with which to smelt it, the annual inroads on the timber ranges were appalling. Indeed, hot mining, as practised in the Falu mine, constituted a singularly outstanding example of brutal and technically backward mining practice, and there is no doubt that in many other ancient mining regions the combination of fire-setting and smelting played havoc with the balance of nature. Where the climate and soil conditions were favourable for timber growth the plundered regions were restored again after a few generations; but elsewhere, around the Mediterranean, in Spain, Britain, and other ancient mining countries, the forests once consumed ceased to grow. The Apennines and the mountain ranges in the Near East turned into sterile, eroded slopes not good for anything by the time the miners and smelters had destroyed the trees. The supply of ore was not used up, but the supply of fuel was.

This is in part the explanation for the northward drift of mining that has progressed since the Bronze Age, at any rate up to the time when explosives and mineral coal came to be commonly employed in the production of metals.

In justice, it should be added to this note on fire-setting that the barbaric practice does contain a valuable technical feature, which explains its enduring use to the end of the last century. In hard, abrasive rock, drilling—even with modern tools—is a costly operation owing to the rapid wear of the bits, and with the manual methods of drilling used a century ago, fire-setting was certainly a more efficient means of extracting hard sulphide ores. It is interesting to note that the method has come back in the modified form of 'jet piercing', using oxygen and kerosene, employed in mining

Fig 115. An ancient transport drift in the Swedish Falu Mine
driven by fire-setting. Surprisingly smooth walls and arches
could be obtained by spalling off the hard rock.

taconite iron ore in the United States. In Sweden, jet piercing is being used in the quarrying of granite.

The Delayed Use of Explosives

Towards the end of the Middle Ages and in the following centuries, the governments of the major European mining countries became seriously concerned over the depletion of their timber resources and tried to stop the waste by various legislative means. But there seems to have been no attempt to encourage the use of explosives in mining, which would have contributed to forest conservation. As it happened, the use of explosives, i.e. gunpowder, in mining was not introduced until the seventeenth century and was not generally applied until a hundred years later, in some countries not until the early nineteenth century. Why this long delay, one may ask.

The development of explosives is a fascinating subject, as evidenced by its voluminous literature, mostly German. For several centuries German scholars have tried to pinpoint the inventor of gunpowder and their attempts make amusing reading. Some insisted that Julius Africanus knew the recipe for gunpowder in A.D. 215, others that it was used in China by A.D. 80. Others cling with delight to the tale of Richard I, in 1191, 'conquering a mighty argosy' off Cyprus stocked with arms and provisions of war, including 'combustible serpents'. At about this time, others claim, powder was used for blasting in the Rammelsberg mine. Some give credit to Roger Bacon as the inventor of gunpowder, but Sebastian Miller in his *Cosmographie*, published in Basle in 1584, very sensibly dismissed the subject with the comment 'the villain that brought upon the earth so injurious a thing does not deserve to have his name remain in the memory of men'. The majority of the old German writers, however, attribute the invention to a Benedictine monk by the name of Berthold Schwartz, who practised alchemy. After shifting his birthplace between a number of towns, later writers settled on Freiberg and that is where a statue to the legendary inventor of the powder was put up. As for the year of the invention, one can choose between 1320, 1354 and 1380.

It appears beyond doubt that the old writers went baying after the wrong scent. Many of them confused the incendiary mixtures that warriors from the beginning of time have been so fond of tossing at each other with powder. But they were not explosive mixtures. An explosive must have a reasonably pure potassium nitrate as an ingredient and there is not the slightest evidence that the 'salt' mentioned, for example, by Julius Africanus, refers to saltpetre.

Modern critical opinion agrees on China as the place of origin of gunpowder. A Chinese author Wu Ching Tsung Yao writing in A.D. 1044 gave a good recipe for making a powder cartridge. The Chinese used powder to fill cylinders of bamboo at about this time, probably earlier. An unknown Chinese colleague of Lieutenant Shrapnel invented a hand grenade by filling a paper tube with powder, stones and porcelain shards.

As with the invention of paper, the knowledge of gunpowder compositions was infused from the Far East via Byzantium and Islam. Recipes incorporating the ingredients of 'black powder' were not uncommon before A.D. 1300. Roger Bacon knew one of them, so did his contemporary the Syrian Al-Hasan al-Rammāh, who described in detail how saltpetre was to be separated from other salts by solution and repeated crystallization, the method subsequently used in western Europe for several centuries. Marcus Graecus, another contemporary, also goes into the details of saltpetre processing and the making of powder 'to make fire flying in the air', as he expresses it in his charming *Book of Fires for the Burning of Enemies*.

Black powder to propel a missile through a gun appears to have been used in China about the middle of the thirteenth century, but the development of cannon into a lethal weapon took place in western Europe during the first quarter of the following century. Guns were used before Metz in 1324, at Florence in 1326, in Britain in 1327. Twenty-five years later the inventive European mind had devised a profusion of designs: there were heavy siege guns, light guns, even breech-loading pieces and rapid-fire contraptions that by stretching the term could be called machine-guns.

The early gunpowder, or 'black powder' as it was also called owing to the charcoal used in the mixture, was a finely ground powder consisting of about 41 per cent saltpetre and sulphur and charcoal in equal proportions. (In later powders the saltpetre content was increased to about 75 per cent.) When rammed too tightly in a gun the early powders either refused to burn at all or else burned too slowly, without explosive effect. The gunners capable of loading a gun with such 'serpentine powder' were few in number and much sought after. Around 1430 a decided improvement was achieved by graining the powders. The mixture, while being pounded in a pestle, was moistened with alcohol or urine (that of heavy wine-drinkers was held to produce the strongest powder) and turned into a cake which was ground into grain in a ball mill. Grained powder did not pack too tightly and produced a greater explosive effect.

Depending on the size of the grains, powders became differentiated according to their end uses—coarser grain for cannon, finer for hand

and shoulder weapons. When, as subsequently discussed, powder began to be used in mining and civil engineering, the composition of gunpowder was changed by reducing the saltpetre content to produce a powder more suitable for blasting.

The Privy Chase

Now began a grotesque phase in medieval economic history. Gunpowder was scarce and costly, owing principally to the difficulty of getting saltpetre. The only source known was the efflorescence[1] produced by decaying nitrous matter, such as the ordure of animals and men. Throughout Europe no stable or privy was safe from the 'saltpetre men'. According to the aforesaid German sources, not even the dead were left alone. In Sweden they said King Gustaf I issued an ordinance against stripping the cemeteries of soil. Not that this northern upstart king would have hesitated to rob graves if there had been a chance of increasing his store of the wondrous crystals, but unfortunately this delightful footnote to sixteenth-century economics must be written off as not quite correct: it seems that the German scholars confounded barnyard with churchyard.

London, however, was a happy hunting-ground for the saltpetre men. 'They digge in dove cotes when the doves are nesting,' cried an M.P. in a debate in Parliament in 1601, 'cast up malting floors when the malt be green, in bedchambers, in sick rooms, not even sparing women in childbed, yea even in God's house, the Church.' But nothing could be done to abate this grievance because 'the Kingdom is not so well placed for powder as it should be'.

In this context it is tempting to quote an order issued by King Charles I in 1626 to his 'loving subjects . . . inhabiting within every city, town, or village, after notice given to them respectively shall carefully and constantly keep and preserve in some convenient vessels or receptacles fit for the purpose, all the urine of man during the whole year, and all the stale of beasts which they can save and gather together whilst their beasts are in their stables and stalls, and that they be careful to use the best means of gathering together and preserving the urine and stale, without mixture of water or other thing put therein. Which our commandment and royal pleasure, being easy to observe, and so necessary for the public service of us and our people, that if any person do be remiss thereof we shall esteem all such persons contemptuous and ill affected both to our person and estate, and are resolved to proceed to the punishment of that offender with what severity we may.'

[1] Referred to in the Mosaic code as 'leprosy of house walls'.

Verily, Englishmen have been called upon to do their duty to King and Country in a variety of ways.

Gunpowder Used for Blasting

This note on saltpetre suggests one reason why gunpowder was not used for such prosaic purposes as mining. There was no ruler in Christendom who would have released one grain of this precious commodity for anything but war, even if there had been a demand for it, which there was not. It would have been equivalent to the American Society of Civil Engineers petitioning the President of the United States to release for excavation purposes part of the stockpile of nuclear bombs.

The use of gunpowder for blasting is, of course, also of military origin. According to some sources the first powder mines were exploded at Merat in 1397. Mines were used before Belgrade in 1441 and again in 1495. Knut Posse, commandant of Wiborg castle on the Finno-Russian border, blew up some of his field-works in 1475 to hold back the Russian besiegers.

But the acknowledged pioneers and experts in mine warfare were the Genoese engineers, Francesco di Giorgio of Sienna, and Pedro Navarro who had a wonderful time blasting Italian castles in the early sixteenth century. While engaged in this work Pedro Navarro, according to some authorities, seems to have devised the method of using drill holes when blasting in rock.

The Turks were also proficient in the use of powder mines. They used them on Rhodes in 1523 and two years later before Vienna. Here, borrowing a page from Vitruvius, the miners attached to the beleaguered garrison intercepted the Turkish sappers by placing a drum on the ground, to discover by the amplified reverberations where the gallery was being advanced. They quickly sank a shaft in the rear of the face and took the enemy sappers by surprise, whereupon they returned in triumph carrying the casks of powder intended for their destruction. It should be recalled in this context that even in remote antiquity military commanders had miners attached to their forces. The custom had persisted, and with the increasing use of explosives from the end of the Middle Ages no army took to the field without a complement of miners. The Turks recruited their sappers from among Armenian, Greek and Bosnian miners. Tilly, the general commanding the Emperor's armies in the Thirty Years War, had 300 miners from Harz when he laid siege to Göttingen. This practice suggests that to the extent to which the miners returned from the wars, the knowledge of blasting, including rock drilling, would have been well dispersed over the mining regions on the Continent during the sixteenth century. The reason for the long delay is found in the dearth of saltpetre, and hence the scarcity of gunpowder, until the establishment of saltpetre plantations, or *nitraries*,[2] had become sufficiently common to ensure a stable supply of the strategic crystals.

With the early application of *Bohren und Schiessen*[3] we are confronted with a situation common to the breakthrough of nearly all epoch-making technological innovations. There is always a desire to pin down the breakthrough to one particular person at one particular time. In their patriotic ardour the historians of different countries are anxious to prove that one of their own compatriots was the inventor, and they waste much effort heaping up proofs to this effect. As previously mentioned, thousands of miners from the time of Pedro Navarro at the turn of the fifteenth century must have become acquainted with drilling and shooting during their military service. When, finally, blasting came to be tried in mining it happened more or less simultaneously in a number of mines, to the confusion of the historians.

According to the oldest German tradition, the method was first introduced by Bergmeister Martin Weigel in the Freiberg mines in 1613. Unfortunately for Herr Weigel, there is no mention of powder in the supply lists of the Freiberg mines until 1643. In this important mining region, drilling and shooting were introduced by a certain Caspar Morgenstern in that year. Of other attempts to pinpoint the first use of explosives in mines the one given by Balthasar Rössler in his *Hellpolierter Bergbauspiegel* (1670) that the method emanated from Hungary is now generally accepted. From there it was introduced to Grosslitz and Chemnitz in 1627 and then to Harz, Freiberg, and other areas.

German miners dispersed the method to mining regions all over Europe, but it met with great scepticism mixed with fear. Nevertheless, powder was used in the Nasa silver mine in Lapland in 1635 and in the Röräs mine in Norway in 1644. Both these mines were situated in regions lacking timber, which explains the early use of powder in Scandinavia. In both cases, the blasting was done by German experts. Those at the Nasa mine were from Clausthal.

These Scandinavian mines were the only two using powder at this early date and they could be supplied only with the greatest diffi-

---

[2] A 'nitre bed' consisted of layers of decaying animal and vegetable matter, mortar from old walls and earth piled to a height of 4 ft. on a floor of wood or tamped clay. The compost was sprinkled with blood and urine for at least two years before the saltpetre was extracted.

[3] Drilling and shooting, or blasting.

culty. The breakthrough of 'drilling and blasting' did not occur until after 1710. In England, the method was first used in the north Derbyshire copper mines after 1670, but it took a hundred years for blasting with powder to become common practice in English mines.

Gunpowder Blasting

The early method of blasting was plug shooting. The holes were $2\frac{1}{4}$ in. in gauge, and about 40 in. deep. They were drilled with crown

Fig 116. Plug shooting as used in the Freiberg mines around 1690. The drilled hole was charged with powder to about one-quarter of its length and stoppered with a scored wooden plug admitting a sulphur match. On top of the hole was placed a piece of sheet iron held in place by a wooden stamp. From a contemporary sketch.

or cone drills of various shapes, one man turning the drill and keeping the holes clean of chips, another wielding the hammer. A hole was charged with about 2 lb. of powder, and shut tight with a wooden plug. The plug was scored along the side through which a match of some kind was pushed to ignite the charge. At first, a straw filled with powder was used, then a sulphur match. It was a dangerous method and many miners were killed by the plug. The effect of plug blasting left much to be desired, the holes were badly set, and in fissured rock the shots had no effect whatever. In many mines plug shooting was abandoned because the cost of blasting proved to be three times greater than that of fire-setting.

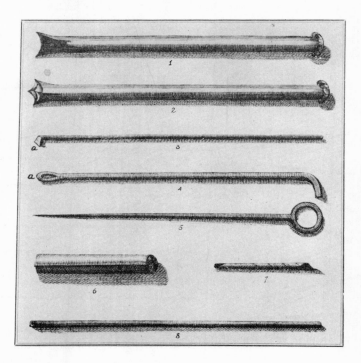

Fig 117. Blasting tools used in German mines during the eighteenth century. From the top down is shown (1) a chisel drill, (2) a four-point drill, (3) a spoon for removing drill chips from the hole, (4) a wiping tool (a water-absorbing rag was placed through the eye a), (5) a pricker (inserted in the hole when it was being tamped with clay and then withdrawn), (6) a powder cartridge of paper, (7) a paper firing-tube, and (8) a hazel-wood firing-tube. These were the type of tools used in all European mines before the invention of the safety fuse. From a mining textbook published in 1774.

A great improvement in blasting followed upon the invention of clay tamping in 1687, attributed to Bergmeister Carl Zumbe at the Clausthal mines in the Harz. In the following year Obergeschworene Singer, also of Clausthal, introduced thin firing-tubes of hardwood

filled with powder to which the sulphur fuse was joined, and soon
afterwards Hans Luft, a bookbinder in Clausthal, invented the paper
cartridge. A few years later, the gauge of the drill holes was reduced
to 1½ in. and the depth was kept within 20 in. The powder charge
was reduced to one pound. In short, by 1700 the technique of blasting with powder had reached an early stage of perfection.

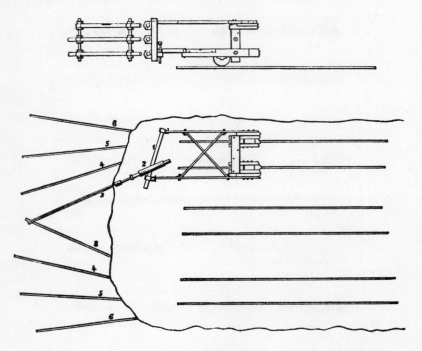

Fig 118. An early V-cut blasting pattern used in American
tunnels during the early 1870's.

There is not much more to add, except that in 1725 rounds, i.e.
several shots fired simultaneously, had begun to be used in Bohemia
and in the Saxon Zinnwald range. Before the century was at an end,
men had begun to blow themselves up with early fulminates, and
in 1829 Moses Shaw of New York set off a number of rounds by
passing an electric spark through a priming compound of silver
fulminate. Finally, in 1831, a 'person in Cornwall'—as he was
referred to in a House of Commons committee five years later—otherwise William Bickford of Tuckingmill, Cornwall, invented his safety
fuse that materially reduced the hazards of blasting.

By the middle of the century electric firing had been improved sufficiently to be adopted in the Hoosac tunnel. It was still a rather treacherous way of firing a round, because it sometimes happened that the man could explode the charge simply by crossing the leads or by holding them in each hand. In the Hoosac, as well as Fréjus, the shot holes were drilled to a standard pattern. At that time, and increasingly in the major tunnelling jobs, the drill pattern incorporated a 'centre hole cut'; i.e. some holes in the centre were left uncharged to provide the hollow space against which the face was blown out. This method obviously called for setting off the charges in a slightly delayed order. As a matter of fact, the blasting used in the Hoosac was in principle the same as that used in modern American practice.

Invention of Dynamite

Space does not permit tracing even in rough outline the development of modern explosives, but it would be a sorry treatise on tunnelling that did not mention nitroglycerine and dynamite, the tunnelling explosive *par préférence*.

By pouring glycerine, drop by drop, into a cooled mixture of concentrated sulphuric acid and concentrated nitric acid, the Italian physician Ascanio Sobrero obtained an oily liquid that he called nitroglycerine. This happened in 1846. For several years it was used as a heart medicine, but apart from its questionable medical virtues neither the inventor nor anybody else thought much of it. Although its explosive property was observed at the outset, nitroglycerine could not be used for blasting owing to lack of a means of firing it.

In 1859, a young Swedish engineer began to experiment with this erratic mixture that refused to explode when struck with a sledgehammer, lit with a match or stirred with a hot poker, yet would go off with tremendous force for no apparent reason whatsoever. By 1862, after blowing a succession of laboratories to bits, Alfred Nobel had discovered the means of exploding nitroglycerine; it needed a shock or, as he called it in his patent, 'an impulse of explosion'. He used gunpowder as a primer initially, but he eventually hit upon mercury fulminate to set off the explosion. From that time on, nitroglycerine owing to its greater blasting effect began to replace gunpowder, first in Europe and, in 1866, also in the United States, where it was used in the Hoosac tunnel.

By that time, however, nitroglycerine was about to be dethroned by dynamite, Nobel's greatest invention. Nitroglycerine was too hazardous for practical use, and after 1862 Nobel devoted himself to making it less sensitive to shock. The best absorbing material discovered by him and still used in modern dynamite manufacture was kieselguhr, a kind of siliceous earth, also known under names such as tripoli and rotten-stone. Nobel's original dynamite consisted of three parts of nitroglycerine absorbed in one part of kieselguhr. It was a safe explosive that could be set off by the use of mercury fulminate detonating caps. It was patented and began to be manufactured in 1867. Three years later it was chosen for the St. Gotthard tunnel.

Two Bangs for Economy

Mining, to put it mildly, is a conservative industry. Once a practice has become established it is adhered to for centuries, sometimes for millennia. It takes a great many big bangs to shake a miner out of his groove. But the bangs may shake a lot of other people out of their set ways and, occasionally, by a roundabout route a new concept may ultimately be forced on the reluctant miner.

For nearly a hundred years dynamite of different compositions has been employed in mines and excavations the world over. But dynamite is certainly not the last word in explosives: for one thing, it gives off lethal gases and countless men have been asphyxiated in poorly ventilated stopes by dynamite fumes. For another, dynamite is expensive, the nitroglycerine alone costing twice as much as TNT, the favourite explosive of military men. The engineering mind being what it is, the high cost of dynamite has produced all sorts of foolish reactions. Men lose their lives loading poorly fragmented rock to enable the site engineer to produce a report showing economy in dynamite consumption.

At the present stage of subterranean construction there is a legitimate need for a cheap explosive. With the enormous development of synthetics one would expect that a cheap civilian explosive would have been made available long ago. Actually it was, but it seems strange indeed that this cheap explosive has not been in common use for the last thirty years. Nobody can claim not to have heard about it, because on at least two occasions it has reminded the mining and construction world, and the rest of the world too, of its existence.

In 1923, the nitrate plant in the German town of Oppau found itself with 4,000 tons of ammonium nitrate, a commercial fertilizer, that by some accident had turned itself into a solid mass. To recover the fertilizer the chemists, no doubt in a temporary lapse of scientific percipience, tried blasting the heap with dynamite. To their great embarrassment the mass exploded and with it went up a good part of the town of Oppau. That bang shook the citizens of Oppau but nobody else. Miners and construction men were not listening, and if by some chance the Oppau bang aroused the curiosity of any explosives manufacturers they kept it to themselves.

Then in Texas City it happened again, when nearly the entire town was wiped out by a fertilizer explosion in 1947. Now at long last inquiries were made to discover what could be done to convert this common nitrogenous fertilizer into a reliable explosive. As it subsequently turned out, all that was necessary to turn an 80-lb. bag of 'prilled' ammonium nitrate into an efficient explosive was to add one gallon of fuel oil and stir. What could be simpler or cheaper?

From the time of the Texas City catastrophe American contractors and quarry men have consumed an enormous tonnage of this home-made explosive that is produced on the site where it is to be used. The ammonium nitrate and oil are mixed in plastic bags, concrete mixers, or simply poured into the hole in alternate layers. To increase the detonation, surplus TNT is added to the fertilizer-oil, but for maximum detonating pressure, water is added to the mixture. In wet holes, the curse of miners and tunnellers, the fertilizer-oil-TNT mixture, plus a cellulose thickener, is pumped into the hole and added to the water already there. To detonate, a primer of TNT or penthrite is required, or a war surplus detonator called Composition B, consisting of cyclonite. But the fertilizer-oil slurry can also be made to detonate with a dynamite primer, as used by the chemists in Oppau back in 1923.

Chapter 13

ROCK-DRILLING MACHINES

ALTHOUGH, generally speaking, there is no great difference between the machines used in extracting ore and those used for excavating tunnels, and although at times the same men are employed on both, there is nevertheless a tremendous difference in the respective approaches to mining and tunnelling. In a mine, a man may be content to go on using obsolete methods and machines, or no machines at all; when put to work excavating a tunnel the same man will be using the best equipment available and he will have to learn how to hustle if he wants to stay on the job.

At one time the tunnel contractor was in need of mining know-how, but it did not take long for the drive essential in contracting work to become reflected in the methods and equipment required for tunnelling. For the last hundred years at least, the cross-pollination has been in one direction—it has been the tunnellers who have inspired the progress made in mining. This is abundantly clear when one considers the early and subsequent development of air-powered equipment and the application of modern explosives. The new methods were first applied to tunnelling, and were then half-heartedly and tentatively adopted for mining. Fifty years after the invention of the rock drill, prominent mining authorities publicly expressed their opinion that no mechanical rock drill could ever compete with manual drilling.

As previously stated, it was the great Alpine tunnels in Europe and the Hoosac tunnel in the United States that definitely broke down the *ancien régime* in underground work. Each of these tunnels in succession constituted a general mobilization of the technical resources of its time. The early ones, Fréjus and Hoosac, directed the interest of numerous inventors to the development of rock-drilling machines; both of them inspired the successful application of compressed air as a means of driving the machines. Compressed air, despite the inane squandering of energy involved in its compression and transmission, still reigns supreme in underground work and, for reasons that will be apparent, is likely to do so for some time to come.

The early inventors of rock-drilling machinery did not suffer from any technical inhibitions. In England alone, patents were granted for six tunnelling machines that were supposed to take out the *full* area of a tunnel. As mentioned in connection with the Fréjus tunnel, the first engineer M. Mauss obtained half a million francs from the Sardinian government to develop his rock-cutting machine that he thought would be capable of cutting out the entire area of this double-track tunnel in one sweep. The idea was finally dropped in 1850.

But the failure of Mauss's idea did not prevent Americans from bringing forth a number of such grandiose inventions. The first machine for the Hoosac tunnel was built in Boston in 1851. It weighed 70 tons and cut a 13-in. groove around the entire circumference of the tunnel, with a diameter of 24 ft. On 24th March 1853 A. F. Edwards, the man who planned and estimated the cost of the Hoosac tunnel to the last dollar, testified about this machine before a committee of the Massachusetts Legislature. The following is an extract from the technical nonsense on which the politicians had to waste their time: 'No machine of the present day should command our attention more . . . than Wilson's patented stone-cutting machine for tunnel excavation in rock. The first model, of 100 tons in weight, is now at the Hoosac Mountain. The result of its working in the natural rock . . . has been from 14 to 24 inches per hour, on a full circle of 24 feet diameter. . . .'

From this, the engineer proceeded to line up a detailed working schedule, substantiated with arithmetic, that with two machines, one at each end, the entire excavation could be performed in 1,005 days.

The Wilson machine seems to have cut altogether 10 ft. before vanishing into limbo. It was followed by a second contraption—the Talbot Tunnelling Machine—made at Hartford and supposed to cut out a core 17 ft. in diameter. Nothing came of that. A third machine, from New York, cutting a more modest core of 8 ft. in diameter, also proved a failure after $25,000 had been spent on it trying to make it work at Hoosac.

The first sensible words recorded in the United States about these tunnelling machines were uttered before the same committee in 1862 by B. H. Latrobe, subsequently appointed consulting engineer on the Hoosac: 'The novel and ingenious machines for driving the tunnel, either by annular groove or a cylinder bore in the centre of the section I could entertain no confidence in, as they require the machines to do too much. . . .' That is to put it mildly. Nevertheless, despite these initial inanities and the otherwise troublesome history of the Hoosac, it was in this tunnel that the seed of mechanical drilling was planted from which grew the great tree of modern technical development in high productive rock excavation. True, a parallel development took place in Europe, in the Fréjus, followed by the other grand Alpine tunnels, but the European line came to an end with the completion of Simplon. The machines used in these tunnels have been discussed in earlier chapters.

Long before these long rock-tunnels were started, however, inventors had been turning out successful rock-drilling machines. Britain, Germany, Italy, France and the United States can all claim valuable contributions to the development of air-powered rock drills. Richard Trevithick of Cornwall, inventor of the locomotive and an early pioneer in steam, invented a rotary drill in 1813 for work in limestone. James Nasmyth, Scottish engineer and inventor of the steam hammer, has also been mentioned as an early contributor to the idea of the percussion drill. He is said to have had a clear conception of a mechanical drill as early as 1839. He produced a drill three years later and in 1852 the machine was tried out in a gypsum quarry in the neighbourhood of Paris. The Singer brothers in the United States invented in 1838 a benching drill that was raised by steam and dropped by gravity. This mechanical drill was employed on some American canal constructions but was eventually forgotten. Isaac Singer made an invention of more lasting value.

In Britain T. Bartlett patented a percussion rock drill complete with rotation and feed, which after successful trials was used briefly in the Fréjus tunnel. In the Rothschönberger Stollen, at Freiberg, an automatic rock drill invented by Schumann was tried in 1856 and patented a year later. Several Schumann machines were used during 1858, after which mechanical drilling was discarded in favour of the old manual method. Some authorities claim that the first European rock drill was invented and patented in 1851 by the Frenchman Cavé. The machine was driven either by steam or by compressed air. Although the Cavé machine embodied the principle of direct action it was not very practical and nothing came of it.

However, there seems to be no doubt that the first rock drill patented anywhere in the world was the machine invented by J. J.

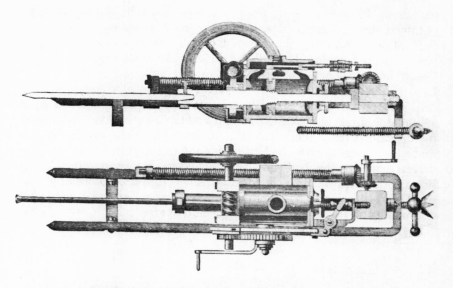

Fig 119. The Schumann machine was an early German rock drill that was discarded in 1858 after two years of trials in the Freiberg mines.

Fig 120. The first steam-operated percussion rock drill was invented by J. J. Couch of Philadelphia who obtained a patent for it in 1849.

Couch of Philadelphia in 1849. On 27th March of that year he obtained the American patent No. 6237 for his steam-operated rock drill. The outstanding feature of Couch's machine was the hollow piston through which the drill rod passed. The drill steel was thrown like a lance against the rock and on the rebound it was caught by a gripper and hurled by the forward stroke of the piston. The drill was Couch's invention, but in building it he was aided by a Philadelphia mechanic called Joseph Fowle. On 9th May 1849 Fowle filed a caveat for a rock-drilling machine of his own which differed materially from the one he had built for Couch. It also was a steam-driven drill, but the drill rod was attached to the piston and followed its reciprocal movements. Rotation was accomplished by ratchet and pawl and the feed by a chain actuated by an endless screw. He obtained American patent No. 7972 dated 11th March 1851. That year the Fowle drill was operated with compressed air.

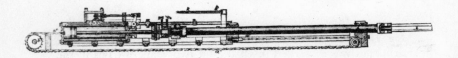

Fig 121. Joseph Fowle's percussion rock drill, invented in 1849 and patented two years later, was not a practical and economic success, but the principles of the design permitted continuous development. From this machine derive all subsequent generations of rock drills.

Fowle's rock drill embodied principles of outstanding merit that permitted continuous development, and all the rock drills made in the world today derive from this machine. Fowle naturally lacked the capital to develop it. Eventually, in 1865, he sold his patent to Charles Burleigh, who, after some improvements, made a success of it. The new Burleigh drill was introduced in the Hoosac tunnel and a large number of them were used satisfactorily for the duration of the work.

As stated in the chapter on the Hoosac tunnel, Thomas Doane, during his incumbency as chief engineer, turned the workings into a testing ground for technical developments, particularly in pneumatic rock drilling and air compressors. In the sorry mess of tunnelling associated with Hoosac, this technical development work constitutes the tunnel's chief claim to enduring fame.

In the Hoosac tunnel, then, after the giant machines had proved a failure, a succession of percussion drills was tried, one of them designed on the Couch principle of the hollow piston. By 1865 it was the turn of a rock drill made by Brooks, Gates and Burleigh, of which forty were made. The drill was attached to the piston in the Fowle manner and was given 200 blows per minute. Although the machine was heavy, weighing 240 lb., it broke down rapidly and the forty units used had to be repaired 250 times a month. Since no improvements could be made on the machines without encroaching on Fowle's patent, Burleigh bought it in 1865 and by adding some constructional features derived from his experience with his early machines under practical working conditions in the Hoosac, he brought out a new model which gave satisfaction. The principal

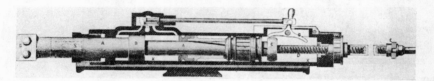

Fig 122. The Burleigh drill incorporated the basic principles of the Fowle machine patented in 1849. The rock drill was employed with great success in the Hoosac Tunnel.

virtue of the improved Burleigh drill was its robustness; it proved to be the first rock drill to stand up to work in hard rock. Otherwise, it was a clumsy machine. It weighed 372 lb. and lacked the automatic features of the competing machines.

These three machines—Couch's, Fowle's and Burleigh's—have been cited because they proved to be the first stepping-stones to the future. But this does not imply that these early machines lacked serious rivals. From 1850 to 1875, something like 110 rock-drill patents were granted to American inventors, as well as seven patents for drill carriages. European inventors were equally active in turning out new rock drills. Altogether eighty-six patents were granted in Europe, sixty-four by the British Patent Office.

Among this throng of hopefuls, one G. A. Gardner obtained a patent for a column-mounted machine. In 1871, a number of patents were issued to another American inventor, Simon Ingersoll, who when starting the Ingersoll Rock Drill Company purchased the Fowle-Burleigh patents; indeed, the entire Burleigh company was merged with the newcomer. Contemporary technical opinion regarded this Ingersoll machine as the best rock drill that had ever been produced. It was a compact machine with all the critical parts enclosed; the rotation was achieved by means of a rifle-bar and the feed by a screw. Nonetheless, what caused the Ingersoll machine to survive was a radical improvement provided by Henry C. Sergeant— a so-called 'Eclipse' valve borrowed from a pump made by A. S. Cameron, who occupied the same shop on Second Avenue in New York as the drill manufacturer. In all previous machines, American

Fig 123. Air-powered Rand piston type drills were used in advancing the tailrace tunnel of the Niagara Falls power house in 1890. To the right the machine is used as a column-mounted drifter, to the left as a sinker. This was the first power tunnel ever advanced.

and European, a number of mechanical devices had been applied for the purpose of reversing the air supply valve at the end of the piston stroke. In the Cameron pumps a tappet operated the Eclipse valve. Sergeant eliminated the tappet and instead operated the valve by having the travelling piston uncover air passages in the barrel, and by using the compressed air to open and close the air-supply valve without recourse to a complex mechanism. Having made this important contribution he set himself up in business in 1882, but only two years later his firm merged with the Ingersoll Company which then put out its famous 'Ingersoll Eclipse' machine.

A rock drill is a machine that tends to pound itself to pieces, and its development has gone hand in hand with the progress in steel metallurgy, but even today a rock drill consumes itself in a year, in the sense that it requires replacement parts of a value equivalent to its original purchase price. The cruel punishment meted out to a rock drill has been appreciated from the earliest times, and much inventive effort has been devoted to developing a mechanism robust enough to keep the machine in service for a somewhat longer time than that spent in repairing it. As W. L. Saunders neatly expressed it in 1889, 'A rock drill embodies more inventions for its volume and weight than any other machine of equal importance.' That statement is probably as true today as it was over seventy years ago.

The Hammer Drill

The drills hitherto discussed had the drill steel attached to the reciprocating piston and following its stroke. This method obviously presented a serious handicap because the heavy mass kept in reciprocating motion put a great strain on the machine and consumed too much air. Naturally it would be much better to design the machine to resemble manual drilling, i.e. to keep the drill steel stationary and use the piston to impact at the end of it in the manner of a moving hammer.

The idea was obvious and had been applied to pneumatic riveting and chipping hammers, but it did not work so well in a rock drill, as many inventors had found out, because of the difficulty of removing the cuttings from the holes.

George Low took out an English patent for a hammering rock drill in 1865 and Henry Sergeant obtained an American patent in 1884. At about this time a hammering machine was put to work in the Manfeld copper mines in Germany. It is supposed to have struck 8,000 blows per minute, weighed 16 lb. and proved rather impractical.

Then, some time before 1890, C. H. Shaw, a machinist in Denver, Colorado, designed a rock drill for overhead drilling which when applied in the mines of Colorado and California was called 'stoper'. This intelligent machine possessed two outstanding virtues. It was of the hammering type; to repeat, the solid steel was loosely held in a chuck and was struck by a piston that shuttled back and forth in the cylinder when forced by the compressed air. As the stoper was used only for vertical holes there was no trouble in getting rid of the cuttings since they dropped out by gravity. In addition to the hammering action, Shaw's stoper was provided with an airleg feed by means of which the machine was held in position and the steel fed into the rock. Shaw apparently did not realize the tremendous value and importance of his pneumatic feed: it was never patented and was free for all to use. To C. H. Shaw of Denver, then, is due the development of the two most important features of modern rock-drilling machines: *hammering action* and *airleg feed*.

If Shaw neglected to protect his interests, one of his associates did not. D. S. Waugh, also of Denver, succeeded in securing patents on stopers and began manufacturing the machines in 1900 under the name of Denver Rock Drill Company, corporate predecessor of the Gardner-Denver Company.

The trouble with Sergeant's and other hammering types of machines was, as previously stated, the difficulty of removing the cuttings from the bottom of the hole. This problem was eliminated by the invention of the hollow drill steel and the provision of a tubular air channel placed in the centre of the machine and connected to the longitudinal hole in the drill steel. In this manner compressed air could be blown into the bottom of the hole to remove the cuttings.

This was J. G. Leyner's historic contribution, the keystone of fifty years of rock-drill development. J. Geo. Leyner, as he had it crudely painted on the front of his little repair shop in Denver, began repairing machines sent in from the neighbouring mines in 1890. A few years later he hit upon the idea of his life and he had made a number of air-blown machines and hollow drills before obtaining a patent for them in 1897. With the Leyner had arrived the modern rock drill; nothing of significance has been added to it since then, except design refinements due to the availability of better materials.

At first, however, things did not go so well for Leyner. In 1897 he made and sold seventy-five of his air-blown machines—and came close to bankruptcy. The miners refused to work with them because they raised too much dust, and Leyner had to take back every one of his machines. The names of these miners deserve to be engraved in the headquarters of the United Mine Workers in Washington. They saved the lives of untold thousands of miners because by their action they forced Leyner to redesign his otherwise fine machine so that water could be admitted and used to flush the cuttings from the hole. The lethal stone-dust was turned into a harmless sludge that ran out of the hole during drilling.

Nevertheless, Leyner's fine water-flushed machines made in the West remained unknown for some years and found difficulty in competing with the light air-hammers resembling pneumatic riveters which, owing to their light weight (20 lb. or less), had found wide favour among the miners. They raised a lot of dust and were too light for the work, but they were preferred to the cumbrous piston drills. Eventually, the Leyner machine gained the universal acceptance it deserved, and when his patents expired in 1914 every drill manufacturer throughout the world adopted his machine. By that time his business, the J. George Leyner Engineering Company of Littleton, Colorado, had been merged with the Ingersoll-Rand Company, in which are vested the traditions of air-tool development extending back to the beginnings of the Hoosac tunnel—actually to 1848 because both Couch's and Fowle's patents were embodied in the Burleigh machines used in driving the tunnel.

In this context it remains only to note the origins of the lightweight airleg machines that have become universal in underground construction and mining since the end of the Second World War. The prototype of these machines is the so-called Jackhammer put out in 1912, a light hand-held hammering type of rock drill meant for hole sinking but widely tried in mines for both drifting and stoping. When copied and used for purposes for which it was not intended this light hand-held machine proved a curse. A man using it had to feed it by pressing with both hands on the handle, absorbing with his arms the recoil of the reciprocating action. This tore both the nerves and muscles of the operator, and countless miners in countries where these unmounted machines were the only ones used became more or less incapacitated for life. Another way of working a light machine, still used by the Bantu miners in the Rand mines, is to lie on the back and push the machine with the legs. Swedish miners did the same a generation ago, the difference being that whereas Bantu miners work in underground stopes in temperatures of 40° C., their northern colleagues lay in open workings in − 40° C.

As usual, nobody cared; here and there some mining engineer scratched his head and tried to find a means whereby the machine could be fed into the rock without having to be pushed in by hand. The solution was there, but no one saw it. The stoper invented by Shaw in 1890 was provided with a long cylinder through which a piston worked by compressed air kept the cutting bit pressed against the rock. All that was needed was to provide the rock drill with the same piston and direct it either straight back against a beam across the drift or, still better, hinge it so that it could be angled to the floor. In the latter alternative it would support the weight of the rock drill and the oblique airleg feed would hold the drill steel against the rock.

Actually, it took twenty years before such a light-weight rock drill provided with airleg feed appeared. It seems to have been introduced first by a German manufacturer in the early 1930's, but the archetype of all existing airleg rock drills which brought about a revolution in

underground work was the Type RH 656 designed by Erik Ryd of
the Swedish company Atlas Diesel, subsequently changed to Atlas
Copco. RH 656 was a fast, light-hitting machine that proved eminently suited to the lengthy and frustratingly slow development work
which ultimately led to the accommodation of the tungsten carbide
bit to rock drilling (see Chapter 14). This combination, the airleg
rock drill and the tungsten carbide drill bit, together with innovations
in blasting, laid the foundation for Atlas Copco, the most familiar

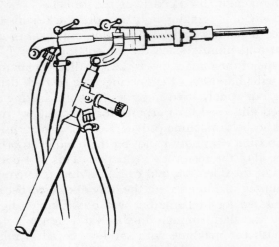

Fig 124. Sketch of the prototype of
the modern light-weight airleg rock-
drilling machines, the Atlas Diesel
RH 656.

name in post-war mining and tunnelling besides being the previously
well-established American manufacturer of pneumatic rock-drilling
equipment.

This brings the 120-year development of pneumatic rock drills, still
the major tools in tunnelling and mining, more or less up to date.
With modern steels and alloys the machines are being constantly
improved. They are being mounted on hydraulic booms, grouped
together in large numbers on multi-story drill jumbos, and in the
more advanced installations they are manœuvred by push buttons.
But despite their tremendous drilling performance, accompanied by
ear-splitting noise, this preliminary to rock excavation must be regarded as a crude way of splitting rock. After 100 years of pneumatic
drilling and 400 years of *Bohren und Schiessen* it is time some other
method were tried.

The Development of the Air Compressor

The cart-horse virtues of compressed air were appreciated in antiquity. Vitruvius relates the charming story of how in about 100 B.C. Ctesibius discovered wind pressure and the principles of pneumatics while as a young boy he helped out in his father's barber shop in Alexandria. It seems that the boy, tired of holding a mirror, rigged up a contraption whereby the mirror could be pulled up and down, remaining in the position where it was left. This was accomplished by balancing the weight of the mirror with a piston sliding in a cylinder against a cushion of air. By means of reeds placed in slits of the cylinder the shifting of the mirror was accompanied by musical sounds.

Much of the work of Ctesibius and his pupil Hero in pneumatics was applied in the temples, to keep the Egyptian peasantry in awe of the mysteries performed by their gods. A sacred fire kindled under a hollow altar generated, by the expanding air, a sequence of events which opened the temple doors; after the fire was extinguished, the doors of the temple closed by themselves to the fearful amazement of the watchers.[1]

However, of more direct bearing on mining and tunnelling technology is the hydraulic compressor described by Pliny. It was already of respectable age when he learned about it, and it appears to have been the prototype of all subsequent hydraulic compressors. Briefly, it consisted of a vertical or inclined pipe through which water, with entrained air, was conducted. Through oblique holes in the upper part of the pipe further air was admitted by ejector action. At the bottom was a leather bag which received the water and the compacted air. The latter rose to the upper part of the bag and was conducted by a supply pipe to a forge, where it was used to supply the blast. The water flowed out through a hole in the bottom of the bag.

This ancient way of producing compressed air was further improved by the Arabs in Spain and used in the twelfth century on the slopes of the Pyrenees to supply blast air to the Catalan forges. The device was called a *trompe* and gave a blast of about 2 lb. pressure.

An early compressed-air device of considerable interest was installed in a Chemnitz mine by the Jesuit, Hall, in 1753. He applied

---

[1] Of more lasting significance was the air-blown organ invented by Ctesibius as an improvement on the ancient Greek musical instrument the Syrinx, or Pan-pipe. It consisted of musical reeds originally played by mouth pressure, but turned by Ctesibius and his pupils into a Syrinx played by hand and known as a *Hydraulis*, from which, apparently, derived the early church organs.

air compressed by falling water to raise water from the bottom of a
114-ft. shaft to the Dreifaltigheit adit. However, the ingenious priest
was not particularly original. An English patent for raising water in
some such fashion had been granted to Rowe in 1726 and fifty years
before that Denis Papin, one of the many inventors of the steam-
engine, air pumps, etc., had carried out successful experiments transmitting air through pipes.

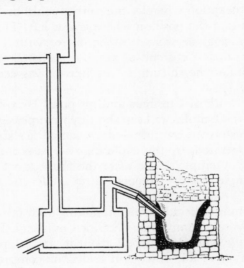

Fig 125. Hydraulic compressor—the
trompe—used by medieval Spanish
iron workers to supply blast air to the
Catalan forges.

The compression of air by falling water is still being used on a
small scale in the United States and Canada, where from 1895
onwards a number of such plants were built delivering air to mines
at 100 p.s.i. One such installation should be mentioned, if only for
the pleasure of recording the creative thinking of men outside the
scientific establishment. This hydraulic air plant was built by a
farmer in Idaho in 1890 for the purpose of lifting irrigation water
over a 300-ft. vertical cliff above the floor of Snake River Valley.
Farmer Priestly owned a few square miles of sterile volcanic land on
the plateau, completely lacking water. About 120 ft. down the cliff an
underground stream of water gushed out and threw itself down to
the river valley below. Priestly constructed a 180-ft. vertical pipe
leading down from the spring and connecting to a closed tank at the
bottom of the cliff. From the tank he ran another pipe to a level

somewhat below the spring where it was joined to a U-shaped pipe, one leg of which extended to the spring and the second one up to and over the edge of the cliff.

Priestly's hydraulic pump worked in the following manner: water with entrained air from the spring gushed out from the cliff-face and was caught in the vertical pipe leading to the tank, where the compressed air rose to the top while the water escaped through a valve in the bottom of the tank. The pressure air rose through the second vertical pipe up to the U-bend where it encountered falling water from the spring and forced it up a height of 120 ft. through the second leg extending over the edge of the cliff. In this manner Priestly obtained all the water he needed to irrigate his scorched acres. This ingenious water lift lacking moving parts would have been admired by the Greek philosophers and would no doubt have been incorporated in classical literature. As it was, Priestly's amazing independent invention has remained unknown except to a few specialists. Compressing air by falling water and utilizing the entrained air is an intellectual and sophisticated technical achievement that has been mastered by inventive individuals far removed from one another in space and time.

In conclusion, another instance will be quoted because of its intriguing implications. In 1908, an American miner found traces of a hydraulic compressor near Teguicgalpa in Honduras. It appears from description to have been constructed on the principles of a modern underground power house. An open supply canal cut in rock conducted water to an underground penstock leading to a pressure chamber and tailrace tunnel at a lower level, where the compressed air was separated from the water. At the time of the discovery, trees estimated to be at least 150 years old grew in the supply canal, and it appears as if the purpose of the hydraulic compressor was to supply air blast to a near-by copper smelter. Is it a pre-Spanish installation or is there some connection, by way of the Jesuits, between the Chemnitz water lift and the Honduras compressor?

What is so amazing about these old hydraulic compressors is that they overcame the seemingly insurmountable difficulties which confronted the designers of mechanical compressors during the entire nineteenth century. Compressing atmospheric air to higher pressure makes the air hot, and cooling compressed air makes it lose its entrained water. But air compressed by falling water is cool and, surprisingly, drier than the atmospheric air before compression. The hydraulic compressor is another example of how, through the centuries, because of faulty communication, excellent ideas and promising impulses have come to nothing.

On the great European tunnels hydraulic compressors were used as late as the 1880's, when they were superseded by mechanical machines. By that time nearly a century had passed in vain attempts to develop a practical, useful mechanical compressor. The first patent was issued in 1829 to William Mann who had a brilliant conception of air compression by the use of a series of cylinders diminishing in diameter as the pressure increased. In 1847 Baron von Rathen in Germany was given the English patent No. 11,932 for his idea of intercooling, i.e. cooling the compressed air after each compression stage. Thus, by mid-century the two major principles in the design of modern air compressors were recognized, but they could not be utilized until some fifty years later.

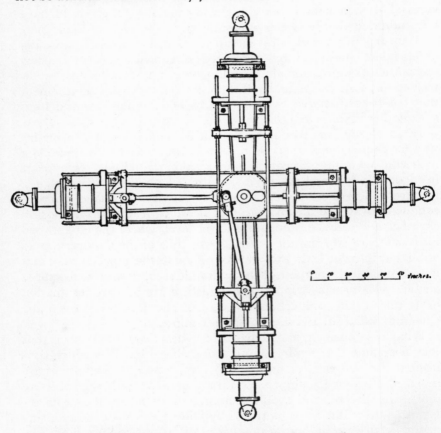

Fig 126. Plan of the original four-cylinder compressor used in the Hoosac Tunnel. The machine supplied 148 cu. ft. of air per minute at 48 p.s.i.

In Europe, the early development of air compressors was pioneered by the Swiss scientist D. Colladon, who devised the compressors at Fréjus as well as at Gotthard. The first Colladon-inspired compressors, as used at Fréjus, were hydraulic, but these were later replaced by water-spout machines. His compressors at Gotthard were, as already described, mechanical machines.

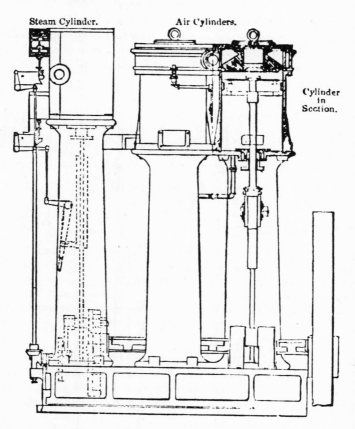

Fig 127. The steam-driven Burleigh compressor, also used in the Hoosac Tunnel, became the prototype for subsequent developments of vertical type machines.

In the Hoosac tunnel, the first compressor was installed in March 1866. This was a four-cylinder machine laid out as a cross, the four pistons being driven by a pitman connected to a crank on the upper end of the shaft of a 120-h.p. water turbine. Each cylinder was

13 × 20 in. and when operated at 70 r.p.m. the compressor delivered
148 cu. ft. at a pressure of 48 p.s.i. A larger machine of the same
type with 25-in. cylinders was also installed to supply low-pressure
air for ventilation. Both machines were developed by the Massachusetts State Commission, although the design work was done by
Thomas Doane, at that time chief engineer of the tunnel. They performed satisfactorily until the end of the work in 1873. The cooling
of the air, always a critical problem in air compression, was accomplished in the simplest possible way. Water was dropped into the
cylinder through a small hole whereby the temperature of the compression fell from 400° F. to about 5° F. above that of the atmospheric air.

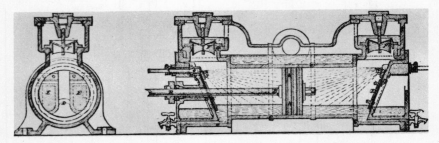

Fig 128. The early European mechanical compressors, such as
the Dubois-François machines used in the early 1870's, were
water-jacketed and generally better than contemporary
American machines. Early promising developments in European compressor design aborted and American engineers took
the leadership in this specialized field.

A number of other types of compressors were subsequently added
to the Hoosac portal installations. Doane invented a horizontal two-
cylinder machine that became the prototype in the United States for
this type of layout. Finally Burleigh produced a steam-driven vertical
type of two-cylinder machine which also became the prototype for
subsequent developments. All these machines were cooled by water
injection.

It is interesting to note that at the time of Gotthard the European
compressors were far superior in design and construction to the
American. They were water-jacketed, provided with better valving
and, being ruggedly built, they were durable and reliable in service.
However, American manufacturers eventually gained a lead also in
compressors and today the best European machines are inspired by
American leadership in this specialized field.

All these machines were single-stage compressors, for no designer had been capable of applying William Mann's idea of multi-stage compression owing to the difficulties encountered in cooling the cylinders. After Mann, the first inventor to advocate compound compression was Ebenezer Hill of Norwalk, Connecticut, and credit is generally given to him for its ultimate adoption. Finally, in 1894 Addison C. Rand, one of America's leading compressor builders, announced that the compressors made by him were compound machines and surface cooled. By the end of the century American manufacturers had mastered the difficulties of multi-staging and cooling. The machines were steam-driven, but within a few years they began to be supplied with synchronous motor drive. By that time, European manufacturers had lost interest in compressed-air machines, because technical opinion held hydraulic machines to be the most promising for underground work.

Chapter 14

TOOLS FOR A NEW AGE

WHAT catches the popular fancy and the admiration of people who should know better frequently makes initiates shudder. People, including directors, journalists, engineers, politicians, major stockholders and even bankers, will travel a long way to gape at and feel properly impressed by the latest piece of black-box magic that a week later is discreetly put away on the scrap-heap.

The small things that work, those that generate dividends, are usually not so interesting to look at. This chapter will be devoted to an insignificant item in modern tunnelling and mining tools that has caused a revolution underground and made possible vast underground construction—'geographical surgery', as it has been called —throughout the world since about 1950. This is a small insignificant sliver of tungsten carbide that is fitted to the business end of modern drill steels. Under the impact of air-operated rock drills the carbide bit sinks into all but the very hardest rock as if the rock were made of cheese, and with it nearly anything can be done in rock at acceptable cost in money as well as time.

The development of the basic tools used in mining is shrouded in the mists of time. Who made the first spade, pick, hammer, wedge? The more recent technical innovations in underground work are likewise subject to debate, and the statements made in the previous chapters can be challenged. It seems clear that Alfred Nobel was the originator of dynamite, but the invention of such an explosive was after all imminent at that time and other chemists may have hit upon methods of taming nitroglycerine before or at the same time as Nobel, but without attracting attention. Also, there were at the time a number of good explosives that, but for the successful promotion of dynamite, could have been developed into equally safe and convenient blasting agents.

The development of tungsten carbide is in one sense much easier to trace, since it lies close to us in time and many of the persons who have taken a part in it are still alive. On the other hand, the fact that so many different persons were involved and, above all, the conflicting corporate interest engaged in its commercial exploitation have confounded the issue by so many claims and counter-claims that it would by now require a special research project to sift truth from advertising. However, the main stream of its technical development has not yet become obscured and can be followed with some assurance.

Tungsten carbide was born out of the German collapse in 1918. The Osram incandescent lamp factory in Berlin found itself without the industrial diamonds essential for the drawing of the tungsten filament wire that emits light. The management ordered a research team to find a substitute for diamonds, and since it was known that sintered tungsten carbide was extremely hard and wear-resisting, work began on the carbide with the aim of making it less brittle. Several years were spent in vain attempts to improve the characteristics of the material, and the team was about to give up the work when one night the laboratory cleaner happened to add iron powder to a charge. His meddling set the research on a new road. By adding iron the carbide crystals had become cemented together and the material was made appreciably tougher, i.e. less brittle. A further search led to cobalt as the best cementing material, and the Osram team could at long last report the development of a new material with excellent characteristics, viz. *cemented tungsten carbide.*

The management were not interested. Diamonds had come back and business was booming. The company allowed the team to do what it pleased with its redundant invention, and one of its members succeeded in raising a flicker of interest in Krupp, who offered him the facilities needed to manufacture the man-made metal.

This is how, in 1926, the first cemented carbides came to be made. It did not take long for the German engineering industry to learn what a tremendously cost-cutting tool had become available. Turning and milling operations could be speeded up by five times. The existence of a few hundred tons of tungsten carbide bits in Germany explains how Nazi Germany was able to re-arm at such speed. This magical machine tool was almost unknown in Britain and in the United States when the war broke out, and it was only when traces of the material were found in the remains of British tanks shot up in

the Western desert that the British military authorities began to take
notice. Rommel's Afrika Korps was supplied with armour-piercing
ammunition tipped with tungsten carbide.

Only diamonds are harder than tungsten carbide. It has a high
melting-point—2,800° C.—and can therefore take heat that will
melt alloyed steels. But in its original composition the material was so
brittle that pieces carelessly packed would fracture in transport. But
this brittleness did not prevent other Germans, such as the Demag
Company, from trying to use tungsten carbide as a bit for steels
employed in rock drilling. Early tests were made in 1928, and some
years before the war very promising results were obtained in German
mines.

By that time the original German research team had scattered and
the members had been forced to leave the country. One of them,
Dr. Hans Herman Wolff, found refuge in Sweden, and on his railway
journey through the country, seeing the granite outcroppings flash
by the train window, he thought idly about the wonderful possibilities for tungsten carbide in such a hard-rock country. Here,
surely, there should be a future for the metallurgical marvel he had
helped to develop as a young man eighteen years earlier.

Unknown to Dr. Wolff the German drills had been tried in the
northern granite and found wanting, as they shattered to bits in the
hard rock. For a while the German powder metallurgist found other
things to do, since a local incandescent-lamp factory was having
trouble with the filaments of their lamps and had to spend a fortune
in advertising to inform customers that it is poor economy to use
an incandescent lamp too long. Eventually the lamp management
employed the German refugee to improve the methods of making
tungsten wire.

With the Russian attack on Finland two years later, Wolff announced his intention of making armour-piercing side-arm ammunition to aid the Finns. Although none of his magic bullets ever reached
the Finnish front, the Swedish army authorities became interested in
his ideas, and to their horror the lamp makers found themselves
saddled with an armament industry as a sideline to their peaceful
electric lamp manufacture.

But while the local lamp factory became geared to a war that
never came, Dr. Wolff found other uses for his growing stock of
cemented carbides turned out behind sealed doors: Erik Ryd, a
designer of rock-drilling machines and the man who had tried out
the German bits, asked for his help in making some rock drills tipped
with tungsten carbide. Thus began a lengthy research development
that went on through the war years, and in which, towards the end,

the entire Swedish mining industry and some of the major construction companies were taking part. This comprehensive effort was directed to the one end of toughening the brittle carbide to accommodate it to drilling in hard rock. It was a slow and frustrating job, and not until 1945 were the new drill bits improved to the point where they were as economical as the conventional steel bits.

From then on they gradually gained on steel. By that time the tungsten department had been spun off by the lamp factory; Wolff had been fired, and the business leased and then sold outright to the Sandvik Steel Company which put one of its men, Wilhelm Haglund, on to the job of turning the still rather erratic material into a stable production item and, not least important, of welding it to steel. In this manner the famous *Coromant* drill steels came into being, and by 1950 had begun to supplant steel drills in mines throughout the world. The tungsten bit had also become the principal tool used in the post-war underground power developments that drain entire catchment areas with power ladders descending from the watersheds down to the sea. This is also the tool used in carving out air-raid shelters, motor tunnels, factories, oil tanks and numerous other subterranean facilities. Some of these post-war underground developments will be discussed in a following chapter, but it is well to recall that they were made possible by this man-made metal that changed the entire concept of rock excavation.

Manufacture of Hard Metal Bits

The manufacture of cemented tungsten carbide bits—or hard metal bits, for short—is an art rather than a science, and the long and complex process could have been borrowed from some secret recipe of a gold-making alchemist. There are still aspects of its manufacture to which scientific methods cannot be applied as a substitute for intuition and know-how. For example, the final crucial test of the material is made by simply placing a bit on a blacksmith's anvil and striking it a number of times with a 2·5-kg. (5½ lb.) hammer. It has not been possible to devise a better and more scientific means of performing this final breakdown test.

Manufacture of·hard metal is still more a laboratory exercise than a factory operation. The long process begins by reducing tungsten oxide slime in an electric furnace in the presence of hydrogen gas, whereby metallic tungsten is obtained as a grey powder. The size of the metal grains, from 0·5 to 8 *mu*, can be controlled by varying the reduction temperature and the hydrogen gas.

The next step is to turn the tungsten metal into carbide. This is done by adding lampblack and heating the mixture in a coal tube Tamman furnace to 1,500° C. (2,370° F.) when theoretically the metal should bind 6·13 per cent of the carbon. The quality of the final product depends on how closely a charge can hit this narrow target. Too much carbon will make the carbide porous, too little will make it brittle.

The cementing metal is obtained by reducing cobalt oxide in hydrogen at a temperature of 800° C. (1,470° F.). The carbide and cobalt is then batched according to a formula which varies for different grades and is kept secret by the manufacturers. At one time they thought that the best material for work in rock would have to contain 11–15 per cent cobalt and the rest tungsten carbide of a small *mu* size.[1] Gradually it has been found from experience that the 'strength' of a bit depends not entirely on the cementing material but also on the size of the carbide crystals. By increasing the *mu* and reducing the cobalt to 7–9 per cent, a more durable bit could be made. But there is a danger in increasing the size of the crystals, because with increasing size the material loses its hardness and resistance to wear. However, after patient trials the successful manufacturers have learned how to devise their own compromise formulas.

Having batched the two components in secret proportions, they grind the mixture in rotary ball mills with acetone or alcohol for as long as ten days. After the mixture has become thoroughly homogenized, the grinding liquid is driven off and camphor or a similar substance added to permit the powder to be pressed into blanks. The pressing is done in hydraulic machines, at pressures varying from 2,800 to 14,000 p.s.i. To add mechanical strength to the blanks and drive off the camphor they are packed with lampblack in a crucible and gradually heated to 900° C. (1,650° F.) in hydrogen. The blanks emerge with the consistency of chalk and can therefore be worked to finished shape and size.

The last operation is the sintering process where the bits acquire their final properties. The bits are placed in a coal tube furnace, or an electric furnace with molybdenum[2] elements, and the temperature is raised to 1,500° C. (2,730° F.) under the protection of hydrogen. Sintering the bits is a critical and highly complex metallurgical process, and the temperature must be maintained to within a couple of degrees either way to prevent failure. The carbon content in the

---

[1] *Mu* = twelfth letter in the Greek alphabet commonly used to denote one-thousandth of a millimetre.
[2] See Glossary.

final bits must not vary by more than 0·01 per cent if a satisfactory product is to be obtained. Despite all precautions, it sometimes happens that a batch of hard metals suffers from 'summer sickness', because a hot and sultry day can upset the result when the margins are so narrow.

A good hard metal suitable for rock drilling has a hardness of 1,800 kg. per sq. mm. when measured by the Knoop method, as against 6,200 kg. per sq. mm. for diamonds, its bending strength is about 175 kg. per sq. mm. (250,000 p.s.i.) and its modulus of elasticity is 62,000 kg. per sq. mm. (88,000,000 p.s.i.). The impact strength is about 175 kg. per sq. mm. (175,000 p.s.i.).

Owing to the complexity of the process, here given only in crude outline, it is customary to make a test series of each batch and subject the bits to a long series of tests employing an array of sophisticated instruments and methods. But the last one is the 'P' test, so called after a Mr. Pehrson who was the first one to wield the 2·5-kg. hammer used to strike the bits to destruction. A bit suitable for rock drilling must stand up to six such blows without fracture. If the test bits perform satisfactorily, the rest of the batch is manufactured.

Another difficulty, just as troublesome as the actual manufacture of hard metal, is bracing a bit to a drill steel, since the steel when heated expands twice as much as the hard metal. As a consequence, the lower part of the bit becomes exposed to pressure after cooling while the top half is subjected to tension. Since the tensional strength of the material is rather low, the bit is liable to fracture when exposed to blows. Therefore, another art has had to be developed for bracing the bit so as to minimize the tensions.

Each manufacturer has his own secret process for welding the bit to the steel, but in most cases it seems as if infra-red furnaces are used to braze the two elements with copper. To test the enduring strength of the braze the manufacturers conduct drill tests in mines with ore possessing different characteristics of hardness and toughness. The wear of the cutting edge is tested in hard ores, the gauge-reducing wear of the corners is tested in highly abrasive ores, and so on. Such routine tests never cease, they are continuing all the time, in mines all over the world.

Drill Steels

Up to 1945, drilling in rock as a preliminary to charging it with an explosive had always been the time-consuming and costly bottle-neck in mining and tunnelling which was the reason for the widespread inventive effort expended on the development of rock-drilling machines throughout the last century. It may be of interest to discuss briefly what could be accomplished by manual drilling some 150 years ago when men began thinking about machines to perform this work. At that time, a three-man drill team working with the best steels available sank a 20-in. hole in average rock in about one and a half hours. The rate of blows varied from eighty to one hundred per minute. The hole was started with a $1\frac{7}{16}$-in. steel and finished with a 1-in. steel. Such a hole required about twenty steels, i.e. one drill per inch. In hard rock the same hole would take up to five hours and twice as many steels.

There was no improvement in the quality of steel for nearly a century. All the great tunnels were driven with drill rods consisting of wrought iron to which a section of carbon steel was welded at the bit end. When drilling machines became common, the entire rod was made of carbon steel of varying grades; after the turn of the century the steel mills settled on a steel with a carbon content of 0·75 per cent as being the best for all types of rock.

When used with a rock-drilling machine the steels wore down very rapidly and had to be re-forged. In hard rock, the bit only lasted a couple of minutes before it had to be sent to the smithy to be re-forged. This meant in practice that one particular drill steel was used perhaps for fifteen to thirty minutes per month; the rest of the time it spent in transit and waiting to be re-forged. In the large Alpine tunnels a whole carload of several hundred steels was required for each round. After being dulled the drills had to be collected and returned to the smithy above ground for re-forging. Not until several weeks later were they sent underground again.

The situation improved somewhat about 1930 when Swedish steel-mills introduced alloyed drill steels containing chromium and molybdenum. This high-bred steel was developed in order to meet the greater drilling rates of the high pressure machines then made. But three years earlier A. L. Hawksworth, a foreman in the Anaconda copper mines in Montana, had invented a detachable drill bit whereby the mines saved $140,000 a year simply by eliminating the transport of drill steels from the underground workings to the blacksmith shops above ground. This became the standard American way of working. The rods were retained at the face and used again and again with different bits which were either thrown away when dulled or re-forged in machines developed for the purpose.

Leyner's invention of a rock drill that required a hollow drill rod put the steel manufacturers in an embarrassing situation since none of them knew how to make a hollow rod. To begin with, Leyner had to make his steels himself out of pipe stock to which he welded a bit at one end and a shank fitting the chuck of the machine at the other. The poor endurance of such a makeshift drill rod no doubt contributed to the slow acceptance of his superior machine. Later, about 1910, drill steels for Leyner's machines were made by drilling a hole through a 4-ft. steel bar in a gun-barrel lathe.

The Swedish mills tried early to roll hollow round or hexagonal drill steel by drilling a hole in a steel billet and filling it with sand. They tried filling the hole with copper and, after the bar had been rolled, pulling out the copper core. In this manner hollow steel for Leyner's machines was made up to 1926 when Harry Brearley in Sheffield used austenitic steel, i.e. chromium-nickel steel, for the core. This material proved more amenable as a core material; the steel bar was rolled into one long rod and when finished the core could be pulled out leaving a uniform and smooth hole accurately centred. This is now the standard method whereby all hollow drill steels are made the world over.

In 1945, when the historic change-over took place in a Swedish power tunnel, a round required 10 tons of high alloy steels provided with forged chisel bits. When drill rods with the new tungsten carbide bits were introduced, the same round required sixty-five drills. These drills stayed on the job; the tungsten bits were reshaped after having drilled some 50 in. in hard rock. The average life of the new drills was 500 ft., some achieving up to nearly 4,000 ft. before being worn down.

Since that time, drill steels have been continuously improved with the introduction of faster and harder-hitting machines. The average life of the drill rod and bit in hard rock is now 2,000 ft. with a drilling rate of 26 in. per minute. This means that the drill sinks into the hard rock as if the rod was being pushed into soft clay. Originally a Swedish speciality, these rods are now made in all major mining countries, although the largest output still emanates from the country of origin.

But this high-performance cutting material has given rise to a number of problems never previously experienced. Some of them began to appear with the introduction of the detachable bits, because when used continuously on the job the drill rods began to fracture owing to fatigue stresses, some of them induced by corrosion in the flushing hole. With the carbide bits the rods were exposed to much more serious fatigue stresses. When struck by a modern hard-hitting drilling machine delivering 2,000 blows per minute, a compressive wave travelling at 16,000 ft. per second is set up in the rod. These repeated shock waves expose the steel to a punishment that would have fractured any alloy steel made only a few years ago. As

made today a Coromant steel is carefully treated against corrosion
and the entire surface is shot-peened to prevent fatigue cracks on the
surface.

Having been static for centuries, the development of rock-drilling
tools has taken on a murderous pace. The never-ending race for
better rock drills, drill rods and bits resembles a dog chasing a cat
chasing a mouse. When the performance of one improves, the others
have to be improved too. The impetus is given by a better, faster and
more hard-slugging machine that will reduce the life of the bit.
Improving the bit will affect the steel of the rod; repeated hammer-
ings for a longer duration will cause fatigue fractures in the steel
which will fail before the carbide bit has been consumed. The rod is
now the weak link that has to be strengthened. By the time that this
problem has been mastered and balance has been reached once more
between the three elements, the machine performance will have been
further improved and a new round of development and research will
have to be started. There is obviously a limit to this race, but nobody
knows where it is.

Back-breaking Loading

One of the most cruel and back-breaking jobs found underground,
or for that matter above ground, has always been 'mucking', i.e.
loading ore or fractured rock into tubs or cars for transport to the
open. This work was done by hand up to the early 1930's. By the
time a mucker reached the age of forty his back was usually damaged
and he was unfit for heavy work.

There were mines where gravity was used to fill the tubs. Ever
since the development of *Fürstenbau und Strossenbau* in Germany
in the 1680's, subsequently known in English mining practice as overhand and underhand stoping, these mining methods have facilitated
the arrangement of the stopes and transport drifts in such a manner
that ore could be loaded by gravity.

But whether ore and broken rock were loaded by gravity or by
shovel was of no concern either to the managements or to the men
themselves, and manual loading continued unabated in both mines
and tunnels until some twenty-five years ago, and continues in
numerous cases up to the present time. The men took a perverted
pride in their back-breaking work, the daily tonnage being something
to boast about. In the Lapland mines, the muckers loaded 30 to
40 tons a day and after the shift walked, with their clothes soaked in
sweat, in a temperature of $-30°$ C. in the face of a raging Arctic
storm, a couple of miles across a bald mountain to a shack made of

dynamite boxes. It took hours before a mucker could thaw out sufficiently to get out of his clothes.

The point of this tale is that it was completely unnecessary. The open-cast mining then used could equally well have been arranged for gravity loading; power excavators were available at the time. The brutal climate, the remoteness, and the technical backwardness made this barbaric practice seem the obvious one to pursue; neither the management nor the men were capable of recognizing an alternative, and if outside influences had not made themselves felt, so it would have remained.

In the United States, a man who had apparently never been down a mine invented a pneumatic loader that has become standard in mines and small tunnels the world over. The excavator with a shortened boom began to be used in tunnels large enough to permit it; the diesel engine was put into lorries and dumpers and used for transport, and now, finally, some smart outsiders have discovered that the sloping plane is a better way of arranging vertical transports than the power-squandering method of hoisting.

A spiralling roadway entering a mine was common in Chemnitz in medieval days, and a slightly inclined adit was standard practice in Armenian Bronze Age mines. For the past ten years transport adits have been driven with a gradient of 1:10 on numerous power developments. Now such approaches are beginning to be used also in mines.

The tungsten carbide drill has forced many changes in underground work in the last decade, generally for the better. It has speeded up the mechanization of the other phases of the working cycle. But there is a difference between men and machines. For one thing, a machine costs money and has to be maintained: a man does not cost anything to acquire; he is something which old-fashioned managements expected to find hanging around outside the gate. For another, a machine needs space, one cannot expect it to crawl on its belly and twist around corners like a miner. A combustion engine needs air to breathe, whereas a man is expected to work and preferably also to keep alive during the shift in inadequately ventilated workings. The immediate environment of a machine requires some consideration, dust and grit are bad for the bearings, water gives trouble to electrical components, whereas a man can work with his lungs full of dust or up to his waist in water.

In short, the heavy plant investments in underground workings which have followed as a consequence of the removal of the ancient bottleneck of drilling have contributed towards humanizing conditions underground. There have, of course, been other forces working to the same end. John L. Lewis, the tough president of the United Mine Workers, no doubt accomplished more during his turbulent career towards rationalizing mining work than all mining managements together. The supply of men suitable for heavy work underground is not inexhaustible; it is getting scarce in many western countries. Union action, then, and the crude law of supply and demand would by themselves have driven up the wages to such levels that managements would have been forced to mechanize, carbide or no carbide. But with the high production brought about by carbide drilling, rationalization of the rest of the cycle became inevitable.

For these reasons, manual work in mining and tunnelling has shrunk considerably in recent decades and so has the number of miners and tunnellers. The few who remain benefit from the improved *milieu* enforced by the machines—more room, better ventilation, less dust and water. Many of the ancient evils have also been eliminated by legislation. With improved production, the earnings of underground workers have risen accordingly and underground labour is usually much better paid than surface labour. But the very fact that a man is well paid puts him in jeopardy of losing his job. His presence becomes an economic irritant that will stimulate efforts to delete him in some manner or other. Where one man a few years ago ran one machine, he now operates two or three. Or he is put to operating a push-button multi-drill unit or a high-powered long-hole drill whereby a whole ore body is perforated preparatory to blasting out a few hundred thousand tons in one gigantic round. Redundant miners, like old soldiers, just fade away. So we have arrived at the paradoxical situation that when, at long last, working conditions underground have become acceptable for humans, the long-suffering miner will have to leave.

It is amusing to speculate on the ultimate end of these rapidly accelerated developments. Russian mining professors have been discussing the automation of major coal-mines for several years. They visualize a continuous production supervised by an instrument panel above ground. Russians also refer to a tunnelling machine whereby they apparently carve out, no doubt in soft ground, a 10-ft. bore in the fashion envisaged by inventors more than a century ago. No details, however, are available about these machines.

If fully automatic mines become a reality, it will of course be nothing new. The Romans mined Spanish gold-mines by water and collected the gold-bearing sludge discharged from the lodes. In the Hallstatt salt-mines the salt has been leached out for many years from sealed-off subterranean chambers, and the brine conducted to evaporation plants on both sides of the mountain. Some 100,000 tons of salt are produced in this manner each year. Instead of hacking out the rock salt as in many other salt-mines, a *Dammwerk* is prepared on one level in the deposit. It consists of a circular chamber about 98 ft. in diameter and about 5 ft. high. After being sealed off, the chamber is filled with fresh water up to the roof, where it leaches out the salt in the rock to a height varying from 19 to 58 in. By the time the brine reaches the desired concentration the water level is dropped and the brine left to settle, whereupon it is pumped to the evaporation plant. Now fresh water is pumped into the works and the process is repeated in this manner some fifty to seventy times, depending on the richness of the rock. By that time the height of the works has been raised to within 5 m. below the next 50 m. horizon (164 ft.) whereupon the leaching is stopped and the works abandoned.

The point of the Hallstatt methods is that having prepared an underground *Werke* in this fashion, the mining of the salt could just as well be conducted by an instrument panel situated in an office in Vienna.

To leach out a rock tunnel or to mine sulphide ores with water would be a lengthy process and nobody would have the patience to wait a few hundred or thousand years for the results. But the instances noted suggest that there are other ways of mining besides blasting out the innards of the earth. It would not be at all surprising if some altogether different methods of extracting metals from the earth were tried out in the not too distant future. Mining in particular has long been an intellectual vacuum; the intelligent men went into mining for a quick kill and were not interested in anything but the profits. Gifted students chose other branches of engineering.

Now a new breed of men is beginning to fill this intellectual vacuum. Major mining corporations, and not least the state-owned mines, have research and development departments staffed by scientifically trained men unburdened by experience in mining. In a few years they have accomplished a great deal in rationalizing the work in mines and underground workings generally. But their most important task remains to be fulfilled—the development of new ways of extracting ore, or metals, or rock, without ravaging the interior of the earth in the present crude fashion.

Chapter 15

UNDERGROUND POWER

IN previous chapters a few of the major tunnelling operations of the nineteenth century, ending with the opening of the Simplon tunnel in 1906, have been discussed in some detail. The vast majority of these underground structures were of course railway tunnels; and most of the existing railway tunnels were completed by the end of the century. The internal communication difficulties of the metropolitan centres were also being solved by putting traffic underground. A vast amount of underground work was also being carried out with the aim of conducting water from unadulterated sources to the cities, and of removing the adulterated tailings of urban life.

Although these tunnels differed in the services rendered, they had one feature in common. They were built with a vast effort of manual labour and with a scant use of power. When building an Alpine tunnel the contractor first had to devote a year or more and considerable capital to developing local sources of water power for conversion, by means of turbines and compressors, into compressed air, or high pressure water to operate his rock-drilling machines. For lack of adequate power due to shrinking water supply in winter, Gotthard came close to ending in catastrophe.

Except for lighting, no electric power was used in Simplon although the tunnel when completed was equipped for electric traction. During the years when the tunnel was being advanced, the art of generating and transmitting three-phase alternating current had progressed to the point where it had become economically viable to develop distant rapids for electric power production.

Although the majority of the early hydro-power plants were run-of-the-stream stations with modest output there were, almost from the outset, occasions for using tunnelling in the construction of these early stations, for diverting the water during the construction stage, sometimes also for the tailrace. The first Niagara scheme had wheel pits sunk 160 ft. in the rock draining into a 21 × 19-ft. horseshoe tail-race tunnel discharging below the falls.

In view of the mid-century developments in power construction, of which more will be said in the final chapters, it is interesting to note that by 1910 the first underground station had been put into service. It was a small 12,000-kW. station built by private enterprise at Mockfjärd, in northern Sweden, in 1908–10. As the years went on and electric transmission lines connecting remote power sites with centres of consumption became common, electric power was made available also on the tunnelling sites. Instead of diverting local torrents, a contractor could build a power line connecting the site with a neighbouring transmission line. Moreover, while building this spur, or in places where there was no power within economic distance, he had by now another prime mover at his disposal, the internal combustion engine, to drive his vital compressors and keep the rock drills going. In short, the advent of the electric age had a profound effect on tunnelling. For one thing, the operations themselves became increasingly electrified. For another, tunnels were put to a further use, that of overcoming the difficulties met with in power-house construction.

This, of course, does not mean that tunnelling became mechanized. There were many types of machines available, new as well as old, and there was cheap power to run them, but there was also plenty of cheap labour eager to be exploited. As a matter of fact, when in about 1910 the first excavating machines had begun to be employed in tunnelling, the workers tried to stop these bread-stealing monsters from being used. It required another thirty years, until the end of the World War in 1945, before conditions matured sufficiently to allow tunnelling to be turned into a mechanized industry. Before that the road to progress was blocked by a superabundance of poor and starving men at large in the western world. These conditions are brutally illustrated in the history of the building of Porjus in northern Sweden, the first major underground power station placed in solid rock. Porjus is a peculiar blend of modern engineering, a quarter of a century ahead of contemporary technical thinking, yet it callously exploited labour in the worst traditions of the nineteenth century.

In 1908, Porjus was not yet a name on the map. It was one of many other anonymous waterfalls on the Lule River on its upper course north of the Arctic Circle, in distant Lapland. Like many of the other waterfalls in this remote wilderness Porjus had become state property by enactments passed during the previous years. The vast Lapland ore ranges, at Malmberget and Kiruna, had been opened up ten years earlier and connected to shipping ports by a railway built under appalling conditions over the Arctic tundras and bogs. It was steam operated and the cost of supplying the railway with imported steam coal was high. The State Railways had plans for electrifying the line and it fell on the State Power Board to find and develop a suitable site for a generating plant. Of the possibilities offered, Porjus was selected as being the most suitable from an economic point of view.

The Swedish authorities worked with admirable speed, not commonly associated with government action. The Porjus site was surveyed for the first time in 1908 and investigated in detail the following year. By 17th December 1909 the Power Board presented the government with a complete plan for building a 50,000 kW. underground power house and a 4,013-ft.-long dam for storing water upstream from the plant. The estimated cost came to Kr. 10,093,000 ($2.7 mil.) and the Board committed itself to building the dam and station in three and a half years from the day when a railway would be extended to the site. A government bill was presented on 4th April 1910 and the Porjus Act was passed by the Riksdag on 5th May, on which day work started on the site.

In addition to the dam, the Porjus programme involved the excavation of a 295 × 40 × 65-ft. generator cavern with the generator floor located 167 ft. below the surface of the ground. It was to be served by a 1,740-ft.-long supply tunnel with an area of 538 sq. ft. ending in a 131 × 56 × 33-ft. forebay from which descended 164-ft. vertical penstocks with a diameter of 11·5 ft. Below the turbines was a tailrace tunnel with an area of 1,076 sq. ft. which, downstream from the station, tapered into a 538-sq. ft. tunnel having a length of 3,780 ft. which returned the spent water to the river. Associated with the tailrace were two large surge chambers with a volume of about 7,860 cu. yds., plus some other ancillary hydraulic structures. The total volume of rock to be excavated was of the order of 262,000 cu. yds.

Porjus was designed to receive 130 cu. yds. of water per second for driving five horizontal shaft turbines directly connected to twenty-five cycle alternators. By placing the power house underground the working head had been increased to 190 ft. But that was not the main reason for going underground. It was feared that a surface

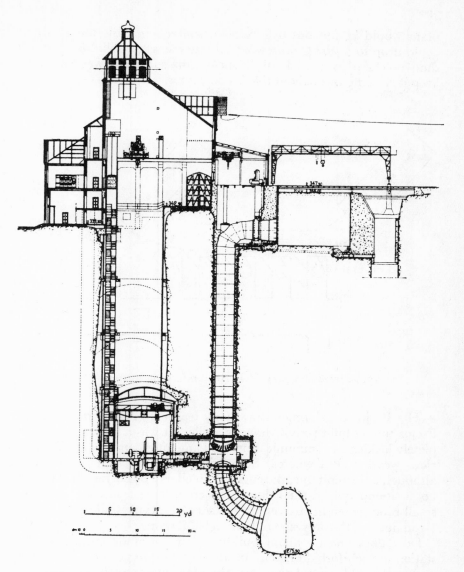

Fig 129. Section through the Porjus power house in Lapland, built 1910–14. This is the first underground power station ever built. Water from the surface forebay at the right falls through 50-metre vertical penstocks and impacts on horizontal turbines driving five 10,000 kW 25-cycle generators, before escaping through the 100 sq. m. tailrace tunnel. The station is still in service supplying traction power to the railway leading from the Lapland iron mines to shipping ports on the Baltic and Atlantic.

plant would be put out of service in winter when the temperature
could drop to −40° C. and would freeze the water solid. By placing
the whole station in rock 164 ft. below the surface it was hoped to
keep it running throughout the Arctic winter.

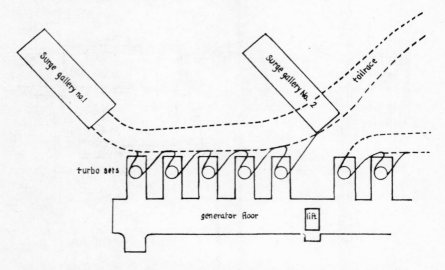

Fig 130. Simplified plan of Porjus underground power house.

The Porjus development has many features in common with the
Fréjus tunnel built sixty-five years earlier. It was a remote site completely lacking in communications and amenities, and cursed by atrocious weather. But whereas Sommeiller could move into a village,
although a decrepit one, the engineer in charge of Porjus, Axel Granholm, found only a small log cabin containing a kitchen and one
small room when he arrived on the site. In a thirty-mile radius, this
Lapp hut was the only sign of human habitation.

How does one go about building a major underground power
station in such forbidding circumstances? Nothing could be simpler:
under the old order one just rounded up enough half-starved
wretches and put them to carrying materials, tools, and provisions on
their backs. Work on Porjus was started up by carrying 5,418 lb. of
food, 1,038 lb. of bedding and 6,756 lb. of tools, on the backs of
workers balancing their burdens on logs laid over bogs for a distance
of 22 miles, followed by boat transport for the remaining 14 miles.
It took a porter twenty-four hours to cover the distance from the
nearest railhead to the site. He was paid Kr. 0·50 (13¢) per kilogram

for his trouble, or something like Kr. 0·83 (22¢) per hour, which was the most generous wage paid at Porjus. Of course, he had to spend the following twenty-four hours walking back to the railhead and sleep a few hours, which cut down the average earnings to half or less, whereby he came on a par with what the Royal Board regarded as a decent wage.

While this portage was going on, another 50-mile transport route was opened up employing horses and boats. By means of this long route 1,692 lb. of saw-mill parts, 17,076 lb. of kerosine, and 14,114 lb. of food, or altogether 32,882 lb., were brought to the site. The time required was three days and the cost Kr. 0·12 (3¢) per kg. (2·2 lb.).

In the autumn and winter when the ground froze, communications improved. The railway was extended over the frozen bogs, and before the ice broke up the following spring 4,458 tons of supplies had been brought to camp over this temporary railway as well as by horse-drawn sleighs. In May and June 1911, a further 660 tons were brought in over the treacherous railway, loaded on light trolleys which were staked ahead by a team of seventy-five men, who were paid Kr. 0·49 (13¢) per hour for their labour.

On 8th July 1911 the permanent railway track reached Porjus and the brutal transport phase was at an end. It was now up to the engineer in charge of the Porjus works to complete the power house in three and a half years according to the commitments made by the Board.

At the end of 1910, the labour force at Porjus was 350 men, a great many of whom were occupied in felling timber for use in building primitive earth-roofed log cabins. That first winter 47,338 trees were felled of which 19,626 were sawn into planks and boards, at first by manual pit sawing, later by means of a circular saw driven by a 20-h.p. kerosine engine. The sawn timber was used for building three barracks, each holding twenty-four men, and a cookhouse. That winter 286 men lived in the primitive log cabins and sixty-four men in barracks, six men sharing a 1,270-cu.-ft. room.

Since the camp administration did not want to be bothered with feeding the growing labour force, the cookhouse was turned over to a caterer who contracted to provide three simple meals a day at a cost of Kr. 1·50 (40¢). Private merchants were also encouraged to establish themselves on the site, and during the winter a few small food and general store sheds were erected. The sale of beer and spirits was strictly forbidden.

In this manner the Porjus site was built up at a fairly rapid pace, step by step, towards a higher state of working efficiency and the establishment of somewhat bleak amenities. A steam generating plant, consisting of a 100-sq. m. Babcock and Wilcox boiler, supplying steam to a 360-h.p. De Laval turbine driving a 3,300-volt Asea generator, was completed in February 1911 and began supplying electricity for lighting and motors. The condensed steam was utilized in a combined laundry and bathhouse adjoining the plant. The bath consisted of a small Finnish sauna and two bathtubs. A bath cost Kr. 0·10 (3¢) in the sauna and the use of a tub Kr. 0·35 (9¢).

It is tempting to compare the hygienic amenities provided by the Swedish State Power Board with those introduced by the Simplon contractor fifteen years earlier. At Simplon every underground worker was required to shower upon leaving a shift and change into clean clothing. Both the bath and the laundry were provided without charge. At Kiruna, the Board charged the workers for these elementary hygienic necessities at an exorbitant rate considering the wages paid. The consequent state of personal hygiene prevailing at Porjus is revealed by the following figures: in 1911, when the labour force had grown to 920 men, only 3,077 baths were served, equivalent to 3·4 baths per man a year. The laundry was kept somewhat busier, and 15·5 tons of clothing were washed during the year. Considering that at least two-thirds consisted of bed linen, the figure suggests that the men had a change of clean underwear once every second month unless they did their own washing.

However, the Board got away with this miserable hygienic standard. The camp doctor reported only 2,561 days lost due to sickness, or on the average 2·5 working days per man each year. There were no signs of epidemics at Porjus.

The discovery that two bathtubs were provided for a thousand men at the Porjus camp obviously prompts further investigation of the working conditions of this underground development. Such were the general economic and social conditions in the country that during the year 4,053 men tried to get work in this deep-frozen hell-hole; only 909 were put to work. A man reporting for work was immediately docked Kr. 12 ($3.23) for his bedding, which consisted of army type mattress and pillow casings and a double blanket. Nothing was paid for the straw used to stuff the mattress and pillow, the only thing not charged for at camp. He paid Kr. 0·15 (4¢) per night for 6 cu. m. (212 cu. ft.) of lodging, including firewood, electric light and cleaning. As previously mentioned, he had to pay Kr. 1·50 (later Kr. 1·60— 40¢) for three meagre meals per day in which salt herring was the staple item.

Depending on his skill he was paid Kr. 0·42 to 0·52 (11¢ to 14¢) per hour. Overtime was paid at 50 per cent higher rate and night and holiday work at 70 per cent. Working hours were nine per day when working a two-shift schedule and eight when working three shifts, or fifty-four and forty-eight hours per week. Timbermen and carpenters had to bring their own tools. Gangs working on contract were provided with tools but had to pay for all materials consumed in carrying out the work, such as dynamite, smithy coal, lubricants, spades, tool handles, buckets, and such like. For heavier tools, such as sledges, drill steels, mattocks, anvils, they were charged according to the metal worn off while in use. The tools were weighed new and when returned after work, and the men paid for the difference in weight according to a price list made up by the site engineer. For some unknown reason forever lost in the mean souls of last-century bureaucrats, the mining teams were not charged for the compressed air consumed, nor for the use of the rock drills. But they did have to pay for the maintenance of the rock drills, and considering that these machines in less than a year require spare parts equivalent in value to the purchasing price of a new machine, the men were in actual fact financing the machines.

To get work at Porjus a man had to agree to a rule stating that 'a worker participating in a strike, open or disguised, or refusing to work owing to blockade or boycott, will be summarily dismissed and his unpaid wages will be forfeited.' The Power Board wanted a lot for its sixpence. To enforce such rules required police, and in the autumn of 1911 a police force moved into the camp.

Mining work at Porjus was conducted by gangs of twenty men working in two or three shifts according to contract. In this way they became the highest paid category in camp, with hourly wages ranging from Kr. 0·75 to 0·83 (20¢ to 22¢). Such a gang was an independent unit working under its own elected boss who negotiated with the site engineer on the over-all price to be paid for a certain length of tunnel, shaft or raise. The gang contracted its collective labour and skill and recruited its own members, subject of course to the approval of the site engineer. It required no supervision beyond a check to see that the work was performed according to plan. The shift boss used a pattern derived from his own experience, determining where the holes were to be placed, how deep they were to be drilled and how much dynamite was to be used. Since the gang paid for the explosive, as well as everything else, there was always a tendency to save on dynamite and shoot the rounds with short fuse.

Conditions at Porjus were typical of those for all northern construction up to relatively recent times, although they were somewhat more callous and formalistic owing to government administration of the site. They explain why in at least one country civil engineering remained stagnant well into the present generation, since such working sites were barren ground for technological progress. They also charged the ground for political explosions. Construction labourers turned anarchic, syndicalist and communistic in their desperate search for a system offering some status of human dignity.

Eventually they got what they wanted although not by their own efforts. The Russian revolution put the fear of Lenin into the hearts of bureaucrats and entrepreneurs alike. A set of modest constitutional changes was hurriedly passed and the tension gradually relaxed. A new dawn rose over the Scandinavian working sites, but the old sins were slow in dying and it required another generation before the economic and social promissory notes issued in 1917 were paid.

Mining Work at Porjus

With the steam plant in service, power was available for driving two Atlas compressors delivering together 953 cu. ft. of air at 7 atm. (99 p.s.i.) pressure, and tunnelling could begin. But this early power supply was inadequate for the large-scale development of the site. In deepest winter—in February 1911—work was started on a temporary hydro-electric station sited below one of the rapids. The station had a working head of 53 ft. and water was conducted through a 131-ft.-long supply tunnel measuring 43 sq. ft., discharging into two wooden penstocks serving two 300-h.p. turbines direct-coupled to 3,300-volt generators. The station began delivering power at midsummer 1911.

By the time, then, that the permanent railway reached Porjus the site was fully electrified. A total generating capacity of 960 h.p. supplied forty-four electric motors of altogether 844 h.p. and 1,322 electric bulbs plus some electric heaters. All buildings above ground and all underground galleries were electrified. Further compressors were installed until in the end there were altogether four units delivering 1,483 cu. ft. of air per minute at 7 atm. (99 p.s.i.) pressure through an airnet totalling 8,530 ft. in length.

By that time, the rest of the site installations were complete. There were stores of cement, steel, petroleum, coal, and 20 tons of dynamite in a frost-proof cellar outside the camp. There was a large smithy, well-equipped mechanical, sheet-metal and carpentry shops, as well as two special smithies for working up drill steels. There were also two rock crushers, each one driven by a 25-h.p. motor, concrete mixers, and a laboratory for testing concreting materials as well as the final concrete.

Underground work began in December 1910 when a 39-ft.-deep shaft measuring 10 × 13 ft. was sunk to the grade of the future supply tunnel. A mining team of twenty men divided on two shifts drove the 538-sq. ft. tunnel by a method of top heading and bench. The heading was first driven to full width of 25 ft. for a distance of 14 to 16 ft. with the use of two column-mounted Atlas Rex 32 rock drills. The lower half of the tunnel was then removed by means of two 10-ft. benches using two hand-held Atlas Cyclops 32 rock drills. The tunnel was mucked out by hand loading in 26-cu. ft. decauville cars pulled by horses. Later, in an attempt to mechanize the loading, a 2-ton electric crane was used.

In this manner 556 ft. of the supply tunnel were excavated to full area during 1911, equivalent to a monthly advance of 49 ft. The rock was first hoisted up through the shaft by a hand-operated crane, then by a 3-ton electric crane and during the latter half of the year by a 2-ton mine skip. The heading was drained by a 10-h.p. centrifugal pump and ventilated by a 15-h.p. fan supplying air through a 16-in. pipe. Two men were killed that year, one asphyxiated by dynamite fumes, the other crushed under the falling counterweight of the skip when the wire broke.

The tunnel was advanced in this manner without further incident until January 1913, when the team encountered a clay-filled fissure surrounded by a crush zone, previously discovered in the generator cavern, which necessitated a change in method. The top heading was taken out full face as previously, but timbered; instead of blasting out the bottom half in two benches, a 7 × 8-ft. heading was driven along the centre line of the tunnel floor. At the end of the pilot heading a raise was driven towards the top heading, and after lining the roof with concrete the remainder of the rock was excavated. After 148 ft. the rock improved and the miners went back to the original method. On 13th August 1913 the two headings met.

It had taken the twenty-man team three years and three months to hole through the supply tunnel, which was 1,752 ft. long and 538 sq. ft. in area. During the best year (1912) the monthly advance averaged 61 ft. The cost of advancing the tunnel came to Kr. 12·8 per cu. m. ($3.44 per cu. yd.) The rock was on the whole of poor quality, as evidenced from the fact that 410 ft. had to be concrete lined. This was a time-consuming and cumbersome job that required fourteen months and delayed the completion of the tunnel until 5th October 1914.

Excavation of the Porjus Generator Cavern

The excavation of the Porjus generator cavern is of special interest since it was at that time the largest room ever excavated. Its dimensions are still impressive: 295 × 40 × 65 ft. Along one wall were five turbine niches, each one measuring 46 × 20 × 20 ft. The floor of the cavern was situated 164 ft. below the surface and in order to get the heavy machinery in place the cavern was connected with the surface by a 16 × 36-ft. shaft. At one end of the cavern was another 10 × 20-ft. shaft leading to the future switchyard above ground.

This 200-sq. ft. cable shaft began to be sunk in February 1911 by a nine-man team working on two shifts, at first by manual drilling, later with the use of three Atlas Cyclops 32 machines. They made 24 ft. per month and reached cavern grade late in summer. The shaft was equipped with a mine skip, pumps and fans, whereupon a heading was advanced across the floor of the future generator cavern. When advancing this cross-heading the team hit upon a 3-ft. wide clay fissure surrounded by a crush zone which upon closer investigation proved to dip diagonally along the cavern into the supply and tail-race tunnels.

The plan chosen for excavating the power house under these treacherous conditions does not lack interest. It was decided:

1. To continue the cross-heading from the cable shaft to the opposite wall of the cavern. This would serve as a haulage gallery.

2. From the end of the gallery and at right angles to it a 7 × 8-ft. heading would be driven in opposite directions, following the long east wall of the cavern along its bottom, as a continuation of the haulage gallery.

3. From the longitudinal gallery, crosscuts would be driven towards the bottom of the five 11·5-ft. penstocks terminating at this grade.

4. The penstock shafts would be driven as vertical raises using shrinkage stoping.

5. Upon completion of the five penstock shafts the five turbine niches would be blasted out.

6. Any niches touched by the fissure would have their roofs reinforced by concrete prior to the excavation of the rest of the cavern.

By the time these excavations were completed it had become obvious that the site was poorly chosen. The granite gneiss was shot through with fissures running in all directions. Confronted with this poor rock it was decided to blast out the cavern in the following manner:

1. Using the cable and main shafts as points of attack, a longitudinal heading would be driven along the crown of the cavern.

Along the shoulders of the vault and just outside the longitudinal walls two other headings would be driven along the entire length of the cavern.

2. The rock remaining between these three pilots would be removed in 20-ft. slabs leaving intermediate 20-ft. slabs to support the roof.

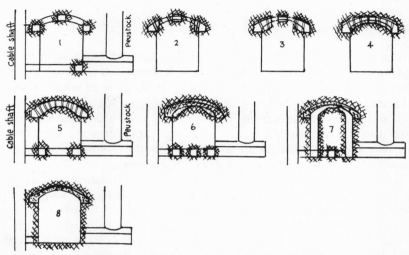

Fig 131. Sequence of excavations used for blasting out the 295×40×65 ft. generating cavern at Porjus, the largest underground structure built up to that time.

3. After timbering the excavated portions of the roof, the remaining pillars would be shot down and supported with timbers.

4. A reinforced concrete vault placed in 20-ft. lengths would be put in along the roof and the space above packed with rock.

5. With the roof secure, a heading would be driven along the floor of the western long wall of the cavern to serve as a haulage gallery.

6. After timbering the two longitudinal haulage galleries, the rock above them extending to the vault would be removed by shrinkage stoping, care being taken against overbreakage along the cavern walls.

7. Another 7 × 8-ft. pilot would be advanced along the centre of the floor.

8. The central core resting on two narrow pillars would be removed by blasting the pillars in sections thereby undermining the rock. The large slabs falling down would be boulder-blasted to suitable size.

The plan worked to satisfaction. Six men working in three shifts were employed in each heading, using two Atlas Rex 32 rock drills. The work of advancing the headings began in the summer of 1911 and the roof vault was in place a year later. In January 1913 the shrinkage stoping of the core was completed, and six months later the cavern was fully excavated. The cost came to about Kr. 20 per cu. m. ($5.38 per cu. yd.).

The Tailrace Tunnel

The Porjus tailrace tunnel is 3,780 ft. long and has an area of 538 sq. ft., except for a distance of 203 ft. behind the draught tubes where the tunnel is expanded to 1,076 sq. ft. Associated with the tailrace are two surge galleries of altogether 1,435 sq. yds.

The tailrace was advanced from two 11 × 16-ft. shafts sunk on line and from the bottom of a circular 212-sq. ft. overflow shaft connecting one surge chamber with a surface overflow basin. During the tunnel advance the shaft was equipped for hoisting.

From the bottom of this 230-ft. shaft a cross-heading was driven to the centre line of the 1,076-sq. ft. tailrace opposite surge tube No. 5. Here the miners drove a raise towards the tunnel roof and widened it to full tunnel width. The rest of the area was benched out in the usual manner. The team working north, along the length of the cavern, had no trouble excavating the large tunnel. It took them about a year to drive the 312-ft.-long tunnel leading to surge gallery No. 1.

The team advancing the southern heading soon ran into the clay-filled fissure and the crush zone associated with it. They passed through the critical zone with a 7 × 11-ft. heading for a distance of 157 ft. and left the rest for the future. The rock got better where the large tunnel tapers into the 538-sq. ft. tailrace and the advance continued by top heading and bench. After some months the rock deteriorated again, and the heading had to be abandoned for the time being.

On the other four downstream headings, driven from shafts, the rock was good all the way and the tailrace, including the surge shafts joining the penstocks with the tailrace, was completed in March 1914. The average advance was 43 ft. per month. Manual mucking with the aid of an electric crane was on the average 32 cu. ft. per man-hour. The critical parts of the tunnel near by the cavern were excavated under the protection of 10-ft.-thick concrete walls. The total volume of rock excavated in the tailrace came to 83,500 cu. yds., which were removed at a cost of Kr. 13·70 per cu. m. ($3.69 per cu. yd.)

By the summer of 1914, the underground work at Porjus was completed, ahead of schedule and from all accounts well within the estimate. The accidents had been held down to a total of fifty-eight, of which only fourteen occurred underground. Eleven lives had been lost, including the two miners killed in 1911. The total cost, including the electrical installation, comes out at something like Kr. 200 ($54) per kW.

Seen entirely from a management and government point of view, the building of Porjus was an altogether admirable performance and the leaders were suitably rewarded, with medals and better positions in the establishment. But in the summer of 1914 when everything was proceeding smoothly six months ahead of schedule, there was trouble brewing.

The first rumours of pending war reached the site on 1st August, but war was very distant and of no concern to the men at Porjus. Two days later they were deeply involved in it. Nearly the entire labour force, including all foremen, engineers, even the site manager, received their mobilization orders, and when the midnight sun stood high over the horizon a special train arrived to take them away to an unknown destination. The site manager refused to obey his order and by making himself inaccessible to the police sent out to arrest him he succeeded somehow, with the aid of the Power Board in Stockholm and political intercession, in escaping being treated as a deserter. He managed also to get replacements for the skilled men taken off to war, and to complete the installations.

The first generator was started at 8.54 p.m. on 17th October 1914 and the remainder towards the end of the year. At the last second of the twelfth hour of the old era, power from Porjus began to surge through the trolley wires of the Lapland ore railway as a substitute for the steam coal that was becoming increasingly scarce as the blockade caught the country in its iron grip during the long night closing in over Europe.

Chapter 16

TROUBLE IN LÖTSCHBERG
'THE CASE OF THE INFILLED VALLEY'

LONG before work began on the Simplon tunnel it became apparent that if this underground link with Italy was to become effective
and economically viable, another tunnel would have to be driven
through the Lötschberg massif framing the Upper Rhône Valley to
the north. To reach Simplon would otherwise require a long detour
along the Rhône Valley to Lausanne, whereas a tunnel through
Lötschberg would join Brig, at the northern portal of the Simplon,
with Berne and Basle and thus funnel the traffic generated by north-
western France, the Rhine Valley, Holland and Belgium. Locally,
it would join the two isolated cantons of Berne and Wallis.

Not less than eight railway projects were put forward and debated
between 1889 and 1899. The one finally adopted envisaged a railway
connecting Brig with Frutigen, on the northern slope of the Bernese
Alps. The length of the line was only 36·3 miles, but they were difficult and expensive miles; 40 per cent of the length consisted of tunnels. Besides the 8·5-mile-long summit tunnel through Lötschberg
there were thirty-three other tunnels on the approaches. After leaving
Frutigen at an elevation of 2,562 ft., the line climbs with a gradient
of 1:50 and between the fourth and eighth miles makes a double
bend spiralling up in a tunnel to gain grade. At about 12·5 miles the
line reaches the northern portal of the Lötschberg tunnel—at one
time the third longest in the world—at an elevation of 3,935 ft.

From the northern portal the tunnel rises with a gradient of 1:143
to a summit 3·75 miles inside the tunnel at an elevation of 4,084 ft.
After running level for a distance of 568 yds., it descends with a

gradient of 1:263 to the Goppenstein portal at 3,995 ft., from where the railway follows the Lonza Valley to the Rhône and joins the Lausanne line a few miles west of Brig.

The total cost of the Berner Alpen Line was estimated at 69 million francs ($13.3 million), of which the double-track Lötschberg would require 32·1 million francs ($6.2 million). The cost of excavating the tunnel was estimated at 1,812 francs per linear metre ($350 per yd.), and the time of completion was put at five years.

The geological profile from the north to the south was expected to consist of lime formations, followed by granite and, towards the south, crystalline slate. No trouble was anticipated with the rock, and the temperature was not expected to exceed 30° C.

None the less, the projectors of the tunnel, F. Hittman and C. Greulich, were not happy about a short stretch on the northern end where the tunnel left the secure cover of the Fisistock peak and entered the narrow Gastern Valley under the Kander torrent. Here the cover was only 610 ft. under the river bed and they expressed some doubts as to whether it consisted of solid rock all the way. There was a risk that instead of being rock the cover might consist of alluvial deposits, silt, sand, gravel. But the two engineers were overruled by a distinguished geological commission of two doctors and one professor, who laid down the scientific verdict that '. . . in spite of the rather shallow cover there is not the slightest risk of encountering alluvial deposits when undercutting the Gastern Valley. The deposits extend to a maximum depth of 60 to 70 metres, leaving a minimum of 100 metres of solid rock cover.' With this emphatic denial of any risks the project was pigeonholed for six years, awaiting the completion of the Simplon tunnel.

With the opening of the Simplon tunnel in early 1906 the Berner Alpine Railway Company ordered the construction work on the line to begin. Work on the double-track Lötschberg tunnel, with an inside width of 26 ft. 3 in. and a height above the rails of 20 ft., began at the northern end on 29th October 1906, with the advance of a 9 ft. 3 in. × 7 ft. 6-in. pilot tunnel. Three days later the southern pilot portal was opened up. By the end of November the pilot was driven with three shifts at both ends. As usual, manual drilling was used while waiting for the portal installations to be completed. By the end of the year there were fifty-two men working in the tunnel. With an advance of 5 ft. 6 in. per day they had accomplished 403 ft.

Again there was a note of caution. An independent geologist, Dr. L. Rollier, issued a warning about conditions in the Gastern Valley. He was convinced that the alluvial fill under the bottom of the river was much deeper than indicated by the official geological profile. It could quite possibly extend to a depth of 660 ft., in which case 330 ft. of the tunnel would have to be driven through treacherous alluvial materials. Would it not be advisable to ascertain in advance the actual conditions by sinking a probing shaft in the critical valley?

The suggestion was ignored. So also were repeated warnings by the people living in the Lonza Valley against erecting a canteen on the slope outside the Goppenstein portal. The contractor was at that time too busy with his portal installations at both ends to be bothered with such idle talk. At Frutigen, on the north side, he was building repair shops, stores, sawmills and accommodation for 1,500 men. He was also building a power line from Spiez to the site. The 15 kV. power was transformed to 125 volts for lighting and 500 volts for driving four 400-h.p. compressors, pumps, fans and other mechanized equipment. The compressors delivered 10 kg/cm² (142 p.s.i.) air for working the Meyer rock drills to be used on the northern end and 120 kg/cm² (1,700 p.s.i.) air for the locomotives subsequently employed in the tunnel. At the Goppenstein end the portal installations were duplicated. Here 5,000-volt power was taken from a station on the Lonza torrent and transformed to 500 volts for driving Ingersoll compressors delivering air to Ingersoll rock drills and compressed-air locomotives. In fact, both sides were electrified and the underground workings lighted with electric lamps.

The Lötschberg tunnel was driven with admirable energy from the outset. The electrical installations were completed in four months and two rock drills were put to work on the northern heading on 7th March 1907. In the following months three machines were put to work on the southern heading. The daily advance rose to 12 ft. per day. Horses were still used for transport.

Throughout 1907 the contractor poured more men and machines into the workings. The pace kept increasing. The tunnel was driven by the Austrian method, by bottom heading followed by intermediate raises to the crown of the finished tunnel from which a top heading was driven in both directions and the tunnel broken out to full width. By the end of the year the northern heading had been advanced a distance of 4,733 ft. and the southern 4,307 ft., or a total of 9,040 ft. without incident.

But during the following year the birds of ill omen came home to roost on both sides of the Lötschberg slopes. On 29th February, at 7.30 in the evening, a snow avalanche came roaring down from the Meigengrat peak and the tremendous air pressure that was generated lifted the canteen from its foundations and threw it into the gorge some hundreds of feet below. When this occurred, a large number of engineers, technicians and visitors were having supper. They were buried under the snow masses at the bottom of the Lonza Valley. Eleven men were dug out dead, another badly wounded engineer died later. Work stopped on the southern end for two weeks while the damage to the portal installations was cleared up. Work was then resumed at both ends; indeed the catastrophe at Goppenstein had not interrupted work on the northern heading for a moment. The progress reported during the next months was the best ever recorded, the average daily advance reaching 25 ft. through the limestone on the northern end.

By July the northern heading had emerged from under the shelter of the Fisistock peak and was driven through the critical Gastern Valley without encountering any change in the rock. The geological forecast was proved right, there were no risks involved and by the middle of the month the chief engineer on the northern heading, Dr. A. Zollinger, left to address a meeting of the Swiss Engineering Society. He expressed his confidence that the worst was over, the supposedly dangerous valley had been crossed and before the month was out the northern heading would enter under the protection of the 13,000-ft. Balmhorn peak.

Dr. Zollinger had barely returned from the meeting when catastrophe struck. The night shift on the northern heading had finished drilling and charging the rock face at 8,775 ft. at 2.30 in the morning of 24th July. Two men had been sent to the rear to collect some gear, when the foreman blew the round. None of the mining crew of twenty-five in the heading lived to give evidence of what actually happened that fateful night, because within seconds they were buried in an avalanche of boulders, silt, mud and sand that kept advancing towards the rear of the pilot tunnel for a distance of 4,300 ft. before it stopped. The only men from the mining crew who escaped alive were the two who had left the face before the round was ignited. When they left, the face did not show any signs that anything was amiss. The rock was firm and no water emerged from the 4-ft. holes drilled for the round.

What had happened was nevertheless obvious to everybody. That last round had blown in the thin rock partition between the solid limestone and the treacherous alluvial that was in direct and continuous contact with the water-soaked sand and gravel rising without a break to the Kander torrent 660 ft. above. With a force generated by a 660-ft. head, the whole infilled valley had discharged into the tunnel and filled it for a distance of 0·8 mile.

Upon learning of the catastrophe Dr. Zollinger sent one of his engineers to report on the appearance of the Kander valley above the break. Nothing is known about what he reported, but other eyewitnesses tell of seeeing a vortex in the middle of the torrent; the shores had sheared and there were deep narrow cracks around a depression in the valley estimated at 480 ft. in diameter.

In short, the alluvial deposits did not end at 245–260 ft., as predicted by the geological commission; they descended much deeper, but just how deep was never reported. In fact, a great many details about the Lötschberg catastrophe were never made public. The heroic age of tunnelling was over, when the triumphs and tribulations of tunnellers were shared by all who could read. There were admittedly not yet any Public Relations men ready to step in to whitewash and confuse the facts, but the elementary techniques of withholding simple truths from the peasants were fully mastered. The principals in the drama were treading on treacherous ground in more than one sense; there were legal aspects to be considered, the shifting of moral and economic responsibilities, there was a lot of money involved, and a great many dead. There was a manœuvring for position. Nobody in authority had anything to say: the Press had to make do with what it could find out for itself.

The railway company appointed an expert technical committee to report on the catastrophe. On 7th September the experts delivered their opinion, accompanied by a demand that the report be published in full after being digested by the railway Board. Nothing came of that. Instead the Board sent a three-man committee, including Dr. Zollinger, on a study tour to Germany. Nothing could be said about what had happened or indeed about the future of the Lötschberg tunnel.

In the meanwhile the Swiss dailies flowed over with rumours and inspired leaks. The expert committee, it was stated, had recommended keeping to the original line, if necessary by freezing the ground. The catastrophe was not due to the Kander breaking through, the real reason was that an underground mud and sand pocket had been struck. It was merely a matter of cleaning up the tunnel and the work could proceed without further risk. The Berne authorities gave the contractor six months in which to recover the twenty-five bodies buried in the sand and give them a Christian burial.

Two months after the slide, the railway put a German firm to drilling through the river deposit to determine its depth. The contracting firm thought it prudent to appoint a commission of its own to investigate the reasons for the catastrophe. The German firm, about to start probing the Gastern Valley, assured the newspapers that with its own system of tunnelling there would be no difficulty at all in continuing the advance along the original axis.

Gradually a few facts leaked out. A Swiss technical journal discovered when its writers visited the site that ten days before the break, at 8,620 ft., a cold spring had been encountered which gave 10 gals. per second under great pressure. The temperature of the water was 6° C., as against 4·8° C. in the Kander torrent above. By placing a number of charges around the spring both the flow and the pressure had been reduced, the water finding another outlet through fissures in the rock. The last rock samples tested 20 ft. ahead of the break had shown geological changes indicating the presence of a dislocation. The incidents had been ignored as not being particularly unusual, and had never been reported. The technical reporters also found that the strange conclusion drawn by the expert commission, as it leaked to the Press, that the Kander was not the cause of the slide, was based on some simple experiments conducted in the valley. Water entering the deep fissure along the shores had been stained red, and it had been found that the stained water appeared downstream. Therefore, the commission concluded, there could be no connection between the Kander and the heading 600 ft. below.

The work of cleaning up the heading continued until well into October. The sand had originally covered the rail as far back as 4,475 ft. from the northern portal. It gradually rose in height and at 4,800 ft. the sand slide was 5 ft. high and nothing could be done to reduce the level. The sand kept pouring in as fast as the miners removed it. Finally they refused to continue with their Sisyphean labour and a masonry wall 33 ft. thick was erected at that point. The twenty-five bodies were left buried in the abandoned heading.

After two months' delay the optimistic German firm managed to get started with the test drilling, and at the end of January 1909 the two holes had reached depths of 145 and 223 ft. At the end of April the drilling work stopped after having reached 722 and 650 ft. Just what was found was not announced. By that time a new heading was being driven around the valley.

What had happened in the meanwhile was that the railway company and the contracting firm had arranged a compromise. The railway abandoned its position that the contractor adhere to the original axis and proceed at his own risk and expense under the Gastern Valley, and accepted the contractor's proposal to go around the valley on a new line. According to a convention signed by the parties on 11th January, the new traverse was not to exceed the length of the original straight line by more than 2,624 ft. (800 m.). The radii of the curves were not to be less than 3,608 ft. (1,100 m.) Outstanding differences since the fatal 24th July were to be settled by arbitration. It was also agreed not to publish the report on the accident.

The reasons for these decisions were delicately touched upon in the Berne cantonal council in answer to a question raised by a member. The Regierungsrat Kanitzer, who also served on the railway board, explained that since the railway had ordered, executed and paid for the investigation into the cause of the slide, the report belonged to the railway. It was a document of vital importance for future litigations. No faith should be placed on newspaper accounts of its contents. The reason for abandoning the original line was the need for using special methods, such as grouting or freezing the ground under the Gastern bed. Grouting could not be applied because of excessive water. To freeze 1,000 ft. of ground would require the erection of thirty drilling towers and a machine installation of 3,000 h.p. It would take about four years and cost something like 20 million francs.

After seven months of stoppage, work on driving the diversion tunnel around the Gastern Valley began on 17th February 1909. The new heading was started at 3,946 ft. and 4,829 ft. of the fatal heading was abandoned. An angle of 41° 33′ 24″ was turned to the east and a curve with a radius of 3,936 ft. (1,200 m.) was laid out. This took the new heading to the east and parallel with the Gastern Valley for a distance of 5,438 ft., where the line breaks off to the south with an angle of 58° 15′ 24″ and a 3,608-ft. (1,100 m.) curve. A few hundred yards along the southern tangent the tunnel crosses the Gastern Valley about a mile and a quarter upstream from the original crossing. Here, according to the contractor's geologists, the rock cover has a minimum thickness of 495 ft. below the bed of the Kander.

After crossing the valley the tangent continues for 17,814 ft. to a point where it joins the original tunnel axis with a left angle of 18° 42′ and a curve of 3,608 ft. (1,100 m.). From the end of the curve the straight line to the southern portal is 13,143 ft. Including the long curves the new traverse has a length of 47,649 ft., as against the original straight line axis of 45,051 ft., or 2,598 ft. longer than the original.

When the work on the new heading was started the southern heading had reached 11,214 ft. The contractor was confronted with a new problem in mountain tunnelling. Hitherto all long tunnels had been driven with a straight axis from portal to portal, and the curves required to connect up the railway line had been put in afterwards. With the new Lötschberg traverse the northern heading had two curves and the southern one, which complicated the survey work immensely. After turning three angles the two headings would have to meet somewhere on the long tangent under the Balmhorn massif.

It was expected that the new traverse would add one year or more to the work of completing the tunnel. But from the very beginning the contractor was determined to make up the seven lost months, and the remainder of the Lötschberg tunnel was driven on a crash schedule. The contractor kept adding more men and machines and drove the northern heading with ruthless energy. One month after starting the mining, teams working with four machines reached a daily advance of 27 ft. in the relatively soft limestone. The daily rate kept climbing to 34 ft. and in April 1909 a world record advance of 43½ ft. was gained in the limestone. Nothing was permitted to slow down the advance. It passed through very nearly everything that the Alps can offer in the way of rock: limestone, quartzite, dolomite, gypsum, slate, anhydrite, decomposed rock of varying mineral make-up. In January 1910 the heading turned a curve in gypsum and anhydrite, and on 13th February the crossing of the Gastern Valley was completed and the heading passed into good granite on the long southern tangent.

In the rear of the pilot heading, nearly 9,600 ft. of top headings had been driven, and for a distance of 9,570 ft. the tunnel had been broken out to the full width of 26 ft. At the time of the valley crossing there were 860 men working in the tunnel.

Meanwhile the work on the southern heading had been going on without interruption, although owing to the granite encountered the advance had been considerably slower, on the average 16½ ft. per twenty-four hours. The heading reached a point at 13,674 ft., where the axis turns 18° 42′ to the right, already in July 1909, and settled down on the northern tangent that eventually would meet the northern heading, provided of course that the surveyors kept their wits. The granite changed to quartz, to porphyry, back to granite, all good solid rock which, however, slowed down the advance due to its abrasive character. In the hard rock a round took two and a half hours to drill, or more than twice the time taken in the loose rock in the northern heading.

To break out one cubic metre of rock required 8 ft. of holes, nine drill steels and not less than 4·34 kg. (9½ lb.) of dynamite. The temperature kept climbing as the thickness of the rock cover kept increasing, from 20° C. it rose to a maximum of 34·2° C. in August 1910 when the heading was 19,800 ft. under the massif. At that time the contractor had 1,340 men and twenty-two machines engaged in advancing and breaking out the southern end of the tunnel. To keep this regiment of men alive required a large ventilation plant, and 2,100 h.p. was needed to drive the compressors and fans. The tunnel was refrigerated in the same manner as Simplon, by spraying the ventilation air with high-pressure water.

By Christmas 1910 the contractor had regained the seven lost months or, otherwise expressed, gained 6,560 ft. over the southern heading. At the end of the year the northern heading stood at 21,871 ft. and the southern at 21,792 ft. The two faces were now only 3,986 ft. from each other and both headings were driven through porphyry.

But February brought a few anxious weeks. On the northern heading the granite suddenly gave way at 23,291 ft. and the miners struck a cave filled with kaolin and a small spring giving off 28° C. water. Here, almost at the very end, the miners were confronted with a situation resembling the pressure zone in Simplon, but the treacherous kaolin proved amenable to traditional forepoling and the 575-ft.-long cave was crossed without incident. The crumbling deposit did not move and by careful manual mining no pressure developed on the timber-lined heading. After this final crisis the heading entered good granite and, since the southern heading was proceeding at its steady rate, a breakthrough was expected at any time, assuming of course that the surveyors had kept the axes accurately aligned.

During the last two weeks the rounds on both headings were coordinated in time. The clocks at both sides were checked with a time signal sent by telephone and the rounds were fired with a seven-minute fuse exactly at 6, 10, 14, 18, 24 and 2 o'clock on both headings. On Thursday 30th March 1911, at 16 o'clock, the remaining partition was calculated to 29 ft. and it was announced that the breakthrough would take place early the following morning.

By 2 o'clock on the morning of 31st March, the two rounds drilled since the announcement had reduced the partition to about 13 ft. An attempt was made to drill a hole through the granitized quartz, but the drill could not be driven more than 6½ ft. The test hole was filled half-way with sand and a round was fired simultaneously on both sides. The partition still stood, although reduced to 2½ ft. in thickness. The probe hole now penetrated the southern heading and contact was for the first time established between the two sides. It was decided that the southern team would retreat and that the final hand-drilling of the short round was to be done by the northern team to a simple pattern grouped around the test hole. The final round was fired at 3.50 o'clock and blew a hole through the partition large enough for the men to crawl through.

After the usual rough masculine scenes of rejoicing, the breakthrough area was immediately widened to conform with the outline of the northern heading. When checking the survey it was found that the two headings had met at 24,115·2 ft. from the northern portal. The deviation of the axis was 10 in. and the error in levels 4 in. The tunnel proved to be 16 in. longer than calculated. The man responsible for this achievement was Professor F. Böschlin at the Technical University of Zürich. He and his team of surveyors had accomplished a masterpiece of surveying under gruesome circumstances that bordered on the impossible. A slight error in setting out the northern 58° curve would have deflected the axis of the long tangent so that the two headings could easily have passed each other.

In spite of the catastrophes at the outset, the Lötschberg tunnel in the end was turned into one of the most admirable tunnelling performances on record. In altogether 1,305 working days 52,478 ft. of pilot tunnel were driven, which produced a daily average of 40·2 ft. as against 35 ft. in the Simplon. The daily advance of the northern heading was 24 ft. and of the southern 16 ft. The maximum number of workers at both ends was 3,100.

At the time of the breakthrough 35,449 ft. had been broken out to full width and 32,846 ft. were lined. The entire tunnel was expanded to full width in March 1912, and on 22nd April at 15 o'clock the last masonry ring was put into place. The Lötschberg tunnel was completed in five and a half years, only five months behind the estimated time.

The infilled valley under the Kander torrent should, it would seem, have given the promoters of other tunnelling ventures food for thought. What would happen, for example, if the miners advancing a tunnel under the English Channel struck an infilled valley, which seems possible? Instead of being flooded by a small, anonymous Alpine torrent they would be confronted with permeable deposits which would carry water from an inexhaustible supply—the entire Atlantic Ocean—under a head of something like 700 ft. But, strange as it may seem, such a possibility was blithely ignored in the century-old debate that by then had raged over the Channel tunnel.

Chapter 17

THE CHANNEL COMEDY

'*Tell the French engineer that if
he succeeds I will give him my
blessings in my personal name and
in the name of all the ladies of
England.*'

QUEEN VICTORIA

ALL grand tunnel schemes have been inspired by a dynamic idea
that in the end has swept aside all obstructions. The dangers, sacrifices and costs have been accepted as being worth the enduring
benefits offered by the subterranean passage. Not so with the tunnel
under the English Channel. Throughout its 160-year history it has
been sea-sickness that has fostered the long succession of schemes for
connecting the two shores with a tunnel or bridge so as to escape
being tossed by the angry waves. Perhaps this is the reason for its
droll history. The Channel has held an irresistible attraction for a
succession of engineering crackpots, and the spell cast has also
affected otherwise sane and respected statesmen and scientists who—
with a few outstanding exceptions—lost their wits once they got
tangled up with a Channel tunnel or bridge scheme. The Channel
tunnel holds the distinction of being the longest *comédie humaine*
ever performed.

The curtain rose in 1802, when the French mining engineer, Albert
Mathieu-Favier, presented a scheme to Napoleon, First Consul of the
French Republic. It involved digging an 18-mile tunnel between

England and France, and to air the long underground passage Mathieu-Favier suggested the building of a picket fence of chimneys sticking up above the water between which ships beating to the wind would have to navigate. On the Varne Bank, to which we shall refer later, he would build an artificial island to enable the horses, and presumably also the passengers in the coaches pulled by them, to come up to snatch a breath of fresh air. James Fox thought it a great idea, '. . . . this is one of the great enterprises we can now undertake together.' Napoleon thought differently.

Not to be outdone, an Englishman produced a better plan the following year. Mr. Mottray thought it would be much easier to level the bottom of the Channel and lay a steel tube on the graded route. Just how the excavations were to be performed under 180 ft. of water, or where the steel was to be procured, were minor matters which did not unduly disturb Mr. Mottray, nor indeed any of his numerous successors.

There is really no need to study the history of the Channel tunnel very closely because everything that follows is a variation of these two themes, occasionally punctuated with a bridge scheme. There were admittedly two brilliant departures from the main trends: in 1855 the French Abbé Angelini combined the two major tunnel ideas into the fruitful suggestion of dropping a prefabricated iron tube from a barge. The tube would by its own weight penetrate through the soft chalk and come to rest 190 ft. below the sea bottom. The other idea was put forward by a Swiss engineer in 1930 and envisaged the building of not one but two parallel jetties across the Channel.

However, the principal actor in the Channel comedy is Thomé de Gamond, the most erudite and gifted man ever bitten by the Channel bug. Seldom has so much formal learning been carried by one man: de Gamond was a doctor of medicine, a doctor of law, a hydrograpic and mining engineer, and an officer of the French Engineering Corps. He was also a wealthy man when, at the age of twenty-six, he became engrossed in the Channel project. When he died in 1886 he had run through all its phases as well as his fortune.

In 1833 de Gamond began his first systematic geological and hydrographical surveys of the Channel. He took numerous soundings and brought up samples from the bottom by the simple method of attaching tallow to the lead. Finally, he turned to diving and, weighted with stones, went down a hundred feet to investigate the bottom. He made two such dives, which he regarded as wholly adequate for his purpose of determining the geology of the bottom.

De Gamond's first scheme was presented in 1834. It envisaged laying a steel tube along the bottom and encasing it in masonry. Two years later he thought it would be more practical to span the Channel with a bridge. To this end he designed four different types of bridge, any one would do. A year later de Gamond had a still better idea: he would build moles extending 5 miles from each shore, the gap between would be traversed by a steam-driven ferry-boat of concrete.

After these early excursions de Gamond settled down to his life's work of thinking up one tunnel scheme after another. But while he brooded over his first subterranean tunnel his rivals were busy publishing their schemes. Dr. Prosper Payerne of Grenoble had invented a diving bell to use in building a 56-ft.-wide causeway along the bottom of the Channel for a distance of 20 miles. Having laid this base, the masons, still enclosed in the doctor's diving bell, would erect a vaulted tunnel 23 ft. high through which an undersea railway between Calais and Dover would be built. This idea did not arouse any interest and Dr. Payerne went back to the practice of medicine in Grenoble.

Of all the amazing schemes put forward while de Gamond was absent from the stage the one proposed by Horeau, another Frenchman, is without a doubt the most charming. He proposed to erect cast-iron turrets at frequent intervals across the Channel, designed in a blend of neo-Gothic and Turkish tent pavilion styles, with heraldic pennants flying in the high wind marking the whereabouts of the air shafts descending to a prefabricated steel tube resting on the bottom.

This scheme was followed in 1869 by one devised by C. E. Young, which envisaged a 25-ft. tube made of ¾-in. cast iron encased in a 1½-ft. envelope of concrete. The interesting feature of this plan was that the concrete tube was to float midway between the bottom and the surface. To prevent the buoyant tube from being carried away by the currents the designer had thoughtfully anchored it to the bottom at short intervals.

Nothing came of these tunnels and the numerous bridge schemes put forth with complete disregard for the fact that the busiest navigational waters in the world would be obstructed by piers, pylons, and towers spaced a few hundred feet apart. At the same time, however, de Gamond kept squandering his family fortune on one scheme after another. In 1856 one of these caught the fancy of Napoleon III and his scientific advisers. It was a circular stone tunnel extending from Cap Griz Nez to Eastwear, between Folkestone and Dover, for a total distance of 21 miles and large enough to hold two railway tracks. An international port—Étoile de Varne—would be built on the Varne Bank where a tremendous oval shaft lined with gently sloping stairs would lead down into the tunnel. The presence of this international port in the middle of the Channel would be marked by a huge gas flame. Just what function this mid-Channel port was to serve was never made clear, but the Emperor became fascinated by the scheme and promised his support. The plan was examined by a commission of French scientists who were strongly in favour of it. Indeed, Michel Chevalier, the French chief of mines and a leading light among the mid-century economists, became as enthusiastic as his imperial master. 'This is work which we must force ourselves to make possible,' he exclaimed, 'a gigantic monument which would stagger people and exercise profound influence on civilization.'

More surprising, in Britain the de Gamond tunnel was backed by the leading engineers: Brunel, Locke and Stephenson were all in favour of it. But, beyond this enthusiastic response by the scientific and technical experts on both sides of the Channel, nothing came of the scheme, principally owing to the deteriorating political relations between the two powers.

Ten years later, in 1866, de Gamond brought forth his most magnificent scheme. It retained the main features of the previous one except in a few respects. For one thing, the approaches to the tunnel on both sides would be taken in open cuttings. But the marvel of the new plan was reserved for the island on the Varne Bank. Here a 1,000-ft. oval shaft descended into the tunnel 150 ft. under the sea. Along the perimeter of this shaft was a gently sloping ramp which brought the tunnel trains to the surface, presumably to allow the passengers to admire the view and sample the invigorating sea air. For some reason now forgotten there were also docks where ships could unload cargoes to the trains and vice versa.

Nobody supported this idea. But de Gamond's last scheme, devised in collaboration with two British engineers, William Low and Brunlees, and presented at the Paris Exhibition in 1867, provoked a response alike from the French and the sceptical British. It caught the interest not only of the Queen but also of the Board of Trade. But this final effort came to nought, partly owing to the Franco-Prussian War, partly to the British interest in a much more practical scheme put forward by the great English engineer John Hawkshaw.

Thomé de Gamond finally gave up. He spent his remaining years in humble circumstances, his daughter supporting him by giving piano lessons. But up to his death in 1876 his fertile mind kept devising one scheme after the other, such as tunnels across the Belts, the Irish Sea, the Sound between Denmark and Sweden, the Straits of Messina, Straits of Gibraltar, the Bosphorus, the Dardanelles, and, more surprisingly, the Straits of Bonifacio between the islands of Corsica and Sardinia. Who knows, perhaps in the future some of the mad dreams of this tunnel visionary may come true.

In the early 'seventies there were two rival tunnel schemes clamouring for attention, both of them British. The one put forward by John Hawkshaw envisaged a double-track tunnel through the Lower Chalk, the second one, promoted by William Low, involved the building of two single-track tubes, also through the Lower Chalk.

At first fortune smiled on the Hawkshaw scheme. In 1872, the English Channel Tunnel Company was formed to promote it. The Gladstone Government encouraged it and in 1875 the French Government authorized the formation of a Channel Tunnel Company, by Michel Chevalier. The company was given a concession to start a tunnel between Calais and Boulogne, and twenty years in which to build it. After completing the tunnel the company was assured of a ninety-nine year operating monopoly.

The French Tunnel Act went into the details of tunnel operation, including the charges to be applied. A live first-class passenger, for example, would pay 50 centimes per kilometre for riding in a glass-enclosed coach, whereas a corpse properly enclosed in a coffin would be charged 1·5 francs per kilometre for the final journey under the Channel.

On the British side a similar enabling Act was passed by Parliament later in the year, whereby the Channel Tunnel Company Ltd. was permitted to acquire land north of Dover to carry out its work. Thus, while tragedies began to haunt the relatively simple Gotthard venture, the two most enlightened governments in Europe gave permission to proceed with a tunnelling scheme which was technically impossible.

Nevertheless, the French company did in actual fact carry out a great deal of valuable preliminary work. Its engineers took 7,700 soundings and collected 3,267 samples of the sea-bed between Cap Griz Nez and South Foreland. With two exceptions they found the strata to be consistent—the depth of water did not exceed 230 ft., the narrowest width of the Channel was 20 miles, the shape of the bottom resembled that of a saucer, the rock was soft, permitting easy excavation, and it was impermeable to water.

The surveys also revealed that the rock, from shore to shore, formed four coherent strata consisting, as reckoned from the top, of white chalk, a rather thick layer of grey chalk, a layer of green sand and, at the bottom, a mixture of clays, the so-called Gault. The strata appeared in this order on both shores and it was hoped that they extended across the Strait in uninterrupted coherence.

According to the Hawkshaw scheme the tunnel descended on a down grade 7 miles in length, entering the impermeable grey chalk at a point north of Sangatte on the French coast. Under the Channel the tunnel had a level grade for a distance of 16 miles followed by a 7-mile ascending grade to St. Margaret's Bay, from which a left-hand curve would lead to a portal where the subterranean railway would connect up with the existing railway tracks of the London, Chatham and Dover and South Eastern Railways.

At Sangatte the French sank a 280-ft. shaft to the bottom of the grey chalk, which was found to be 180 ft. below sea-level at low tide. They also drove a pilot tunnel for a distance of over 2,000 yds. under the Channel and found that water seepage did not exceed one litre per linear metre of gallery (about 1½ pts. per yd. per minute), which was well within the capacity of existing pumping facilities. Later, a second 17·7-ft. circular hoisting shaft was sunk at Sangatte and a steam-driven compressor was installed to provide ventilating air for the pilot tunnel.

While on the southern shore the French were busy as moles, nothing happened on the British side, for the British company had failed to raise even the modest sum required to sink a shaft. Thus ended a promising beginning. The Hawkshaw scheme was dead.

In 1880 the time was ripe to try out the Low scheme which seven years earlier had been adopted by a rival tunnel company. Sir Edward Watkin, chairman of the South Eastern Railway Company, brought new life into the dormant Channel Tunnel Company and succeeded in obtaining £20,000 from the railway for preliminary investigations. An Act of 1881 enabled him to sink two shafts on a site west of Dover, at Abbot's Cliff and Shakespeare Cliff. From the bottom of one shaft a 7-ft. circular tunnel was extended 2,026 yds., while the pilot from the second shaft was advanced 800 yds. before it was abandoned.[1]

On the British side there was a workmanlike approach to the job. The French had advanced their pilots by the conventional method of drilling and blasting, a method ill-suited to the soft chalk since the shooting risked fracturing the rock and producing leaks. The British

[1] The shaft at Abbot's Cliff has been filled in, but some time between 1921 and 1924 a 480-ft. adit was driven towards the Watkin's tunnel and abandoned. This 7-ft. circular tunnel was advanced by an electric machine developed by the Royal Engineers for tunnelling under the German lines during the 1914–18 war. The machine still remains on the site as a heap of rusted scrap-iron. By means of this adit access can be had to the Watkin's tunnel which is in a surprisingly good and dry condition after eighty years. In the chalk can still be read the legend THIS TUNNEL WAS BEGUN IN 1880 WILLIAM SHARP.

engineers introduced a tunnelling machine driven by compressed air which cut a circular tube 7 ft. in diameter while it progressed through the soft chalk. The cutting arm revolved about two turns per minute and produced an advance of 40 ft. in seventeen hours. The cut chalk was removed by an endless chain of buckets and dropped into wagons at the end of the machine. Two men worked the rail-bound machine and, as usual in those days, were expected to live in the exhausted air.

With work finally proceeding at both ends, French speculators went wild; founders' shares in the tunnel company skyrocketed from 5,000 to 130,000 francs. On the British side Sir Edward was busy holding luncheons in the pilot tunnel to promote the raising of the £270,000 needed to proceed with the tunnel. Then, in 1882, the Board of Trade stopped all work on the British side. The official reason was that the Government wanted a scientific inquiry conducted into the feasibility of the project. Actually, the Gladstone Government bent to a protest storm, long brewing, which now gained in violence as the work was getting under way. A national panic, fanned by hysteria, swept the country. The Queen had changed her mind and now thought the Channel tunnel highly objectionable. Alfred Tennyson, Lord Leighton, Robert Browning, T. H. Huxley, Herbert Spencer and a host of lesser lights saw nothing but evil in the scheme and thought that the tunnel would be an open road for the invader into England.

The military attack against the tunnel was led by General Sir Garnet Wolseley, seconded by the Commander-in-Chief His Royal Highness George, Duke of Cambridge. From all accounts the gallant gentlemen had no faith whatever in the troops under their command. Gone for ever, apparently, were the sturdy virtues of the British infantry; it could no longer be entrusted with the defence of a front less than 10 yds. wide! Between nightfall and dawn the French would be able to pour an army of 20,000 through the tunnel. To seize the English end, with the telegraph wires, all the mechanical contrivances designed for the destruction of the tunnel, together with forts and batteries, was assumed to be a small military operation, requiring so little preparation that it would attract no attention whatever. Nobody, it seems, looked into the logistics of transporting 20,000 men, with arms and provisions, through the tunnel in a single night.

With sinking hearts the French promoters watched the fantastic debate raging on the opposite shore. As a last desperate attempt to save the tunnel scheme they offered to bring out the tunnel railway from the security of the Sangatte cliff and run it in the open on a looped viaduct built in the sea so as to provide an easy target for the Royal Navy. After all, if the British Army professed itself incapable of defending a 10-yd. front on its home shore, surely Her Majesty's Navy could be relied on to blast the viaduct into rubble.

The offer did not save the tunnel. On 12th May 1882 the technical commission appointed by the Board of Trade reported that it would be dangerous to rely on any measures for rendering the tunnel useless. A year later, when the rival British tunnel companies renewed their Bills for concessions, a Select Committee subjected a panel of witnesses to 5,396 questions, after which it recommended the Government to refuse the Bills.

That was the end of the Low scheme. Work ceased at Sangatte on 18th March 1883, and the shafts and galleries were abandoned.

Looking at this amazing British performance from the vantage point afforded by eighty years of time, there is not the slightest doubt but that the action to stop the tunnel venture was right, although the reasons for doing so were wrong. It would have been impossible to excavate the tunnel with the facilities available in the early 'eighties. The geological survey was purely superficial and the enterprise would have ended in catastrophe. It would not have been possible to ventilate the tunnel while advancing the headings during the construction or after its completion.[2] But that is a small matter: the miners would inevitably have struck an infilled valley, with even more tragic results than in the Lötschberg tunnel a quarter of a century later.

Although the Channel tunnel sank into a twilight sleep lasting until 1929, at least officially, the fascination of bridging the Channel did not pale, and fertile engineering minds kept producing one scheme after the other. A president of the Institution of Civil Engineers suggested closing the strait by a pontoon bridge. Another president of that august body proposed sinking a 4-in. cast-iron tube 13 ft. in diameter and prefabricated in 10-ft. lengths. The sections were to be joined by men working inside an 80-ft. shield pushed forward by hydraulic jacks. An American contribution envisaged building prefabricated 18-ft. cast-iron tubes encased in masonry in a drydock, joining them together and then towing 20 miles of assembled sections across the Channel and dropping the long tube to the bottom.

There was also an early suggestion of a train ferry, 'a huge railway station travelling at high speed between the English and French coasts'. This floating railway station was to be 450 ft. long, 57 ft. in beam and 12 ft. in draught. Engines were to drive it at 20 knots. The

---

[2] To prevent the train passengers from suffocating from smoke the promoters planned to use compressed-air locomotives, the air being carried by tank cars in the rear of the locomotive. The exhausted air was to be relied on to ventilate the tunnel.

designer had thought of getting the trains on and off the ferry at high and low tides by means of lifting the ramps with hydraulic jacks. The strange ship and the hydraulic ramps at both shores were hailed as eminently practical by contemporary engineering opinion.

Then there was another bridge scheme involving a structure 23½ miles long supported on fifty-five piers sunk into the sea-bed. The French Ministry of Marine, however, did not approve of it.

In 1906 Sir Francis Fox, the great tunnelling expert, fell under the Channel spell. Together with Sartiaux, the chief engineer of Chemin de Fer du Nord, he looked into the old material and found it all impracticable. The new scheme presented by these two eminent engineers indubitably had its points. The route followed was the old Hawkshaw one, but otherwise their scheme had a number of novel features. There would be two 20-ft. tubes 50 ft. apart and connected by cross-galleries. The railway would be electrified, whereby the gradient could be increased to 1·5:100 and the curves made tighter. The ventilation problem would also be simplified. A separate gallery would drain the tunnel to the north. The scheme was worked out in admirable detail, but even such a capable engineer as Sir Francis did not escape the fantastic spell cast by the Channel. Since he was convinced that the grey chalk dipped and rose under the Channel and he regarded it as essential to keep the structure encased in this impermeable mantle, the Fox-Sartiaux tunnel would have been a veritable switchback. Passengers riding over this pitching and rising grade would experience the same feeling as when on a ship following an ocean swell. The cost of building the tunnel was estimated at £16 million. *thereby bringing back seasickness*

An enabling Bill was introduced in 1906 but ran up against the classical military arguments. This time the military spokesmen, while admitting the fire-power of modern rifles, nevertheless thought it impossible to deploy a thousand troops in a busy railway terminal 'with movement to and fro of trains'. The commander of Dover, speaking from his own experience, had 'found it impossible to insure a night when he could safely turn out the garrison in such a way as to protect the town ... frailty of human vigilance would prevent blowing up or flooding the tunnel'.[3] It was indeed an appealing age, and it is a pity that it has vanished for ever. At any rate, the Bill was withdrawn and Sir Francis's reputation as an engineer remains intact.

In 1929, owing to the enthusiasm of a Member of Parliament by the name of Sir William Bull, the Channel tunnel was brought to

---

[3] Channel Committee reports.

life again. A Committee was appointed to investigate the economic aspects of the tunnel, which had never been done before, but since it found both the geological and engineering data scanty and out of date it decided to make a thorough inquiry into the whole issue. The 1930 Committee met twenty-five times and considered all means of joining the British Isles and the Continent by tunnel, bridge or ferry. It employed a firm of consulting engineers to inquire into the technical aspects of the numerous schemes put forward. No scheme was too wild for scrutiny and a polite commentary. 'We have felt it our duty to consider on its own merit any scheme submitted to us.' The Committee lived up to its promise and did an admirable job in the best traditions of Parliament. Consider, for example, what the members had to deal with:

A Swiss engineer proposed, evidently in earnest, to build a double jetty or causeway extending across the strait from Deal to Calais. The two parallel structures would enclose a cross-channel canal that would join the British canal system with the canals on the Continent. On top of each causeway would run a double-track railway and a two-lane motor road. At each end there would be tall bridges permitting the largest ocean vessels to pass. The cost came to £80 million.

This scheme of building a barge canal across the Channel still occupies the pinnacle of engineering fantasy, and the Committee turned it down with the forbearing comment that it would become an obstacle to navigation.

The other suggestions pale in the presence of this great idea. There was a plan for building a bridge 22 miles long, carrying two railway tracks and a four-lane motor-road. For some reason best known to the promoter there was to be a mid-channel railway station. At each end would be 2,000-ft. spans with clearance of 200 ft. This bridge would cost £75 million. The Committee thought it would become a navigational hazard. An Italian engineer had a better project: he suggested joining short sections of steel tube encased in concrete by flexible joints on the surface, and gently dropping the jointed tube to the bottom in the manner of a submarine cable. The scheme required only two ventilation towers rising above the surface. The best aspect of the whole idea was its cost, only £2 million. The Committee pronounced it slightly impracticable.

When inquiring into the tunnel traffic the Committee had to listen to some strange arguments. The Tunnel Company thought that by 1936, 1,890,500 passengers would use the tunnel, 'plus 1,687,000 foreigners', making a total of 3,577,500. The Southern Railway knew the traffic load to the last passenger: by 1936 the exact number of people using the tunnel would be 1,524,943. The French, however, went about it in a more elegant fashion. When studying the traffic figures back to 1894, the forecasters had discovered what amounted to a natural law of traffic growth which had enabled them to construct a logarithmic curve with a 4 per cent gradient. According to French mathematics, 2,200,000 persons would use the tunnel by 1940. Having duly contemplated these three estimates the Committee ordered an independent forecast which gave the result that about 2,357,000 passengers could be expected to use the tunnel by 1938.

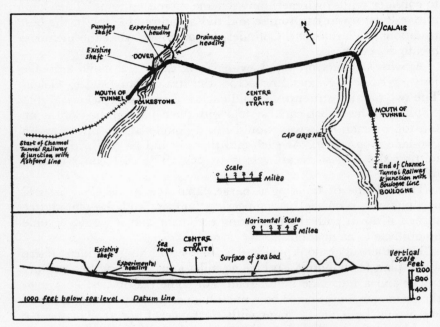

Fig 132. Plan and section (simplified) of the Channel Tunnel scheme developed by the Channel Tunnel Company and accepted by the 1930 Parliamentary Tunnel Committee. Subsequent plans for tunnelling the English Channel conform in more or less detail to this basic scheme.

As for freight, the Committee accepted the view that the tonnage would be about 50 per cent more than the freight carried by the short sea-routes across the Channel.

From the many tunnel schemes presented the Committee finally settled on that of the Channel Tunnel Company, embodying two 18½-ft. tubes with a joint 7-ft. drainage tunnel between the rail tunnels. The French company proposed to drive a small pilot tunnel to explore the ground and expressed its willingness to invest 10 million francs for exploratory work, with the aim of developing excavation technique and trying out an idea of pumping out the chalk slurry into the Channel water. Driving the pilot tunnel would require two and a half years and cost £5 million, whereas the twin traffic tunnel would take four years and cost £25 million.

The Committee accepted the view of the consultant geologists that the grey chalk continues without a break from shore to shore, but that nevertheless there was a chance of encountering fissures or perhaps even infilled valleys. The engineers consulted thought that small fissures could be coped with, either by grouting or freezing. Infilled valleys, however, presented a more serious challenge since the gallery would be flooded with water under a pressure of 150 p.s.i. But even then it might be possible to push through by means of a closed shield flushing away the mud and silt in front of the shield by using powerful jets. The tunnels would be lined with cast-iron segmented rings of which about 500,000 tons would be needed. Excavation of the tunnel would be performed by rotary cutters similar to those employed in the London clay.

Finally the Committee estimated that 250 men would be required for five years to drive the pilot tunnel and 1,500 men for three years on the traffic tubes. It concluded: 'The tunnel could be built by private enterprise at a cost that would permit of the traffic through it being conveyed at rates not higher than those at the present in force on the short cross-channel routes. Its construction, by creating new traffic and thus increasing trade, would be of economic advantage to this country.'

The Ramsay MacDonald Government turned down the report. A White Paper subsequently issued declared (1) that the tunnel would be no relief to unemployment, (2) more Englishmen would travel to the Continent than foreigners to England, and (3) the defence measures required would cost £2 million.

The Channel tunnel had run into another dead end. In 1936, a non-tidal train ferry dock was completed at Dover at a cost of only £1 million and the British and French railway systems were joined for the first time in a hundred years. It did not eliminate the *mal de mer*, but the ferry service nevertheless constitutes a substitute for the tunnel.

The Present Position

With the exception of the 1930 Committee report, which can be accepted as a sober, competent and intelligent summary of all the factors bearing on the Channel tunnel, all or nearly all of the previous schemes and the reactions to them possess amusing or frustrating overtones, depending upon how one regards them. The tunnel belonged to the realm of nineteenth-century science fiction that excited the fanatics and presented an irresistible temptation to the lunatic fringe of the engineering profession, but reputable engineers and level-headed politicians also came under its spell.

The post-war phase of the history of the Channel tunnel has not been without its ludicrous features. A few years after the war a Parliamentary study group brought the 1930 scheme up to date, but then dropped the whole idea when it found that the cost had grown to £65·5 million. To raise this vast sum by private finance in the depressed British post-war economy was not deemed possible.

In the early 'fifties a French visionary attracted interest by his scheme which involved the building of a gigantic elliptical tunnel holding a double-track railway in the lower half and a four-lane road in the upper, capable of swallowing 12,000 motor vehicles per day. This scheme was encouraged by NATO, but sober-minded engineers shuddered at the thought of what would happen if the lanes were blocked by a car wreck piling up a 15-mile-long line of cars behind it, all of them spewing carbon monoxide. The first post-war flurry subsided.

But not for long. Two French sisters married to American businessmen were seasick crossing the Channel and, upon returning to New York, suggested jokingly to their husbands that they ought to do something about a Channel tunnel because the surface crossing was so dreadful. One of the men actually did. He discussed the idea with a friend who was commissioned to proceed to Europe to look into the matter.

As was to be expected, events took a droll turn. After seeing the Managing Director of the British Channel Tunnel Company, which had been kept alive in spite of its many frustrations and failures, the investigator arriving in Paris to discuss the matter with the French Tunnel Company went, under a misapprehension, to see the Director of the Suez Canal Company. The conversation between the American emissary and the Canal Director took place at a critical time. The latter was still suffering from the insult of having had his company's valuable asset seized by President Nasser, with small hope of getting adequate compensation. The Suez concession had been due to lapse in 1968 and the company had considered the possibility of a Channel tunnel as a suitable successor to its immensely profitable Canal business. The precipitate action of Nasser had brought the issue to a head.

It was indeed an awkward situation. On the one hand, complex and difficult negotiations for compensation from the Egyptian Government were pending, and it would be impolitic to proceed with plans for another major investment before they were concluded. On the other hand, here was a group of Americans who seemed to mean business and were likely to snatch the Channel tunnel from under his nose. The Canal Director kept silent and let the American talk, but when on 3rd March 1957 it was announced that an American company called Technical Studies, Inc. had been formed and backed by two prominent New York banks and, moreover, joined with the ancient British Channel Tunnel Company, Ltd., with the intent of making a comprehensive survey of the old issue, he could not keep silent any longer. On 26th April the Suez Canal Company announced its intention of financing a geological survey of the Channel as a preliminary to building a tunnel.

Now began a few months of quiet wrangling between the four interests, out of which emerged, on 26th July 1957, 'The Channel Tunnel Study Group' wherein the two old British and French tunnel companies each retained 30 per cent, the Suez Company another 30 per cent, while Technical Studies Inc. was elbowed out and left with a mere 10 per cent. But the Americans did not allow themselves to be put off in this manner. After further discussion the original protocol was amended so that each one of the four parties obtained a 25 per cent share in the venture.

The surveys, financed by £270,000 contributed by the four partners, began in the autumn of 1957, but long before that the shares of the old Channel Company had taken a new lease of life. Whereas they had previously been available at 6d., in April that year they rose to 10s. and kept rising under the impact of the heady news. On 20th May the shares were quoted at 26s. 9d., or 6s. 9d. more than when originally issued in 1876. They reached a high of 50s. in 1959, since when they have fluctuated between 19s. and 30s. as the news from the Study Group has kept fanning or damping the enthusiasm. What were the realities behind the boom?

There was, first of all, the economic study carried out by *The Economist Intelligence Unit*, and published in March 1960. Assuming a peak capacity of twelve trains per hour for eighteen hours per day, traffic through the tunnel would be 216 trains per day. With 700 passengers per train and 300 vehicles carried piggy-back, the peak-hour capacity would be 8,400 passengers and 300 motor-cars. A different combination of six vehicle trains and six passenger trains would put the capacity at 1,800 piggy-back vehicles and 4,200 passengers.

In 1957, 5·75 million passengers crossed the Channel, 3·2 million travelled by sea and 2·55 million by air. The charge for the Dover–Calais ferry was £1 10s., and the total charge for a second-class ticket London–Paris was £4 13s. The cheapest air ticket between the two cities was £5 14s., including the coach services to and from the airports. The charge for using the tunnel has been calculated at 32s. per passenger, i.e. slightly more than the ferry charge.

The economic study concluded that it would be reasonable to assume that 68 per cent of the total surface passenger traffic would be diverted to the tunnel, whereas for a number of reasons only 10 per cent of the air passengers could be induced to use the subterranean crossing. It was also estimated that the sea traffic would expand by 42 per cent from 1957 to 1967; if a tunnel existed by then, the traffic through it would increase by 3·6 per cent per year, declining to 2·1 per cent after 1980.

To sum up, the tunnel traffic was put at 3·2 million passengers in 1965, rising to about 5 million in 1985. At an assumed fare of 32s. the revenue from passenger traffic would be £5·2 million in 1965, rising to £8·2 million in 1985. To this should be added the revenue from motor vehicles carried piggy-back through the tunnel. The total number of vehicles carried across the Channel in 1957 was put at 285,000, of which 80 per cent went by sea. Of the so-called 'accompanied' vehicles, 166,000 were carried by the sea-routes which would be put out of business by the tunnel. It was estimated that 71 per cent of the accompanied vehicles, each one carrying on the average three passengers, would be diverted to the tunnel by 1965 at a charge of £7 16s. as against the present £10 16s. on the Dover–Boulogne ferry. The number of vehicles carried through the tunnel was expected to grow from 776,000 in 1965 to 1·2 million in 1985, and the revenue from £5·3 to £9·4 million.

Then there was the goods traffic. The freight susceptible to diversion through the tunnel was put at 1·6 million tons in 1960, with an average annual increase of 24,000 tons. The expected revenue from goods was £2·6 million in 1965, rising to £3·4 million in 1985. If Britain joined the European Economic Community the revenue would rise to £6·5 million by 1985. If the revenues expected from the three main sources were added up, the total would be about £13 million in 1965 rising to £21 million in 1985.

There is no point in considering the economics of a highway tunnel. Apart from the ugly potentialities of exposing a million amateur drivers to the psychological strain of driving through a 26-mile-long underwater tunnel, the revenue would be 35 per cent less than from a double-track railway tunnel. Moreover, such a tunnel would cost a great deal more to build. Whereas a railway tunnel is estimated at £112 million, a highway tunnel would cost £129 or £153 million, depending on the scheme chosen.

A Channel tunnel, therefore, could obviously be made to pay. There still remained the question of whether it could be built.

A number of first-rate technical surveys carried out by the Study Group went a long way towards providing an answer to this basic question. By implication they revealed that at no time in the past could any one of even the more sober schemes put forward have been carried out. The geology of the tunnel route is far too complex for that.

A short geological excursion will explain the difficulties involved. The Straits of Dover were formed when the sea broke through the Isthmus some 6,000 years ago, and its bed consists of rock formed in the Jurassic and Cretaceous Ages. The strata dip towards the north-east, but they are certainly not as regular and homogeneous as de Gamond and his successors assumed from superficial soundings and investigations of mainland strata. The White Cliffs of Dover are Cretaceous, at Cap Griz Nez the rock is Jurassic, a word that makes the skin of experienced tunnellers creep. Under the Straits the rocks are mixed and, as amply brought out in previous chapters, any mixture of rock spells danger. Also at one time during the Jurassic Era a tributary of the Old Rhine flowed through the Straits and deposited there its burden of erosion debris, subsequently concealed by later Cretaceous deposits.

For this and other less important reasons the shortest route, namely Cap Griz Nez to Dover or Folkestone via the Varne Bank, on which so much mental effort had been expended in the past, was ruled out. The route abounds with faults and fissures, and at least one of these, just outside Cap Griz Nez, would have proved disastrous.

The Dover–Sangatte route, as proposed by the 1930 Committee, appeared to be the soundest of all alternatives. Here the Lower Chalk, laid down in Cretaceous times, appears to extend as an un-broken bed with a thickness varying from 262 ft. on the Kentish coast to 197 ft. on the Artois shore. Although soft the rock is reason-ably impervious to water, and from geological investigations it seems to contain no serious fissures. Nevertheless, the team of distinguished geologists retained by the Study Group, although agreed on the continuity of the rock, cautioned about the possibility of an occa-sional fissure or indeed infilled valley.

Why, one may ask, should prominent geologists hedge on such important points? The answer is simple: as any practical tunneller knows from his own experience, a geological forecast may be

99·9 per cent or more correct, but the remaining 0·1 per cent can spell disaster for a tunnelling venture. One never knows what may be encountered until the rock is opened up. For this reason the 1930 Committee recommended a pilot tunnel as an essential preliminary to advancing the traffic tubes. At that time the conventional method of obtaining core samples by diamond drilling was standard practice in both tunnelling and prospecting on land, but to carry out such investigations through 200 ft. of water from a heaving barge was beyond contemporary drilling techniques.

Such deep-water drilling has since then been developed for use in offshore prospecting for oil, and although costly no longer presents any particular difficulties. The trouble is that to be of any use the bore-holes should be placed so closely that the method becomes prohibitively expensive. As amply proved in Simplon and in numerous other tunnels, an interval of only 100 ft. can conceal serious trouble.

The geological consultants rightly dismissed a continuous series of borings as impractical, although a number of shore drillings were carried out to depths varying from 420 to 814 ft., and eight holes were sunk in the Channel beds at certain points to check on indications obtained by other means. For a continuous profile modern geophysical methods were applied instead. In 1958 the bottom was surveyed by the Sonar method, but since this reflective method only reaches at the most 100 ft. into the bed, the survey was repeated the following year using a newly developed instrument whereby a 12,000-volt spark is discharged in water. The 'sparker method' makes possible a penetration of 1,500 ft. into the sea-bed. The profile obtained by these methods showed a number of distortions, and eight holes were sunk into the bed for closer investigation. Microfossil studies were also carried out on the rock samples gathered from the beds. This combined attack revealed, *inter alia*, that the boundary between the Lower and Middle Chalk was not quite what the geologists had deduced, and led to a change in the tunnel route.

It appears, then, from all accounts that the level section of the subaqueous tunnel could be driven through an uninterrupted bed of impervious chalk, whereas the gradient sections sloping for 7 miles on the English side and 3 miles on the French would of course pass through less homogeneous beds where faults and fissures can be expected.

On the basis of the geophysical explorations, the consultant engineers proposed to drive two rail tunnels with a diameter of 21 ft. 4 in., joined by four cross-galleries. Between the tubes and slightly below them would be a service tunnel 10 ft. 10 in. in diameter which would be advanced ahead of the tubes. While advancing the service tunnel the ground ahead would be probed by horizontal as well as vertical long-hole drilling. Any fissures encountered would be grouted; any infilled valleys would be crossed using a closed shield, employing compressed air if needed.

The circular tubes would be excavated by a rotary boring machine similar to the ones used in the London clay, advancing at a rate of 80 ft. per day. The soft chalk would be crushed, mixed with water to a slurry which would be pumped through a pipeline extending to the portal shafts, or pumped into the sea by a method originally suggested by the French engineer Fougerolle in 1919, assuming that a suitable foolproof valving system could be developed.

The invert of the tunnels would be lined with precast concrete, whereas the rest of the lining would be cast *in situ*, using collapsible shutters. A 15-in. lining was proposed for the traffic tubes and a 6-in. one for the service tunnel. Ventilation of the headings during the advance, and subsequently with the tunnel in service, presents no particular difficulties with a rail tunnel. For one thing, the trains would serve as pistons pushing the air ahead; the vacuum created in the rear would immediately be filled by air flowing through the cross-galleries.

The tunnel would have a total length of 33 miles, of which the subterranean part would be 23 miles and the approaches 10 miles. The submarine part would reach a summit 125 ft. below the bottom at a point between mid-channel and the French shore, from which the tunnel would slope towards both shores for gravity drainage. At the points of juncture with the approaches, drainage galleries would carry off the seepage. The time of construction was estimated at five years and the cost put at £112 million as previously stated.

From published accounts, then, it appears as if the Channel tunnel at long last has emerged as a serious engineering proposition. As a long-term financial venture the scheme also has its merits. Considering an annual maintenance cost of £1·5 million on the tunnel and railway plant, and a further million for administration and other expenses, the return on the investment would be attractive.

Nevertheless, several years after having spent £270,000 on investigations proving that a Channel tunnel can indeed be constructed and made into a profitable business, at the time of writing no attempt has actually been made to go ahead with the scheme. What are the reasons for this delay?

For one thing, and that is no doubt the main reason, it seems quite obvious that British opinion is not wholeheartedly in favour of any Channel tunnel. The psychological climate does not appear to have changed appreciably since 1936 when Sir Winston Churchill, always in favour of a tunnel, wrote: 'There are few projects against which there exists a deeper and more enduring prejudice than the construction of a railway tunnel between Dover and Calais. Again and again it has been brought forward under powerful and influential sponsorship. Again and again it has been prevented.' Judging from the response of influential newspapers to the new plans it does not appear that the ancient prejudice has been laid.

Chapter 18

GEOGRAPHICAL SURGERY

'Man knoweth not the price thereof.'

THE atom bomb that scourged Hiroshima on the morning of 6th August 1945 served at least one good purpose. With its loud explosion it sounded the birth of a new age in a manner not to be mistaken. Future generations, if there be any, will not be burdened with generalities such as the Iron Age, Middle Ages and similar abstract divisions of history, invented for the convenience of historians. Here one is confronted with a sharp line dividing the past from the future.

This date, within a year or so, also divides old-time rock tunnelling from industrialized rock excavation which provides the only means so far discovered of surviving a nuclear war, since it enables rock shelters to be built rapidly and economically. This meeting in time is purely coincidental. Geographically also, the two developments are far apart, technically they are not. Both draw their nourishment from western science and western ruthlessness. The common force that steered the bomb to Hiroshima and to the construction of rock shelters in distant Sweden is war, offensive war and defensive war.

By the time the Second World War ended in 1945, Swedish military authorities had concluded what was at that time the largest programme of underground construction ever undertaken within the course of five years. Fortifications, command posts, stores, entire armament factories, not to mention air-raid shelters, had been placed underground, in caverns blasted out in solid granite. In this large-scale underground construction a new generation of tunnellers was trained, while Swedish engineers lost their respect for hard rock. Whereas before the war a tunnel in hard rock was a time-consuming and costly venture only resorted to for lack of other alternatives and hence used at such long intervals that no technical codex could evolve, now engineers, foremen and miners, in large numbers, became permanently occupied in underground construction.

The art of tunnelling that had developed during the previous century was largely forgotten. Upon the completion of the second Simplon tunnel and some others in the 1920's, a professor in Zürich wrote a book simply in order to preserve for future generations of engineers the technical know-how acquired in driving the long Alpine tunnels. The age of railway tunnelling was gone, and the author saw no further need for long tunnels for many years to come. It is highly probable that the acccumulation of technical data contained in this excellent book was not absorbed by anybody but his students, because copies in technical libraries have obviously never been opened since they were catalogued. There was no longer a need for such information.

Although a great deal of military work had to be improvised, both for lack of mature methods as well as suitable equipment, the very fact that it provided continuity enabled the experiences gained on one underground development to be rapidly adapted and improved on the next. The tunnel areas attacked became larger. Following what were in fact American precepts, the rock was attacked 'full face', that is to say a section 500 sq. ft. or more was drilled up by numerous miners working on multi-deck drilling platforms and then blasted out with one round. To get rid of the fragmented rock, electric excavators were employed, since the areas were large enough to accommodate such machines. A new type of light rock-drilling machine provided with airleg feed, subsequently known as a jackleg and in its effective version developed by Atlas Diesel, was also being used in increasing numbers. When this military work got under way, blasting was still a job that fell within the province of the shift boss. From long experience he decided how a round was to be drilled and charged, utilizing to advantage faults in the face. Depending on the character of the rock facing him he decided how it was to be attacked, and each round was accommodated to the appearance of the face. In this manner the economics of the operation came to depend to a large extent on the individual know-how of the boss.

This traditional system came to an end during the early 1940's. The large-scale underground developments, military and civil, inspired systematic investigations of the numerous technical and economic factors involved in rock blasting, such as the resistance of rock to blasting, size and length of drill holes, charging, burden, and numerous other details. New drilling patterns were developed and the traditional ones improved upon. The entire working cycle was analysed to the last detail with the aim of obtaining rhythmic advance without time-wasting interruptions.

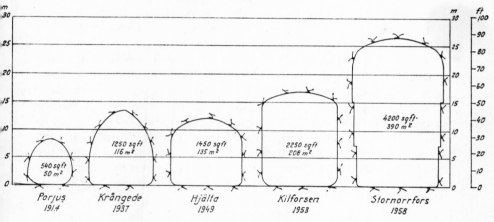

Fig 133. Development of Swedish power tunnels.

Peculiar as it may seem at first glance, this type of technical analysis had never been previously undertaken in the field of rock blasting, although it had long ago become a vital necessity in other fields of production. Simply as a result of these systematic studies, undertaken in part to keep contractors in check, rock excavation was lifted to a higher technical plane without the need for any dramatic improvements in equipment. But these early rationalization studies also fertilized the formerly barren ground permitting it to absorb research and technical advances in other fields, in geology, explosives, mechanized transport, metallurgy, and so on. These things were not new, but previously they had been too sophisticated to be applied to the rough business of rock excavation.

These developments were crowned in 1945 with the successful accommodation of tungsten carbides to rock drilling, as briefly discussed in Chapter 14.

Other technical innovations followed. Milli-second blasting permitted a full-face tunnel area of 1,600 sq. ft. or more to be fragmented in one dull thud without shakes or throws. The old primitive drilling platforms turned into large, hydraulically operated drill jumbos equipped with numerous services to facilitate the work of drilling and charging. They were in fact the tunnelling machines dreamed of by inventors a century before, although perhaps not exactly what they had in mind. Instead of the old-time timbering and concrete reinforcements of poor rock, weak tunnel roofs became secured by rock bolting. Since there was no longer any time-consuming effort involved in drilling, it was an easy matter to drill through blocky rock into sound rock beyond and anchor it by steel rods inserted into the holes and either expanded or grouted in place. In this manner any hazardous tunnel roof can be secured like a beamed structure.

Previously, throughout the long history of underground work, the broken rock was hoisted to the surface through shafts of different depths sunk to tunnel grade. Only the long Alpine tunnels were driven without shafts, simply because no shafts could be sunk. Now it became customary to drive adits, sloping haulage-ways with a gradient of 1:7 at the midpoints of long tunnels, from which the advance could proceed in both directions. These tunnel ramps are now made wide and tall enough to allow two 20-ton diesel trucks to meet, and permit transport of 170,000-h.p. turbine wheels and similar bulky equipment.

Adits as well as tunnels are well lit; sometimes they are provided with traffic lights. Since the fleet of heavy diesel trucks trails exhaust which, with the daily tonnages of exploded dynamite charges, raises the carbon monoxide level to lethal heights, the ventilation of tunnels has become of major concern; the amount of fresh air supplied by the ventilation plant keeps the concentration of carbon monoxide to less than 0·1:1,000 at all points of the tunnel. The air supplied is also heated or refrigerated if conditions warrant it. A well-managed underground working has better air than many factories and offices above ground.

New Hazards and Rewards

Underground work has been made safer also in other respects, as a result both of legislation and of the employers' own concern with the welfare of their high-production labour. A tunneller now works in a safety uniform that has become more or less standard in all countries: a hard hat protects his head against rock falls, steel-reinforced rubber boots save his feet and toes from being crushed, thick rubber overalls keep him warm and dry, rubber gloves shield his hands, and ear-plugs cut out the damaging frequencies of the ear-splitting noise emitted by a battery of pneumatic machines. However, despite all precautions accidents still occur, and it is seldom that a major underground development can be carried out without loss of life. The gains made in safety are cancelled by the speeding up of the working cycle. Men die from many causes: from being crushed by falling rock, pierced by drill steel shot with lethal force by high-pressure water, from electrocution, from being scared to death. The massacres that reach the papers derive mostly from premature igni-tion of rounds. Electrical ignition of the blasting caps is still a treacherous business that is not fully mastered. The caps commonly used require only 0·3 amperes to detonate, and stray currents of this strength are difficult to guard against on a highly electrified under-ground development, indeed in any electrified community.

Nobody knows how many miners have been blown to bits owing to accidental ignition of charges produced by a stroke of lightning in the vicinity. The current induced in the ground by a passing thunder-head will also set off an electric blasting cap. For this reason, it is now common practice to organize a meteorological service on the site. Its principal duty is to keep track of all thunder clouds in the vicinity. If a cloud comes closer than four miles to the site all charg-ing work stops underground. By such means as these many blasting accidents are prevented. But new causes of premature blasts appear as fast as they can be detected and prevented. Radio transmitters emit energy that can and in fact has brought about premature ignition of charges in underground workings some distance away. Electrical welding machines used in the tunnel also serve as radio transmitters capable of setting off a round. The electric lighting on the drill jumbo, if not heavily insulated, will also prove lethal, and so will electrical excavators, loaders and other machines. In recent years the awareness of the hazards created by induced and stray currents has brought about a technical retrogression in blasting. The con-venient but sensitive blasting caps are being superseded by caps that require five amperes to ignite. But such caps need heavy and cumber-some blasting machines working at 2,500 volts, which of course is a decided disadvantage to men accustomed to light equipment.

Alongside these rapid technical developments, sometimes pushing them along, have come just as revolutionary improvements in wages. As the rapidly expanding post-war economy kept soaking up labour above ground, it became increasingly difficult to get men to work underground. Wages rose, by 100 per cent from 1935 to 1945, by another 100 per cent during the following four years, by another 100 per cent during the next three years, and so on. By 1957, tunnel miners were earning five times more than they did before the war. Their earnings have been rising since; in the early 1960's Swedish tunnellers make about £2 an hour and have fallen victim to the stress diseases accompanying high income.

Gone, too, are the cheap and crude construction camps. The better camps are laid out like tourist hotels in the wilderness, the best ones resembling luxury motels in their appointments. In isolated areas, the amenities of camp life stand in dramatic contrast to those prevailing in the neighbouring communities and dwellings. A modern tunnelling man usually lives better in camp than at home.

Gone also are the mean attitudes, the crude exploitation of labour. The men get paid for what they do. It is up to management to provide suitable machines and improve upon methods; the gangs put them to work. The job of the site engineers is to keep records and see that the established working cycle is followed. On a well-administered development, the boss steers the work with charts and statistics. He has no more reason to enter the workings than a managing director of a motor company has to hang around an assembly line.

There have also been profound changes in other ways. Formerly, as shown in the history of the building of Porjus, a site engineer was content to hire excavation skills. The gangs hired were in actual fact sub-contractors without capital and therefore had to be supplied with tools for which they were charged. The men were supposed to know their work when they arrived at camp; an untrained man in a gang was taught the tricks of the trade by his mates if they liked him well enough to let him stay with them. The engineers knew little except what they picked up by watching the work being performed. That is not quite so any more. Owing to rapid technical developments, it has become necessary to train and keep training men, as well as engineers. Courses are going on all the time, informing and training on all levels. Pilot studies for the purpose of evaluating new equipment and methods are conducted elsewhere, in test mines and experimental workings, before being introduced on the sites. To prevent drilling from becoming the monopoly of a few experts who could drive their earnings to any height, it has become customary to instruct locally employed men in drilling and blasting before starting up a new underground development.

In very recent years, the training has become directed to other ends than imparting information and skills. Not unexpectedly, it has been discovered that after fifteen years of good living, social welfare, higher school-leaving age, motorism, etc., teenage boys no longer possess the physical robustness still required in underground work. At the mining school in Kiruna it has been found necessary to build up the physical condition of mining apprentices unaccustomed to hard work by various means, including a game known as 'miners' rugby'. In other words, the crude law of supply and demand has brought about a revolution in outlook during the last fifteen years.

The men labouring underground, just by becoming fewer, have gained economic status and human dignity that could not have been obtained in any other way. Their earnings, as previously noted, have increased by leaps and bounds, considerably faster than the cost-of-living index. But their productivity has increased at an even faster rate, so that the cost of tunnelling has declined by 30 per cent or more in terms of 1935 tunnelling costs. Nevertheless, by becoming members of the surtax-paying class, the miners have put themelves in danger of becoming redundant. All technical efforts are being directed towards eliminating as many of them as possible.

Not surprisingly, this development has gone further in Scandinavia than elsewhere. In Norway, for example, a 2-mile tunnel, 540 sq. ft. in area, was being driven by one foreman and seven miners per shift, plus two men in the repair shop, or a total labour force of thirty-six men, including ancillaries. Another Norwegian power-tunnel 10 miles long and 160 sq. ft. in area was driven by thirty men. The advance in these two tunnels was 118 and 197 ft. respectively per six-day week. In these Norwegian tunnels the time required to blast and remove one cubic metre of rock is 0·62 man-hours.

This brief account of the post-war developments that in the course of ten years have turned tunnelling into a rationalized industry applies mainly to Sweden. From this source the equipment and methods have spread throughout Europe and been applied with due consideration to local conditions. Subsequently, there has been a cross-pollination so that the codex of rock excavation here discussed can be termed the European method of tunnelling.

The American Way

In the United States, where throughout the years more underground work has been carried out than anywhere else in the world, developments have also been rapid. But for various reasons, ranging from differences in geology to uniquely American economic conditions, high labour costs, abundant supply of labour, union policy, and so on, American progress has taken another course. To begin with, American machines were much heavier than their European equivalents when the post-war era began, and they have continued to increase in weight and power. Another reason is the overriding importance of time in American contracting. To gain time it pays to use more labour, more power to drive heavier and costlier machines, far more explosives to charge broad-gauge holes. Although a contractor no doubt would like to cut down on his labour force, he is required by contractual obligations, to satisfy union requirements, to employ more men than he actually needs. For example, on an operation almost exactly similar to benching out the Stornorrfors tunnel, of which more below, where the Swedish Power Board used four men, an American contractor was required to employ thirty-six men.

The essential difference in modern American and European tunnelling is highlighted by the West Delaware system which forms part of the New York water supply, and the Täby drainage tunnel north of Stockholm. Both tunnels have the same area, or 134·5 sq. ft., and were driven simultaneously in the middle of the 1950's. On one of the sites of the Delaware development, an intermediate shaft serving two headings, the contractor employed twenty-one staff and 204 workers; the total labour force in the Täby tunnel was thirty-seven men. In the American tunnel, each round produced an advance of 11·6 ft., as against 15·7 ft. in the Täby; the volume of rock pulled per round was 55 and 78·6 cu. yds., respectively. Each cubic yard of rock excavated required 9 and 11·5 ft. of drill holes and 5 and 4 lb. of dynamite, respectively.

Looking at it from a purely economic point of view, there is of course no doubt about the technical superiority of the manner in which the Täby tunnel was driven. But that is not quite the full story. If the time element is taken into consideration, an altogether different picture emerges. In the Delaware tunnel the advance per shift was 22 ft., against only 8 ft. in the Täby. In twenty-four hours the American teams made 132 ft., whereas the Swedish team made only 47 ft. The volume of rock excavated was 662 cu. yds., against only 235 cu. yds.

The figures quoted are of particular interest because it seldom happens that two underground developments lend themselves to such comparison, and they bring home the essential difference between the American and European methods of tunnelling. In Europe, it is the unit cost that matters beyond all. A low over-all cost per cubic metre of rock removed is, everything else being equal, a measure of the engineering performance. Time of completion is of lesser importance, and the projects are usually phased so as to obtain the best possible economy. If a tunnel is scheduled for completion on a certain date, as determined by other economic considerations, it is started early enough to ensure that the completion date can be met with a minimum expenditure of labour, equipment and explosives. Unions do not force employers to use more men than required, nor do they prevent the introduction of methods and equipment designed to save labour.

In the United States the aim is to get the tunnel completed as fast as possible. A contractor goes all out on explosives, installs oversized compressed-air and ventilation plants capable of clearing out the blasting fumes in a couple of minutes, uses heavy and powerful rock drills and, beyond all, puts on labour so as to be able to push through the job in the shortest possible time. The unions have a voice in deciding how many men should be employed. On public contracts there is as much as 50 per cent 'featherbedding' imposed by the union politics. Under such conditions there is not much point in cost cutting, neither is there much use in carrying out rationalization studies aimed at developing sophisticated techniques. In America, tunnelling has become mechanized to save time but not cost. Whereas a light jackleg drill of the type commonly used in Europe costs $335, American boom-mounted drills cost something like $11,200. The total cost of American tunnelling is not necessarily reflected in these figures, but it comes shockingly high when viewed by European engineers.

Post-war Power Houses

The new post-war tunnelling technique has been applied throughout the world almost entirely to the classical purpose of tunnels, that is to say the conducting of water, either for irrigation or for the insatiable needs of metropolitan areas. Since a water tap must discharge into a drain, there has also been a concomitant need for expanding the network of sewers.

There have been few occasions to build railway tunnels, but the rapid post-war growth of motor traffic has made road tunnels economically viable in mountainous regions where the motor roads are blocked with snow several months of the year. At the beginning of the 1960's, there was one 7·5-mile motor-tunnel being driven under Mont Blanc and another 3·6-mile tunnel under the Great St. Bernard, while five other Alpine motor tunnels were in different stages of projection.

However, there is no doubt but that the character of post-war tunnelling has been shaped by altogether different aims than those applied in the past—by the large-scale application of tunnelling for the development of water power. In Europe, the annual growth of generating capacity since the end of the war has been, on the average, 7 per cent, with peaks of 9 per cent for some years. Of this new capacity something like 5 per cent has been hydro. During the years 1956–60, $5,000 million was invested in European hydro power, while the estimated capital requirements for 1961–65 reach $6,900 million. During the second half of the decade hydro-power stations of a total value of $8,000 million are expected to be built. The figures suggest the tremendous scale of post-war tunnelling, because regardless of how the station is placed, above or below ground, tunnels will have to be excavated, to divert the water during the building stage, to conduct the water to the station, to get rid of the spent water after it has done its work.

But in the building of post-war hydro stations, it has become increasingly common to place the entire hydraulic plant underground. There is today hardly a country in Europe that cannot boast of at least one power station wholly enclosed in rock; a few of the largest stations built on the American continent during the 1950's were underground stations. This modern practice of building power plants in rock evolved in Sweden, where in 1961 there were thirty underground stations with a total capacity of 3,650 MW. producing 53 per cent of the country's output of hydro power. By 1966, seventeen new underground plants will have been put in service, adding 1,600 MW. to the generating capacity. In that country, not only hydro stations are put underground but thermal and nuclear plants are also being placed in rock.

Clearly there are reasons for this modern predilection for troglodyte engineering. One is obvious: by placing these vital plants underground, protected by a rock cover of several hundred feet, they should be safe against conventional and perhaps also nuclear bombs.

But that is not the main reason. Briefly, a power station is placed underground to save money. A power plant is more economical to build and operate the larger it becomes; also the unit costs decrease with increasing head. In Sweden, owing to the rather even flow of the rivers along slightly sloping valleys, the heads are modest; few existing stations use heads exceeding 400 ft. In other words, topographical conditions do not favour the economics of scale in hydro development.

But these defects of nature can be remedied by placing the generating plant underground. In this manner a 'concentrated head' can be constructed, by damming the river and placing the station deep underground. Since the generating plant is situated well below the water level of the river at the site, the tail water will have to be conducted by a long tunnel discharging into the river a considerable distance downstream. Therefore the creation of an artificial head in excess of 100 ft. is one reason for placing a station underground. By increasing the cross-section area of the waterways, the hydraulic characteristics of the plant are improved, while at the same time the cost of excavating becomes lower. By suitable regulation, by means of dams and barrages upstream from the plant, a large supply of water can be stored to suit daily, weekly or annual variations of the load. In this way the volume of water, or flow, available to work the station becomes very large.

Then there are the not inconsiderable economic benefits derived from using the rock as a construction element. Instead of building with concrete, self-supporting caverns and tunnels are created by hollowing out the rock. The excavated material is used for building the upstream dam. Moreover, as a consequence of the large water-ways through the station the vertical axis generating units can be reduced in number, to two or three very large sets. The largest tur-bines installed are rated at 178,000 h.p. per unit driving an alternator with a capacity of 150 MW. To prevent cavitation, the stainless-steel runner is placed below the normal water level at the down-stream outlet of the tailrace tunnel, while the generator is placed above the highest downstream level.

If the rock is good the waterways can be left unlined, except for the penstocks and draught tubes. In places where it is desired to reduce friction, the rock walls are smoothed off by a special blasting technique. Sometimes the large generator cavern is given a protective concrete vaulting, but generally it is sufficient to rock bolt the ceiling and apply a layer of wire mesh and gunnite to prevent rock falls. The cavern walls are left untouched, although a stark architectural beauty can sometimes be achieved by accentuating the mineral formations in the rock.

So much for the Swedish underground power houses. Their large number and the size of the underground plant are obviously due to the means offered by post-war tunnelling techniques for performing large-scale excavations in rock with great economy, speed and safety.

Elsewhere, for example in the Alps, where the topography is en-tirely different, the Swedish technique has been modified to conform with local conditions. Here water is gathered by tunnelling systems which scoop up snow water as it descends from the peaks and con-duct it to storage dams. Long pressure tunnels driven many hundreds of feet above the river furrow, through the mountains framing the steep valleys, bring water with high head through penstocks leading to underground power houses situated level with the valley floor. The spent water is discharged through a short tailrace into the river.

The variations are many. One may cut through an intervening mountain ridge with a tunnel and bring water from one valley to a power house situated on the floor of a neighbouring valley. It is being done in a small way in the Alps. In Australia's Snowy Mountain scheme the direction of the rivers is reversed by tunnelling through the divide to bring the water into the arid interior where it is needed, rather than letting it go to waste in the ocean. When turning water around by this geographical surgery, the head obtained in the man-made water courses is used for generating power.

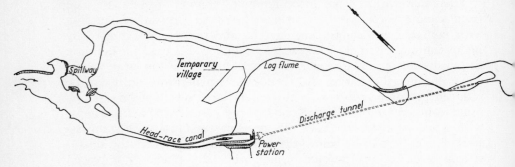

Fig 134. Plan of the Stornorrfors development.

It seems fitting, by way of illustrating the performance of the post-war tunnelling industry, to choose the Stornorrfors power plant in northern Sweden as the subject of a case history in the manner previously used, particularly as this huge underground plant seems destined to remain the largest ever constructed in Europe. On the Stornorrfors development, post-war tunnelling reached its full flower-

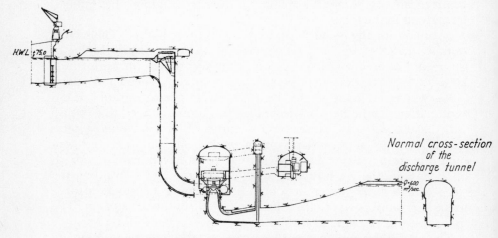

Fig 135. Section through the Stornorrfors underground power house.

ing. The scale of operations was not only huge—something like 2·8 million cu. m. (3·7 million cu. yds.) of rock were excavated, in addition to 2·9 million cu. m. (3·8 million cu. yds.) of alluvial—but being huge, the unit costs were reduced to what appear unapproach-able lows. The 4,200-sq. ft. tailrace tunnel, the largest ever advanced, was excavated at a cost of $1·87 per cu. yd., and the entire station, including the electrical installations, was built at a cost of $137 per installed kW., as compared with a European average of $352 for hydro and $156 for thermal stations. The finished station generates power at 0·19 cent per kWh., in terms of 1959 prices.

If, as has been claimed, the basic function of technology is to reduce costs, surely such an achievement in power engineering de-serves notice.

Building History of Stornorrfors

Stornorrfors also sums up the last fifty years of hydro-power developments. Along one series of rapids of the Ume River over a distance of 8 miles there were by 1954 three small run-of-the-stream stations, the oldest one—now turned into a museum—built in 1899. The most recent one situated on the site was completed in 1926 and had a capacity of 26 MW., which was all that could be accomplished thirty years ago. The new station replaces all three, and by concen-trating the head to one point along this stretch of the river a working head of 244 ft. was obtained. By regulating the sources of the river and its tributaries, a water storage of 5,000 million cu. m. was achieved which eventually will supply twenty power stations along a stairway formed by the river system and capable of producing 8,000 million kWh., of which 1,900 million will derive from the Stornorrfors plant. The waterways of the station are designed to handle a flow of 600 cu. m. (786 cu. yds.) per second.

To describe in technical detail the different civil engineering and electrical features of the Stornorrfors plant falls outside the scope of tunnelling. Suffice it to say that the development is very simple in concept. From a rockfill dam upstream from the station the water is conducted by an open canal for a distance of 7,872 ft. into three 1,830-sq. ft. intake tunnels blasted in rock for a distance of 174–206 ft. The level of the water entering the forebays is 246 ft. above sea-level. Three vertical penstocks 26 ft. in diameter conduct the total flow of 21,186 cu. ft. per second to 178,000-h.p. Francis turbines driving 150-MW. alternators.

The machines are installed in a cavern measuring 406·7 × 60·6 × 95 ft. Alongside it is a 305 × 58 × 47·5 ft. transformer gallery where the 18-kV. energy generated by the alternators is stepped up to a transmission voltage of 380 kV. The leads are run through vertical shafts 8·5 ft. in diameter to a switchyard above ground.

The spent water leaves the turbines through concrete-lined draught tubes discharging into a tailrace tunnel having a cross-section of 4,200 sq. ft. The 13,120-ft.-long tunnel runs horizontal for a mile or so after which it dips 130 ft., whereby the bottom comes 200 ft. below sea-level. The tunnel discharges into an open canal which empties into the river.

The underground plant also includes a 492 × 65·6 × 72-ft. surge gallery connected with the tailrace by a 1,022-sq. ft. cross-gallery. About midway between the generator cavern and the transformer gallery runs a 40-ft.-wide crane gallery to facilitate shutting off any one of the draught tubes with a gate. In addition, there are an underground water-tank, elevator shaft, control room and, not least, a 29·5 × 21-ft. access tunnel permitting heavy machine components to be brought into the station.

As previously mentioned, building the Stornorrfors station required excavations on a large scale. A total of 3·8 million cu. yds. of rock was removed, 2 million from the tailrace tunnel. The headrace canal required the removal of 0·8 million cu. yds. of rock and 17 million cu. yds. of alluvial. Owing to good rock, concrete construction required only 79,000 cu. yds. Another way of putting it is that one kW. of installed generating capacity required the removal of 10 cu. yds. of rock and 10·2 cu. yds. of alluvial and the pouring of 0·17 cu. yd. of concrete. Considering only the power house, the cubic space per kW. comes to 0·26 cu. yd. These figures sum up better than words the benefits derived from underground construction.

Starting up the Work

The work on Stornorrfors began in the autumn of 1953 and was conducted by the owner, that is, the State Power Board. A village with a number of permanent features was quickly built from prefabricated light concrete elements erected on steel frames. Housing was provided for 950 employees and their families; the communal amenities included a hotel, club-house, canteens, cinema, shops, post office, telephone exchange, offices and so on. The mechanical repair-shop was built on a large scale and equipped to undertake complete overhaul and repair of a fleet of forty 20-ton diesel dump-trucks, fifteen excavators, as well as bulldozers, tractors, mobile cranes, etc. There was also a large rock-crushing plant and concrete mixers serving a precasting plant since little concrete was cast *in situ*. The electric substation serving the site had a capacity of 9,750 kW. There were altogether three compressor stations delivering 11,650 cu. ft. of air per minute. The cooling water from the 6,400 cu. ft. village-station was used to heat the service shops through pipes in the concrete floor slabs. The lighting both above and below ground was by sodium lamps.

According to the original schedule, the first Stornorrfors generator was to be phased into the grid on 1st April 1959. However, after the work got under way the power consumption suddenly increased beyond forecasts and the building time was shortened by six months, to 1st October 1958. To enable the machine installations to be made, the shortened schedule required that the generator cavern, together with its intake, penstocks, and draught tubes, involving excavations of altogether 432,000 cu. yds. of rock—plus roof reinforcements—be completed within twenty months.

The work on the cavern was performed in four stages, and since the methods employed represent the full flowering of modern tunnelling they will be described in some detail.

To get work started, a 2,165-ft.-long adit with a 581-sq. ft. area was driven with an incline of 1:7 into the ground where, after 1,574 ft., it hit the level of the future machine deck in the cavern; the remainder was a spur leading down to the level of the tailrace tunnel. This main haulage tunnel was made 29½ ft. wide to enable two 20-ton trucks to meet. One half of the floor was paved with concrete to carry the heavy outgoing traffic, the other half with macadam for the return traffic. After serving as a haulage way, the 1,574-ft. tunnel was kept as the permanent access to the underground plant.

The first stage in excavating the generator cavern consisted of driving a 581-sq. ft. top heading for its entire length, or 406·7 ft. The crown of the heading was 2·4 ft. below the finished roof, and slabs about 3 ft. in thickness were left along the two sides of the heading. The reason for not removing the full area is interesting since this is probably the first time that smooth blasting was carried out on a major scale. With the rough top heading completed, contour holes were drilled rather close together along the theoretical outline of the cavern and charged with a slow explosive. In this manner the roof and sides were dressed smoothly and accurately in the tough gneiss. While this work was going on, other teams drove a top heading through the transformer gallery and a number of large headings on the turbine and draught-tube levels. This ended the first phase, which required seven months.

During the second phase of four months, the roof of the cavern was reinforced with rock bolts grouted in cement and finished with gunnite. The three penstocks were also completed.

There now exist a number of improved mechanized shaft-raising methods that vastly facilitate this work which was formerly so time-consuming and hazardous, but the method used at Stornorrfors still deserves mention because it is the grandfather of them all. The procedure was as follows: during the first stage a heading had been driven on a level where the three penstocks terminated underground. From above the ground a 5·8-in. vertical hole in the centre of the future penstock was sunk by a rope drill down into the heading below. A hoist was placed above the hole and a wire dropped down into the heading where it was connected to a cage. Two men equipped with stopers entered the cage which was hoisted up to the face where they drilled a ring of holes along the circumference of a circle with a 5·2-ft. diameter. After charging the holes, the cage was lowered into the heading, disconnected from the wire and removed to the side. Firing the round produced a circular hole and the fragmented rock dropped into the heading where it was mucked out.

The wire was once more lowered through the hole and the cage connected to it and hoisted up into the bottom of the shaft where a new round was drilled to extend the raise upwards. In this way, the raise was extended to the surface, whence the team began working itself down by enlarging the pilot shaft to the full 26·2-ft. diameter of the finished penstock. The rock was shot down through the shaft. In this manner a team of two miners per shift produced an average of 230 ft. per month, sometimes 50 per cent more. Elevator and conductor shafts were similarly driven.

During the third phase, which also lasted four months, the top bench, measuring 55·7 × 25·4 ft., was removed in the cavern. This brought the miners down to the level of the permanent haulageway through which the broken rock could be removed. The bench was drilled up with wagon drills, but a 3-ft. slab was left along the sides for subsequent removal by smooth blasting. The roof of the transformer gallery was finished and so were the draught tubes.

The fourth phase, also of four months' duration, included the blasting of the second 26-ft. bench and the third 36-ft. bench. To facilitate transport through the top and, later, the bottom adit, the benches were given a slope of 1:7. The benches in the transformer gallery were also removed and finished by smooth blasting. The necks of the draught tubes, crosscuts from the generator cavern to the transformer gallery, the cooling-water tank and other details were also concluded, so that concrete work could start in October 1956. Machine installation began on 1st September the following year.

The cost of building the power house with its immediate waterways came to Kr. 12·7 million, or Kr. 35 ($6.75) per kW. A surface plant built at the same time cost Kr. 145 ($28) per kW.

Tailrace Tunnel

From the point of view of brute size, the Stornorrfors tailrace tunnel exceeds anything that has hitherto been accomplished in tunnelling. The tunnel it 52·4 ft. wide and 86 ft. high, which produces an area of 4,200 sq. ft. The length is 2·5 miles, and 2 million cu. yds. were excavated. But apart from its sheer size, the Stornorrfors tailrace is worthy of notice from the manner in which it was advanced. By introducing a new type of mechanized drilling, record advances were made and the unit cost reached new lows. The tunnel was driven on four fronts, from the power house adit, from both fronts of a midway adit and from a downstream adit, but only three were used at one and the same time since speed was of no paramount importance. The midway adit had the same area as the permanent upstream one, or 581 sq. ft., and was driven full face with an average advance of 14 ft. per day.

The top heading of the tailrace was given a more generous area, or 1,721·6 sq. ft., which appears to be the largest area blasted full face. A round was drilled from a three-decked jumbo by a team of twenty-one miners per shift. Using Atlas Copco BBC 21 'Lion' jack drills the team perforated the rock face to a pattern of 172 holes for a total length of 4,000 ft. A V-cut was used which with a tunnel width of 52·4 ft. should produce a theoretical advance of 8 m. (26·2 ft.). The steel sets had a maximum length of 9·6 m. (31·4 ft.) and were provided with 34-mm. carbide insert bits. The relievers and trimmers were drilled with a set ending with 8-m. steels and 35-mm. bits. The holes were charged with 35 per cent dynamite and the trimmers with a powder having a slower ammonia nitrate base.

The top heading of the Stornorrfors tailrace is probably the last instance of such a large area being drilled up by 'manual drilling', meaning in this case that the drill steel was directed by the machine operator. Not even the most skilful operators are capable of placing cut holes with such accuracy that they meet each other 26·2 ft. in the rock. As a consequence of this unavoidable inaccuracy it was never possible to approach the theoretical limit of 26·2 ft. per round; the best advance recorded was 25·9 ft. From this time on the requests for mechanical steering of the long steels became more urgent. They have subsequently been met by the introduction of the Swedish ladder method which in addition to doubling the output of an operator also facilitates better accuracy when drilling the holes.

With the V-cut the round required five hours to drill and charge. Including food breaks, portal time, withdrawal of drill jumbo, and so on, a full eight-hour shift was consumed in preparing and blasting

a round. It produced an advance of 21 to 24 ft. and on the average
1,450 cu. yds. of fragmented rock suitable for loading. A cubic yard
of the tough gneiss required 2·8 ft. of hole and 1·8 lb. of dynamite.

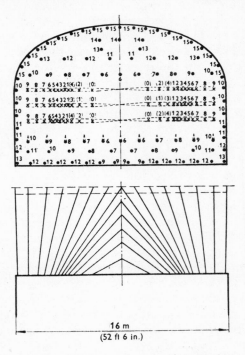

Fig 136. The V-cut blasting pattern
used to advance the 160 sq. m. top
heading of the 390 sq. m. tailrace
tunnel of Stornorrfors, the largest ever
advanced.

The rock pile created by a round was mucked out during the following sixteen hours using an electric excavator with a 3-cu. m.
bucket and a fleet of 20-ton diesel dump trucks. The cost came to
Kr. 21·36 per cu. m. (£1 3s. 0d. per cu. yd.) of which only Kr. 10
(13s. 7d.) applies to drilling and blasting.

After the top heading, there remained 52 ft. to the bottom grade
of the tunnel. The rock was removed in two 26-ft. benches in a highly
mechanized operation. Across the full width of the tunnel extended a
steel frame mounting 13 Atlas Copco 'Lion' rock drills with chain
feeds. The machines were spaced on 5·4 ft. centres, except at the
ends. They were fixed to the frame at an angle of 45° and drove

Fig 137. The benching machine used in drilling up the two benches in the Stornorrfors tailrace tunnel was operated by four men. The drilled rows ahead of the machine were charged with dynamite as the drilling proceeded in the rear. Six rows were blasted in one round which produced 2,200 cu. yds. of rock and lowered the floor 26 ft.

Fig 138. The Stornorrfors underground power station on the Ume River in the Swedish North was brought into service in 1959. Its three generator sets have a capacity of 350,000 kW. The installation of a fourth set will raise the capacity to 500,000 kW, whereby Stornorrfors is likely to remain the largest underground hydro-power plant in Europe.

34-ft. steels provided with 39-mm. bits into the bench. Only four men operated the thirteen machines. After one row of holes had been drilled across the bench the jig was advanced 5·6 ft. for a new row. In one shift the four-man team produced six and a half rows, or a total length of 2,360 ft. of holes. The average output per man and shift was 587 ft., with a maximum of 722 ft.

The front rows were charged as the rear ones were being drilled. The bottom was tightly packed with 13 lb. of dynamite, followed by 7 lb. of loosely placed sticks. The total charge per row came to 263 lb. and the round to 1,709 lb. It was ignited by a milli-second blasting machine.

The rock produced by such a round was on the average 2,200 cu. yds. It was mucked out by an electric excavator with a 4-cu. yd. bucket, with a bulldozer helping to scrape together the rock for good bucket fill. It required two eight-hour shifts to muck out one round and a fleet of 20-ton trucks to remove the broken rock to the dump. By working on two headings, a total advance of 55·7 ft. per day was gained. The second bench was removed in exactly the same way, with similar results.

The economy of this operation also set a record. To remove one cubic yard of rock required only 1·6 ft. of hole and 0·8 lb. of dynamite, or in terms of money Kr. 5·20 per cu. m. (5s. 6d. per cu. yd.). The time required was 0·25 hr. per cu. yd.

The actual building costs of the dam, power house and waterways came to Kr. 77·1 million ($15 million), but to this should be added a number of so-called general costs: interest on capital, administration, social costs, road building, bridges, compensations and so on, amounting to Kr. 132·5 million ($25.6million). Turbines and electrical installations came to Kr. 44·4 million($8.6million), whereby the total became Kr. 254 million ($49 million), as against an estimated Kr. 217 million ($42 million). Total cost in terms of installed kW. capacity comes out at Kr. 680 per kW. ($131.34) about the lowest attained in post-war hydro developments.

Technocrat and St. Barbara

The Stornorrfors power station was completed in 1958. As reflected in the notes on its building history, post-war tunnelling is principally a matter of economics and an account of tunnel advance is told in statistics. The human aspects of tunnel advance, the triumphs and disasters, are no longer permitted to obscure the economic realities and are in the process of being deleted in major underground operations.

After Stornorrfors, tunnelling entered into the bleak impersonal realm of the computor. Tunnelling, like large-scale mining, has become increasingly the concern of technocrats. The excavation of underground structures in good rock, and ripping ore out of the ground, require no subtleness or concern for creative engineering. Underground work is clinically free of human contamination and hence lends itself to technocratic treatment. Since the advance of such a tunnel consists essentially of linking up innumerable details into an arithmetic progression, the planning and supervision can equally well be turned over to an electronic data-processing machine. Whether in actual fact tunnelling by computor has been put into effect is a minor point. There exists now, after years of continuous rationalization studies, such a tremendous store of data on all phases of underground work that by feeding it into a computor one could obtain a site manager capable of giving an objective technical answer to all questions put to it. Given the nature of the rock, the water flow or the traffic expected, the time available for the work or some such elements, the rest can be turned over to the computor which would come forth with the design of the underground plant, blasting patterns, the men and machines needed to execute the work, and so on.

No doubt for some time to come there will still be a need for old-time tunnelling engineers on the site, men in hard hats who sleep in their boots. But they are already yielding their status to anonymous technocrats remote from the site, rationalizers who have no occasion to get their feet soiled by sloshing around in a tunnel and are aghast at the very idea.

Under technocratic conditions both the men and the machines used to break rock are of no particular interest in themselves, except as units in an organization designed to perform a given operation at a minimum cost. The naïve ideas of inventors a century ago of building huge machines capable of carving out the full face of a tunnel as it advances through hard rock can perhaps be realized now; at any rate there is the power available to drive such a machine. But who would want such clumsy mechanical monsters when by blending men and available mechanical facilities a much more flexible and economical excavating 'machine' can be designed far removed from the site? A balanced task force, its complement of men, mining machines, transport, and work orders determined long in advance by computor, can be sent out to perform the work, and the output supervised by distant computor. When the work is accomplished it can be broken down into its constituent parts and put together in different combinations to suit conditions on a new site.

These reflections, it should be emphasized, apply to current trends in countries where underground construction has become a continuous and large-scale business conducted by government authorities and specialist contractors in good, reliable rock perfectly understood and mastered. Unfortunately, this technocratic vision shatters when confronted by the ugly realities of badly fissured, crumbling stuff, the calcareous, Jurassic and Alpine rocks encountered almost everywhere around the globe, except Scandinavia, the Canadian Shield and some other isolated regions where the igneous rock has been left undisturbed since the crust cooled. In such treacherous rock a tunnel advance remains what it always has been—a hazardous venture where anything can happen from one minute to the next, where in the end the tunnellers, their modern machines and organization notwithstanding, stand naked, stripped of their mechanical facilities and power resources, and must rely on their courage, determination and sacrifice in order to keep advancing.

Under such conditions distant technocrats and their computor programmers become as futile as a faulty geological prognosis, and the faith of the tunnellers becomes centred on St. Barbara, patron saint of miners and artillery men, to keep them alive and unscathed until the end of the shift. On Alpine developments it is customary to place an effigy of the saint in a niche cut into the portal rock, which seems as good a safety measure as any other that can be devised under such conditions.

Thus it was St. Barbara rather than a computor in distant Milan that was chosen to keep watch over the miners in Mt. Blanc, the 7-mile-long motor-tunnel under Europe's highest mountain, the insurmountable barrier which for more than a hundred years had challenged successive generations of tunnellers. When at long last the attack was launched in early 1959 the tunnellers had at their disposal the latest methods and machines evolved on both sides of the Atlantic, and they went to work with high hopes and with the assurance that the mighty massif would be pierced in a couple of years. What actually happened will be described in the next and concluding chapter.

Chapter 19

THE KNIGHTS OF MT. BLANC

'Sometimes a balance is struck between the rock and man. Then the miner can rely only on his personal qualities, his courage, physical endurance and spirit of sacrifice.'[1]

'THE day will come when we will build a safe road through Mt. Blanc and unite the two valleys of Aosta and Chamonix', prophesied Horace Bénédict de Saussure, the Swiss naturalist and mountain climber, when he stood one day in 1787 on the top of Europe's mightiest mountain and looked out over the peaks and bluish glaciers glistening in the sun.

Time and again during the next 150 years the people in the economically and socially backward Aosta valley reverted to the old dream, the tunnel that would break their isolation and turn their poverty into riches overnight. Some twenty times railway surveyors intent on finding a route through the Alps stood at the foot of the mighty massif and contemplated an attack. But one team after another had to give up before the obstacle. The promise of a tunnel through Mt. Blanc was for generations the surest way for a local politician to get himself elected. 'I cannot give you the exact hour or the day, but I give you my word that if I'm elected it will not be many weeks before you have a tunnel through the mountain,' shouted

[1] Loris Corbi, managing director of Società Italiana per Condotte d'Acqua, contractor of the Italian end of the Mt. Blanc tunnel.

one politician electioneering some forty years ago. The whole valley celebrated his victory but nothing more was said of the tunnel.

Then in 1946, one year after the end of hostilities and when Italy lay economically prostrate with the Communists within reach of power—a situation in many ways reminiscent of the unrest in 1857 when the Sardinian government decided to go ahead with the Fréjus tunnel—Count Dino Lora Totino, a wealthy woollen manufacturer in Turin, thought the time propitious for a tunnel through Mt. Blanc. He floated a company, had a scheme drawn up by Professor Vittorio Zignoli, also of Turin, and a triangulation survey carried out by Pietro Allaria, a *geometra* with little experience of high mountain work. Two professional mountain guides ended their lives on the eternal glaciers, but Allaria survived the ordeal and descended the massif with a net of accurate triangulation angles in his field-books.

Count Totino's private tunnel scheme was quite a modest affair. To escape installing a costly ventilation system, traffic through the tunnel was to be limited to 200 vehicles per day, spaced at such intervals that the carbon monoxide concentration would remain below the lethal level. His miners advanced a pilot tunnel for about 660 ft. and broke out the first 150 ft. to a full-sized tunnel. Less than a year later, when the Italian army had begun to attain some resemblance of peace-time order after the collapse, the military authorities became aware of what was going on at the northern rampart which protected the classical invasion route through the Aosta valley, and began to wonder who had given Count Totino permission to bore a way through it. No one had; in the general post-war confusion the Count had simply gone ahead with his scheme without bothering to inform the authorities about it. By the time the Italian army moved in and stopped the advance, he and his company had sunk 200 million lire ($320,000) in the heading.

Although Count Totino and his company ceased to have anything further to do with the tunnel, his outrageous initiative and daring had nevertheless aroused the interest of official circles in Italy and the idea was not permitted to die. At the instigation of Italy a study group was formed in 1949 with Italian, French and Swiss experts to pursue in detail the political, financial and technical issues involved in advancing a vehicle tunnel through Mt. Blanc, connecting Paris and Rome by the 'White Way'. The French were against it from the outset. Their General Staff did not take kindly to the idea of opening up the hitherto impregnable southern bastion and, like their British colleagues, the French strategists dreaded another Caesar leading his legions into the heart of Gaul. The neutral Swiss, however, who had visions of Geneva becoming the major stopping-place

along the Route Blanche, managed to bridge the differences, and
in the end, on 14th March 1953, a convention was signed in Paris
by the Italian and French governments for building a vehicle tunnel
through Mt. Blanc. The fears of the French military authorities had
been allayed by the provision that they would be able to blow up
their own end in time of war.

The Italian Parliament ratified the Mt. Blanc convention the following year and an Italian state corporation was set up for building
and administering the tunnel. The town and canton of Geneva
entered as a minority party to the convention in 1956, and finally, in
April 1957, the French Parliament too ratified it; the following year
a French tunnel authority was formed. According to the financial
agreement the French were to contribute $17 million and the
Italians $8.96 million to the cost of the tunnel, which was originally
estimated at $31.4 million (19,500 million lire). The town and canton
of Geneva agreed to pay $1.59 million for their minority interest. As
usual, it was an altogether too optimistic estimate. After the work
got under way the costs had to be progressively revised, to $32.8
million, to $35.0 million, to $40.0 million, and they kept rising until
the completion of the project.

The protocol formalities and financing having been agreed upon,
the stage was set for the great push through Mt. Blanc. Among the
many bidders the Italian tunnel authority chose Società Italiana per
Condotte d'Acqua as its contractor for the southern end. The French
selected the contracting firm of A. Borie, which allied itself with five
other French firms into Société d' Enterprises Travaux Publics André
Borie, for building the northern half.

Work on the Italian side began on 4th December 1958, and on
8th January 1959 drilling began at the portal. The French start was
deferred until 30th May 1959, when the French miners attacked not
the main vehicle tunnel, which enters on a slight curve to avoid an
avalanche slope, but a short pilot tunnel driven as a continuation of
the main axis of the tunnel, in order to facilitate accurate alignment of
the tunnel axis. During the first two months the French team worked
on temporary scaffolding with light-weight rock drills, and the heavy
advance did not get under way until August.

Tunnel Data

The two contractors working towards each other established their
camps on shelves cut into the mountain-sides close to the tunnel
portals. The French terminal is situated a short distance from the
hamlet of Les Pélérins, about a mile and a quarter from Chamonix,

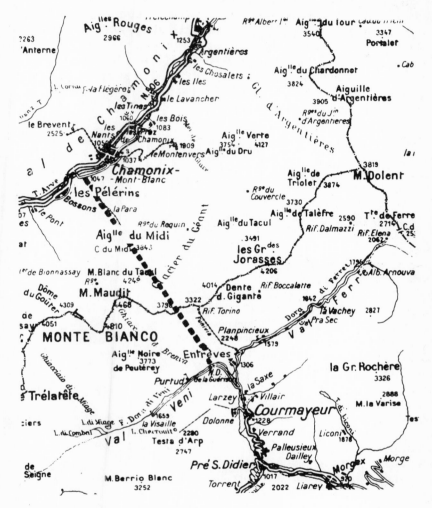

Fig 139. The Mt. Blanc Tunnel runs roughly from Chamonix, north of the massif, to the town of Courmayeur in the south. The northern portal is situated close to the hamlet of Les Péllérins and the southern in the proximity of Entrèves.

at an altitude of 4,179 ft. The Italian portal is situated near the hamlet of Entrèves, near the exclusive mountain resort of Cour-mayeur. The tunnel runs in a straight line for 38,060 ft. with a rising grade of 2·5:1,000 from the southern portal to a summit at 18,374 ft., at an elevation of 4,583 ft., from which it descends towards the northern portal with a gradient of not less than 24:1,000. Since the southern portal is 350 ft. above the northern it was hoped that the mechanical ventilation plant would be aided materially by the natural draught. The air needed to ventilate the tunnel was origin-ally estimated at 800,000 c.f.m.[2]

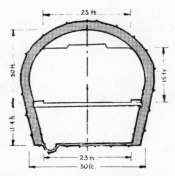

Fig 140. The horseshoe section of the Mt. Blanc Tunnel was excavated to 796 sq. ft. in the protogine granite and to 861 sq. ft. at the ends, but the finished section is 678 sq. ft. for the entire length.

The tunnel passes directly under Aiguille du Midi, Mt. Blanc's sister peak, and under the glaciers Vallée Blanche and Glacier du Géant. Under the Aiguille du Midi the rock cover is 7,972 ft.

At every 1,000 ft. along the tunnel there is a 100 × 11 × 15-ft. emergency bay, and on the opposite side a recess 20 × 23 ft. to facilitate turn-arounds if needed. The tunnel is horseshoe-type in shape, with a total height of 31 ft. and a shoulder width of 29 ft. 6 in. The vehicle deck is situated 11 ft. from the rock floor, and provides for two 11 ft. 6-in. lanes and on each side a 2 ft. 6-in. pathway. The 23 × 11-ft. area below the deck is to hold ventilation and evacuation air ducts and other services.

The tunnel was designed for a traffic capacity of 300 vehicles per

[2] c.f.m. = cubic feet per minute.

hour, or 350,000 per year, carrying about a million passengers and about 100,000 tons of freight. In addition to linking up the three metropolitan centres, London–Paris–Rome, the Mt. Blanc tunnel will reduce the road distance from Paris to Milan by 194 miles and cut the winter road distance between Geneva and Turin from 491 miles to a mere 168 miles.

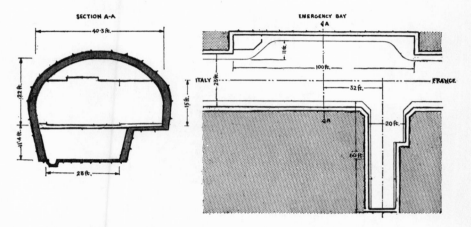

Fig 141. Turn-around and emergency bay, placed at every 1,000 ft. along the tunnel.

The geological profile of the Mt. Blanc massif, which for apparent reasons could not be determined by test drilling but was based largely on deductions, is roughly as follows: at the northern end there is a thin fold of metamorphic gneiss, followed by the core of the massif which consists of a protogine granite, a post-crystalline deformed rock that rapidly loses its cohesion when the rock pressure begins to act on it after a round has been fired. On the Italian side the protogine core is followed by succeeding folds of gneiss and sedimentary rocks, such as shales intermixed with schists, so soft that they form a sticky mud when wet.

Nevertheless, the geological survey, as well as Count Totino's test tunnel, seemed to indicate that for at least the first few thousand feet the rock would stand up to a careful full-face advance. On the French side, however, the miners could expect firm rock from the beginning, in accordance with past experience in Alpine tunnelling. When during the Mesozoic and Miocene periods the crust of the earth, caught as in a vice, rose in recumbent folds to form the great massifs of the Alps in a series of mighty heaves from the south, the granitic intrusions became oriented along the northern side and folded over

Fig 142. The motor tunnel through the Mt. Blanc barrier
joins up the industrial centres of northern Italy with
those north of the Alps. It reduces the road distance between
Geneva and Turin from 491 to 168 miles and the distance
Paris–Rome by 194 miles.

with crystalline schists and gneisses, together with metamorphosed sedimentary rocks from the south.

Plans of Attack

This geological drama which took place some fifteen million years ago determined the choice of methods and equipment on the two sides. The Italian contractor, with his instinctive distrust of the rock facing him, chose light, manually operated airleg rock drills supplied by Atlas Copco, and Montecalvi diesel-powered dump trucks

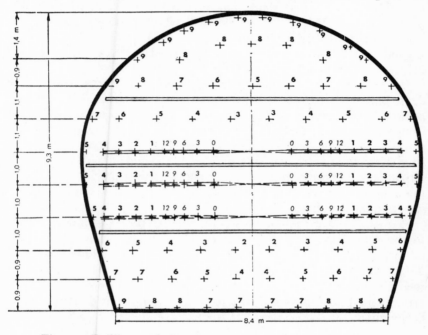

Fig 143. Drilling and charging pattern used at the Italian end of the Mt. Blanc tunnel. Area 80 sq. m. (861 sq. ft.). Dimensions in metres. Such a full face round, the few times it could be used, produced 537 sq. yds. of broken rock.

with a 10-cu. m. (353 cu. ft.) loading capacity. The facilities, although highly mechanized—about seven tons of machines per worker —were flexible to permit their rapid adaptation to changing rock conditions. The mucking was performed by two Eimco 105 loaders with a full bucket capacity of 39 cu. ft.

According to plan, the rock was to be attacked 'full face' from a three-deck drill jumbo on which eighteen to twenty-one miners drilled into the 861-sq. ft. front to form a blasting pattern consisting of 120 to 150 holes, to a depth of 14 ft. 6 in. Using a conventional V-cut, an advance per round of 13 ft. and 39 ft. per day was expected.

The anticipated good rock on the French side inspired an altogether different method of advance employing radically different types of drilling equipment and transport. The French contractor adopted the American practice of heavy rail-borne equipment. On a seventy-five-ton three-decked gantry jumbo, provided with electric traction, were mounted fifteen heavy Ingersoll-Rand chainfeed DC 35 WD rock drills on articulated hydraulic booms. On the top deck (fourth working level) were four booms, on the second deck was mounted a DHD 400 Downhole drill which followed its 8-in. bit into the hole drilled. With this type of drill none of the energy is wasted which otherwise would be required to turn the long and heavy steels needed for such a large-gauge bit.

On each side of the burn-hole drill were two booms, and on the deck below were four booms mounted in vertical pairs. On the bottom level, finally, were another four booms, also in vertical pairs. One man operated each machine, which he could manœuvre to place seven to nine holes within a limited area of the face. Hydraulic power to operate the booms was supplied by five Ingersoll-Rand 516 HBD air-driven hydraulic pumps. To operate these machines requires miners possessing a specialized mechanical know-how not commonly found in the rough business of tunnelling.

With this outfit the contractor planned to drill 130 holes parallel to the tunnel axis to an average depth of 13 ft., using 14-ft. steels provided with 1¾-in. Series 116 Carset tungsten carbide cross-bits. The contour holes were charged with 40 per cent dynamite, intermediate and lifter holes with 60 per cent, while the eight relievers around the burn-hole were charged with 92 per cent dynamite. The large-gauge burn-hole was left uncharged, in order to release the tension of the rock. The blasting pattern was wired to obtain fifteen zones, blown inwards towards the burn-hole with half-second delays.

The advantage of this method of blasting, as against the conventional V-cut, is that it eliminates the need for the skill required to angle holes so that they converge as nearly as possible in the rock beyond the face. In narrow tunnels the burn cut is the only alternative for getting a satisfactory advance since there is no room for angling long drill-steels. In the nearly 30-ft.-wide Mt. Blanc tunnel, however, there was ample room for a V-cut, which in good rock gives the most economical advance.

On the Italian side the miners used Coromant drill sets beginning

Fig 144. The 75-ton drill jumbo used on the French side is here shown assembled outside the northern portal prior to the advance.

with 39-mm. (1½ in.) and ending with 32-mm. (1¼ in.) bits. Owing to the larger holes the French miners used 450 kg. (995 lb.) of dynamite per round, as against 330 kg. (729 lb.) on the Italian side. The air plant capacity also reflected the difference in the two methods. At the Italian portal four Atlas Copco AR-4 compressors delivered 3,530 c.f.m., whereas the French required a 1,500-h.p. plant delivering 10,000 c.f.m. to operate the drilling equipment. However, with the continued advance additional units were installed on the Italian side until in the end there were ten AR-4 compressors delivering altogether 8,800 cu. ft. of air per minute.

The cost of the drilling equipment was also quite different. The light airleg rock drills used by the Italian miners cost £140 per unit, whereas the heavy American drills on the French side cost something like $11,200,including the hydraulic booms. The French tunnelling machine cost about $504,000, as against $28,000 for the equipment used by the Italians.

As previously mentioned, the transport on the Italian side was motorized. On the French side it was railborne. Along the entire length of the tunnel ran a double-track railway laid with 30-kg. (66-lb.) rail. To muck out 750 tons of rock in three and a half hours required sixty to seventy cars, each one of 10-cu. yd. capacity, divided into a number of trains pulled by 30-ton electric locomotives. Loading was accomplished by two electric Conway 100-1 machines, each one provided with a 33-cu. ft. bucket.

With railborne transport there arises the problem of getting an empty car to the face and removing it when filled. This can be done in several ways, for example, by means of switches. In the Mt. Blanc tunnel the American 'cherry picker' method of ranging was employed. This simple and clever way of solving an annoying problem that has bothered tunnellers since rail transport began to be used a century ago has not previously been discussed and deserves to be described in some detail.

Briefly, this is how it is done. The drill jumbo is provided with a hoist. While mucking is in progress the jumbo is removed to the rear of the tunnel for a distance exceeding one full train-length from the face. A train of empty cars pulled by a locomotive is driven up to the face, where it stops to enable the *last* car of the set to be picked up off the rails by the jumbo hoist. With the last car hanging in the hoist the train reverses until the locomotive has cleared the jumbo. The hoisted car is dropped on to the rails in *front* of the locomotive and is pushed by it to a position in the rear of the loader. Before the train backs away the last empty car is picked up by the cherry picker. When the first empty has been filled up at the front, the train backs away far enough to allow the second empty hanging in the cherry picker to be dropped down on the rails and pushed up against the loader. In this manner all the empty cars behind the locomotive become ranged as full cars ahead of the locomotive as the loading continues. When all cars are full the entire train is pulled out. By switches in the rear the track is cleared of any trains on the way in.

After this digression to a transport detail, let us return to the main stem of the narrative. Since the entire French operation was electrified except for the drilling, ventilation was no problem, and the air requirements were of the modest order of 1,070 cu. ft. per second. On the Italian side, where the contractor had to consider the exhaust of the diesel tractors, ventilation was on an altogether different scale. Each second, 2,450 cu. ft. of fresh air had to be supplied to the workings and the same volume of polluted air evacuated. The total capacity of the ventilation plant was therefore 4,900 cu. ft. per second. Two ducts, one 6½ ft. in diameter and the other 8 ft., conducted and evacuated the air, generated by a 450-kW. fan outside the portal, plus two 180-kW. booster fans inside the tunnel. The total power requirements on the Italian side were 4,500 kW.

Since the temperature of the rock was expected to reach 45° C. (104° F.), owing to the thick rock cover, arrangements were made to refrigerate the air by injecting cold pressure water through nozzles in the airline, in a manner used in Simplon, if necessary combined with heat exchangers. To prevent the tunnelling crews from being exposed to the great differences in temperature the French contractor built a *chambre chaude*, a heated locker room, close by the portal to provide a healthy transition between the heat in the tunnel and the cold mountain-air above ground.

The French contractor planned to use about 330 men on his side, with ninety men per shift inside the tunnel. Towards the end of the advance in 1962 he had 432 men employed. The Italian contractor expected to use 350 men, with 100 men per shift inside the tunnel. In 1962 he used 453 men. Considering only the underground operations, the Italian side had 7 tons of mechanized facilities per worker as against 17 tons on the French side. Above ground, the French contractor invested in 8 tons of machines per man, as against 5 tons on the Italian side.

With the heavy investment in plant, the French contractor planned to produce 12 m. (40 ft.) of tunnel advance per twenty-four hours. The time required to excavate and line 5,800 m. (19,024 ft.) of tunnel was estimated at thirty-four months, i.e. the French half of the tunnel was to be completed by 15th February 1962. By then the French team would have excavated 550,000 cu. yds. and placed 92,000 cu. yds. of concrete lining.

On both sides the concrete lining was to be placed by the use of collapsible shutters. From the concrete mixing plant outside the portal the concrete was brought in by truck on the Italian side and by rail on the French and shot into the space between the rock and the form by pneumatic placer. The thickness of the lining was 30 cm. (11·8 in.), increasing to 50–60 cm. (20–24 in.) at points of severe overbreakage. The lining was to follow the heading about 2,300 ft. in the rear.

These, then, were the plans for advancing the 861-sq. ft. Mt. Blanc tunnel and the equipment gathered for the work. From a purely technical point of view it promised to be a very interesting operation because, in addition to the scale of the job, here the two post-war schools of tunnelling were meeting head on. Upon the outcome of the advance depended the reputation of the American method, employing heavy and highly capitalized excavation plant that requires a high rate of production and speedy advance to be made profitable. On the Italian side there was not so much at stake. The advance was to be made with light and relatively inexpensive machines requiring more manual drillers and, being portable, adaptable to changing conditions of rock. Yet, with these machines the Italian mining teams were expected to produce the same output as the heavy plant used on the opposite side of the hill.

Tunnelling the Italian Way

But the advance did not go according to plan. Work began on the Italian side on 8th January 1959, under the camp management of Signor Ercole Ruggeri,[3] and a tunnel area of 861 sq. ft. was attacked full face in the schistous rock. A daily advance of 26 ft. was recorded until a spring was struck at 1,209 ft. and the tunnel had to be evacuated until the water subsided. After resuming the work at a greatly reduced rate of advance owing to the water, the mining team had reached 1,644 ft. on 6th April when it ran into a zone of crumbling phyllite. Several hundred tons of debris came crashing down on the jumbo, crushing it under its weight. There had been warning rumbles and the drill team had retreated taking their machines with them before the roof caved in. No life was lost.

[3] Signor Ruggeri directed field operations to the end of 1961, when he was succeeded by Signor Virginio Scavarda, who brought the job to a conclusion. The assistant manager, Giulio Cesare Meschini, saw the job through from beginning to end.

But the full-face advance was interrupted. The phyllite so unexpectedly encountered necessitated a change in method, at first to a top heading with an area of 508 sq. ft. The phyllite zone proved to be 327 ft. long and had to be dug out by hand. It took one hundred days to cross the zone, by means of a pilot tunnel which was subsequently enlarged to half-tunnel section. In other words, after 1,640 ft.

Fig 145. A heavily timbered top heading was used by the Italian team to cross the 154-ft. zone of crumbling schists encountered at 2,654 ft. from the portal.

the Italian team was clawing at the rock in the manner of classical miners, and the rate of advance was about the same as it would have been 2,000 years ago, or less than 3 ft. per day.

After passing through the phyllite, the advance continued at half section through crumbling schists until on 12th August at 2,654 ft. the roof collapsed a second time for a length of 20 ft. The marly schist necessitated a reversion to a 91-sq. ft pilot tunnel trussed up with heavy timbers; indeed, one particularly bad section had to be armoured. The team spent fifty-nine days working with pick and shovel to gain 154 ft. After that the schist became somewhat better and the advance could continue at half section until on 15th December the eagerly expected protogenic granite was reached at 4,278 ft. After excavating 101,000 cu. yds. of crumbling stuff the contractor, engineers and miners drew a sigh of relief and looked forward to working in the firm rock constituting the heart of the mountain. From an economic point of view the situation began to appear bleak to the contractor. The average advance had been 12½ ft. per day, or less than one third of that planned.

Having reached the granite, further advance was stopped and the first four months of 1960 were spent breaking out the tunnel to full area and putting in the lining. With the arrival of a new 40-ton jumbo, the rock was attacked full face once more. For the next few months an advance of 14 ft. per round and 28 ft. per day was recorded, but as the mining team kept advancing under the massif other serious trouble began to develop. The rock was heavily stressed under a cover of 3,280 ft., which exerted a pressure estimated at 3,550 p.s.i. Sharp slivers of spalling rock began to shoot out from the sides with cracks like pistol shots. Following the bursts, large slabs of rock came sliding down from the walls and face, or dropping from the roof. This situation continued to worsen until the 6,600-ft. point was reached. The roof had to be bolted and a strong steel net capable of catching falling rock was placed under it. The planned advance in the granite had been 40 ft. per day, but progress was impeded by the necessity of securing the heading after each round. During May and June, the two most difficult months of 1960, as much as forty-one hours had to be spent after each round scaling, rock bolting and netting. Despite these precautions there was a fatal accident, the first one at the face, when the mining foreman, Pietro Mauri, was buried under rock collapsing from the face.

At 6,930 ft. the full-face advance had to be abandoned once more in favour of a 10 × 13-ft. pilot tunnel, undertaken principally with the idea of relieving the stress in the rock. At a distance of only 30 ft. in the rear, the pilot was broken out to full tunnel area. On 12th December the advance was stopped at 8,183 ft., after a total advance of 3,906 ft. during 1960, or an average of 16 ft. per day. About 171,000 cu. yds. of rock had been excavated. By then the operation was hopelessly in arrears, and under normal conditions of contracting the contractor would have suffered great financial loss.

On 8th January 1961, two years after starting the work, the mining team stood at 8,251 ft. in reasonably good granite which permitted full-face operation. The newly developed ladder-drilling method was adopted, whereby nineteen miners worked twenty-six machines, and during the first four months of the year a full-face advance of 1,968 ft. was recorded. But then, on 28th April, at 10,098 ft. the miners ran into a zone of deteriorated, highly mylonitic

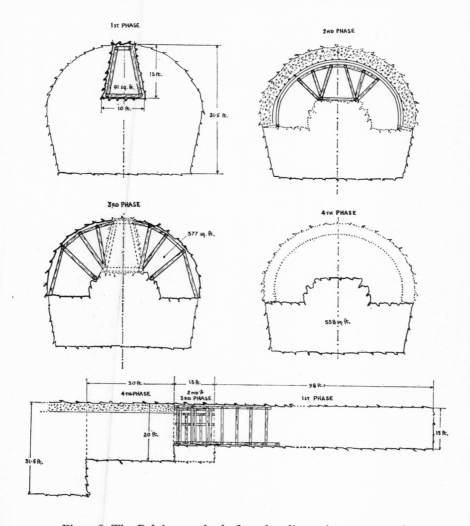

Fig 146. The Belgian method of top heading using a 10 × 13 ft. pilot that was subsequently broken out to full tunnel width and the arch put in before removing the 538 sq. ft. bench. The method was employed in poor and crumbling rock.

granite shot through with springs. The roof had to be trussed up with steel arches placed on 3-ft. centres. Once more, modern methods and machines had to be abandoned for time-tried methods using pick and shovel. Large blocks of rock, from 6 to 12 ft. in length, came tumbling down at the face, having lost their coherence due to the water jetting out through the fissures. On 25th May the jumbo was buried under 39 cu. yds. of mylonite.

The period from 28th April to 10th October 1961 was the worst in the history of the Mt. Blanc advance. During these 163 days the total progress made was 788 ft., or an average of 5 ft. per day. The working shift had to be reduced from eight to four hours. The rock ahead was probed by long-hole drilling using jointed steels, an operation which was the direct cause of the second fatal accident at or near the face. When retracting the steels after one probe the tremendous pressure built up by the water in the hole shot the final steel rod into the tunnel. Every precaution had been taken, the miners at the face stood aside and no one was in the way of the steel javelin as it flashed into the rear, flung with the strength of a giant. Some 60 yds. away it struck the jumbo, changed its direction and pierced the chest of the miner Giuseppe de Fazio, fatally injuring him.

On 9th October at 10,887 ft. the heading struck firm rock and full-face attack was attempted again, despite the heavy cannonade of rock bursts. Ladder drilling was abandoned in favour of hand-held drills and the depth of the holes was reduced to 16 ft., which gave an advance of 13 ft. per round, or 25 ft. per day. But although the rock was firm enough to permit full-face advance, that did not mean that everything was well. The roof and sides of the tunnel required bolting and netting, in addition to steel arches, to prevent collapse. Even the face had to be bolted to keep it in place. The number of bolts used varied from 15 to 25, and all told the Italian team placed 54,347 bolts to a total length of 270,000 feet. In addition, nearly 500 tons of protective netting was placed to catch falling rock. Water kept pouring in at a rate of 3,000 gals. per minute. However, the most embarrassing phenomenon of all was the temperature of the rock. According to all geological decencies it should have been around 40° C. (104° F.); actually, it was only 12° C. (54° F.). This extraordinarily low temperature raised the ghost of Lötschberg, because it could signify that water from the Toula glacier some 4,000 ft. above was seeping through fissures and porous material into the tunnel, and the miners could expect at any moment to be buried under the collapsing masses.

However, no catastrophe occurred. But the engineers and geologists spent a few anxious months waiting for the temperature to rise.

Eventually it did, although never beyond 28° C. (83° F.). On 10th December, when the heading had reached 11,808 ft., the miners struck a succession of cold springs, and for two days water jetted out of the face at a rate of 18,000 gals. per minute, in addition to a steady stream of 6,000 gals. per minute in the rear of the heading. After a few days the water subsided, and when only a foot of water was flowing throughout the length of the tunnel the miners went back to

Fig 147. View of the Italian portal installations, with the tunnel entrance to the right. A series of avalanches at left destroyed some of the buildings in 1962.

work. Up to the end of the year the advance was about a foot per day.

On 1st January 1962 the Italian team stood at 12,142 ft. During the previous year a total advance of 3,956 ft. had been made, or 11 ft. average daily advance. About 132,000 cu. yds. of rock had been excavated. The water flow had dropped to 4,500 gals. per minute, but the rock was still friable and the face had to be bolted and netted to keep it intact during the drilling. The time spent on scaling became excessive; about five hours were occupied with this safety work after each round, and during the first month of 1962 the advance was only 518 ft.

In February, however, the Italian miners struck good rock for the first time since they began the advance three years earlier. The full-face attack was resumed with "Lion" machines, and by the end of

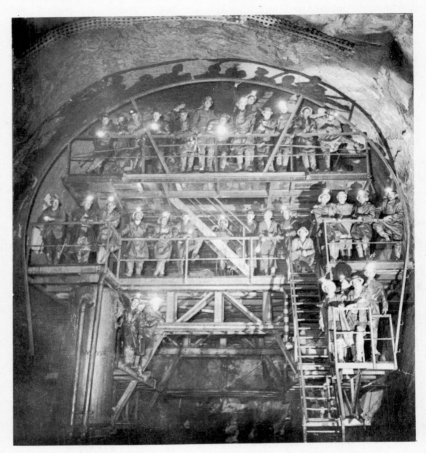

Fig 148. Italian drill team a few minutes before the advance began in protogine granite, encountered at 4,278 ft. from the southern portal, constituting the heart of the Mt. Blanc massif.

the month the mining team had progressed 807 ft., or nearly 29 ft. per day, the best monthly result recorded in the Mt. Blanc tunnel.

The good rock lasted only three weeks and in March the Italian team was again working in deteriorating rock. It was now decided to abandon full face altogether and instead to advance a tunnel of 565 sq. ft. in order to meet the French at mid-point of tunnel, at the 19,029-ft. mark. It was a wise decision. The protogine granite, although still treacherous and extremely dangerous after a round had released the rock tension, proved amenable to fast advance with the reduced area, and the Italian team advanced 919 ft. in March. It began to look as if the worst was over.

When the Avalanche Struck

But the Italian troubles were not yet over. The portal installations on the shelf hacked into the steep mountain-side were exposed to snow slides although no serious ones had actually hit this particular strip for many years. Then on 6th April 1962, at one o'clock in the morning—a few hours after European televiewers had witnessed the breakthrough in the neighbouring Grand St. Bernard tunnel—the Italian camp was struck by an avalanche. Three of the camp buildings were destroyed and three men killed; a fourth was dug out of the snow some hours later. It happened to be an important night in the Italian camp. Many of the visitors for the St. Bernard breakthrough were expected in the morning, and the management of Condotte d'Acqua, the contracting firm, was in camp when the avalanche struck. The time, however, was most fortunate; a new shift had gone on and the old one had not yet returned to camp when the snow and stone masses buried and destroyed the two dormitories at the extreme left of the camp. Work stopped and the engineers got busy with the rescue work. Everyone was ordered out from the security of the tunnel and the men were standing shivering in the cold night outside the portal when a silent uncanny force hit them and hurled 200 of them head first into the deep snow lining the slope. Some were completely buried, others were found with their legs sticking out of the snow.

A second later the cause of the mysterious force became all too evident to the men still remaining on their feet. A second avalanche came crashing down 500 ft. to the left of the first one. This was a big one; about 260,000 cu. yds. of snow and rock slid down from the mountain and destroyed and buried everything in its way. No one was actually hit, but the compressed air wave preceding the slide possessed such tremendous force that it lifted off the shelf every man it encountered. Actually, those buried in the snow were better off than those left standing at the portal, because during the next phase those who had remained unscathed came as close to death as they were ever likely to come. The fine dry snow filled their nostrils and lungs, some had their entire face enclosed in an airtight armour of fine snow compacted under tremendous pressure. Nearly everyone came close to choking to death; thirty men lost consciousness and had to be resuscitated with oxygen. Panic broke out among the survivors, but was quickly brought under control and the interrupted rescue work was resumed. When dawn rose over the peaks it was found that the second avalanche had in actual fact not caused any loss of life. Ten buildings had been destroyed or damaged during the night, by being hit by the first slide and by the pressure wave of the second. When digging into the wreck of one dormitory the rescuers found a Swedish drill-master sound asleep. He was the only one in the camp not aware of what had happened.

But such is the business of tunnelling that nothing must stop the advance. The badly shaken mining crew returned to the heading and left it to others to clean up the site.

The rate of advance was stepped up, and by the end of April the heading reached 14,596 ft. In May the team made record advances of 215 ft. per week, at the end of the month the heading was pushed ahead 52 ft. per day. On 4th June the heading passed the 16,405-ft. (5,000 m.) mark, and there remained only 2,625 ft. (800 m.) to the breakthrough. The total advance for May was 1,042 ft.

June was an even better month, with an advance of 1,327 ft. and a record daily advance of 57 ft. During July a further 1,335 ft., the fastest progress yet, were made without incident, and on 3rd August the mining team reached the half-way mark at 19,029 ft. (5,800 m.) The rumble of the French mining machine some distance away could be heard through the rock partition. The Italian advance had come to an end, and the team could relax waiting for the break-through.

Contrary to all expectations the tail end, usually the most difficult, lent itself to the best performance. During the seven months of 1962 a total advance of 6,885 ft. was made, or a daily progress of 31 ft. During these months 173,000 cu. yds. of rock were excavated, or about as much as was accomplished during the entire year of 1960, previously the best of the whole troublesome period spent in the bowels of Mt. Blanc.

Tunnelling the French Way

While the Italian operation was hampered by all the difficulties commonly associated with headings advanced from the southern slopes of the Alps, the French were spared some of the more gruesome aspects of Alpine tunnelling. The rock consisted of gneiss and schist for a distance of 1·2 miles, after which the heading entered the protogine granite core of the massif. As the advance continued the French miners had to struggle with unstable rock, but conditions never deteriorated so far as to necessitate a change of method. Whereas on the Italian side full-face advance could be used only for nineteen months all told, the French tunnelling machine was employed throughout the job.

The original French plan envisaged a three-shift operation with one 13-ft. round per shift and a daily advance of 40 ft. The mining and mucking team was to consist of forty-five men who would drill, blast and muck out 750 tons of rock per shift. The drilling of 1,800 ft. of holes was to occupy two hours, charging and firing a round one hour, ventilation twenty minutes and mucking three and a half hours. But it proved difficult to keep to this schedule. Although the initial rock proved generally firm, as predicted, there were some spots near the portal that were highly unstable and required 160 tons of steel arches for support. The miners were also troubled by water at the outset, although to an insignificant degree compared with the Italian side. For the rest of the advance the French were favoured by dry rock; the total flow did not exceed 160 gals. per hour.

None the less, the French had their share of trouble. The working cycle kept increasing in length. The time of drilling a round was exceeded by one hour, sometimes as much as four hours. Charging a round took longer than planned. Beyond all, mucking proved more time-consuming than the three and a half hours allotted to it. Getting rid of the muck took one to two hours longer; in some weeks six and a half hours were spent mucking out a round.

But serious and disappointing as were these delays to a site management responsible for getting maximum output from a highly capitalized productive plant, the greatest trouble was caused by the need to secure the rock on a scale never before required in rock tunnelling. Extensive rock bolting proved necessary from the outset, and as the heading advanced into the massif the need for securing the overstressed rock kept increasing. At first one or two hours were spent in securing the unstable ground, then the time grew to three, four, at times ten hours. At the end of two years, 72,000 bolts of a length varying from 3 to 6½ ft. had been placed to secure the roof and shoulders of the tunnel. The face, too, had to be bolted to keep it in place. There were times when the roof and sides had to be secured by five bolts per sq. m. (10·76 sq. ft.), while the face required fifty bolts to keep it from collapsing.

But poor rock was not the only trouble that M. André Gervais, the French site manager, had to deal with. His fine operation, including

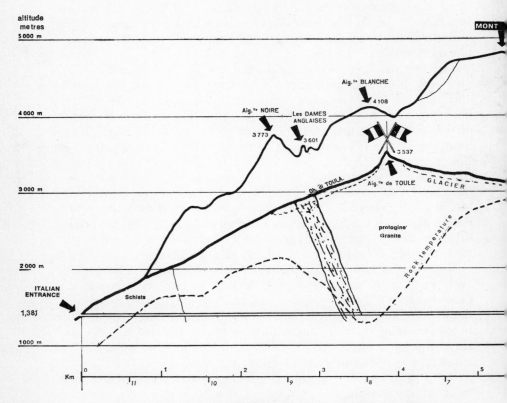

Fig 149. The Mt. Blanc Tunnel. Diagram showing distances, altitudes, rock formations and rock temperatures. Measurements are in metres.

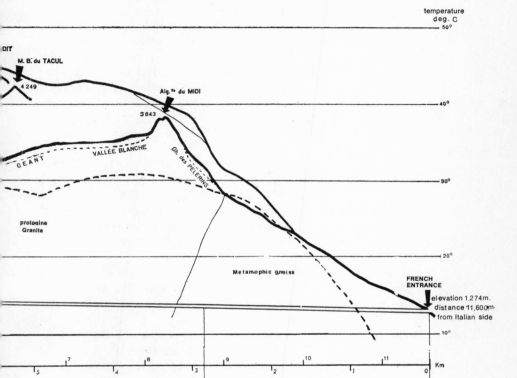

the best camp facilities ever installed on a construction site, was repeatedly held up for some reason or other. Work stopped after every accident involving loss of life. The mining team struck for higher pay, or in protest against incidents in the Algerian war, or for other political reasons. Over three months were lost in labour disputes. As a consequence, the average advance was 11½ ft. per round, or 35 ft. per day during the first year, an excellent performance under the circumstances and nearly three times better than the Italian advance. But as the advance continued the average kept declining, to about 22 ft. per day during the second year. The French half of the tunnel was scheduled for completion on 15th February 1962. That day the mining team stood at 15,880 ft. and about 13,200 ft. of lining had been placed. The rate of advance had declined further, to 18½ ft. per day.

Contrary to what happened on the Italian side, the temperature kept climbing as the French miners pushed ahead towards the heart of the mountain. In June 1961, at 11,500 ft., the rock temperature was 31° C. (88° F.), the highest recorded. Then it began to drop, and in April 1962, at about 16,200 ft., the temperature was down to 29° C. (84° F.). At no time did the rock temperature reach the 40–45° C. (104–113° F.) variously predicted.

Up to February 1962, the average French advance had been 544 ft. per month against an Italian average of 492 ft. Then came the Italian record month with 807 ft. full-face advance, compared with 525 ft. on the French side, and from that time on the Italian team began to gain on the leader. When in early March the Italians made the decision to concentrate on a top heading of 565 sq. ft. instead of the full area excavated by the French, the Italian speed of advance began to accelerate in spite of their other trouble. As the French passed the 5,000-m. mark (16,405 ft.) on 9th April the Italians were busy cleaning up their camp after the avalanches, but the team nevertheless gained 344 ft. on the French that month. The Italians passed the 5-km. mark (16,405 ft.) on 4th June, when their pace had been stepped up to 43 ft. per day, nearly three times as fast as the French progress which had slowed down to 15½ ft. per day. At the end of June the Italian team caught up with the French, and at exactly 22·01 o'clock on 3rd August they shot their last round which brought them to the midway point. The French reached their journey's end, at 19,016 ft., on 11th August, and a rock partition 13 ft. thick separated the two teams.

The breakthrough was postponed until 14th August, when the Chairman of the French syndicate, Edmond Giscard d'Estaing, had the honour of shooting the last round. The partition separating the

Fig 150. From the breakthrough in the Mt. Blanc. The Italian team enters the French half at noon on 14th August 1962.

two halves of the world's longest tunnel was shattered at 11.45 a.m., and the hour of celebration was at hand.

It was subsequently shown that the deviation of the axis towards the east was 5·3 in. and the difference in levels 8·3 in. The reported length of the tunnel was 7 miles 1,099·5 ft. (11,599·97 m.) but this figure is likely to be amended by the final check.

Fig 151. Italian Premier, Signor Amintore Fanfani, presents an Italian miner with the insignia of the Order of the Italian Republic.

So the tallest mountain in Europe had at long last been holed through. The cost in life came high. Altogether seventeen men had been killed, twelve of them in the tunnel; and 800 men had been injured, out of a total work force of 955 men when at maximum strength. The risk of being killed had been one in fifty-six and the chances of getting hurt came uncomfortably close to certainty. In cost of money, the Mt. Blanc tunnel also came high, something like £9 per cu. yd. of rock according to preliminary calculations, as against £1 4s. per cu. yd. for a 646-sq. ft. tunnel simultaneously driven in northern Scandinavia. The dynamite consumption had been 2·5 lb. per cu. yd. on the French side and 2 lb. on the Italian. The length of hole drilled to break out a cu. yd. of rock was 4 ft. on the French side and 3·8 ft. on the Italian. These critical unit figures are about double those normally required in firm gneiss and granite.

Fig 152. View of Mt. Blanc from the town of Courmayeur. The site of the southern portal, on a shelf cut into the mountain-side, can be seen roughly in the centre of the picture. The fourth peak to the left of a line drawn through the site is Europe's highest mountain, 15,781 ft. tall.

The total length of roof bolts put in by the French alone reached about 465,000 yds. For the entire tunnel the figure came to more than one million yards, an all-time record in rock bolting.

It is not to be wondered at if under these conditions all cost and time estimates were shattered. Fortunately for both contractors, it proved possible to adjust the original contract prices to fit the actual conditions. Old-time tunnel contractors, held to their original estimates, would have been forced into bankruptcy at the end of their struggle with the stubborn mountain.

The breakthrough marked the end of the dramatic phase, but much work remained to complete the tunnel. For one thing, the Italian team had to bench out the bottom part that had been left behind in the final spurt towards the midpoint. After that the traffic deck had to be put in, followed by the installation of the ventilation plant and other services required to make the tunnel viable. Another year or a year and a half would be required before the Mt. Blanc tunnel would be open for traffic.

None the less the job was done, or at any rate the part that matters in the advance of long mountain tunnels. The time was at hand to put official approval on the heroic feat of piercing the last and most formidable barrier on the continent of Europe. On 15th September the French and Italian political establishments, headed by the premiers Messrs. Georges Pompidou and Amintore Fanfani, went through the tunnel and descended on the mountain town of Courmayeur to place the oratorical cap stone deemed suitable for such occasions.

But something else happened on that memorable day, something unique in the long and grim history of underground work. One by one, some seventy Italian miners were called to the reviewing stand in front of the tunnel portal and were ordained Cavaliers of the Order of the Italian Republic for their courage and devotion to duty during three years of bitter struggle with the mountain. At long last the anonymous peaceful heroes of the western world had become recognized and honoured for their accomplishments. Perhaps, after all, there is some truth—in a wider sense—in the words attributed to Galileo, *Eppur si muove*.

GLOSSARY

Ajutage. Roman term designating size of water delivery pipes and outlet spouts.

Anhydrate. Dehydrate.

Anhydrite. Anhydrous calcium sulphate, related to gypsum.

Argillaceous slate. Clayey slate.

Basalt. A fine-grained black and hard igneous rock.

Batter legs. Sloping legs.

Black powder. Gunpowder, when used for blasting of a different formula from propellant powder.

Blende. Any one of several minerals, chiefly sulphides, with a bright but non-metallic lustre.

Blocky rock. Rock ore that breaks into large blocks.

Bloom. A mass of wrought iron obtained by the direct process of iron making.

Brattice. A wall of separation in a gallery, erected for deflecting air towards the working-places.

Buddler. A workman who works an inclined trough or plane for washing out the light particles of a crushed ore.

Cadastral survey. Survey for the purpose of delineating landed property.

Carbon-14 dating. A method of determining the age of an artifact by means of measuring the rate of radiation of the carbon isotope C-14 present in all organic matter. The so-called half-life of C-14 has been determined at 5,568 years. If, for example, a piece of charcoal gives off radiation at half the rate of a modern piece of charcoal it is 5,568 years old. An object giving off a different rate can be dated by interpolation on the radiation scale.

Centre core method. Method of tunnelling whereby the centre is left to the last for excavation.

Decauville car. A narrow-gauge railway car, named after its inventor Paul Decauville (1840–92).

Dimensional stone. Building stone cut to measure.

Dolerite. A hard, dark, green igneous rock used as a tool by ancient Egyptian stone masons.

Double-jack. Method of hand drilling using three men, two wielding heavy hammers and one turning the steel.

Drift. A horizontal passage underground, or tunnel, driven into an ore deposit and used for communication purposes.

Extrados. The exterior arc of an arch, as in a tunnel.

Feldspar. A group of crystalline minerals, usually white in colour.

Fire-setting. Process of cracking or spalling a working-face with fire.

Fuller's earth. An earthy substance resembling potter's clay but lacking in plasticity.

Fulminate. A salt of the highly explosive fulminic acid.

Galena. Native lead sulphide, the principal ore of lead.

Geodosy. Branch of surveying that takes account of the curvature of the earth.

Geothermic (Geothermal) gradient. Increase of the temperature of the earth from the surface downwards, averaging about 1° F. for each 60 ft.

Gneiss. A laminated or foliated metamorphic rock corresponding in composition to granite.

Graded; to grade. A slope upwards or downwards; to determine the rate of its increase or decrease.

Grouting; to grout. To fill out or finish with mortar or cement.

Gunnison granite. A type of granite found at Gunnison, Colorado.

Gypsum. Hydrous calcium sulphate.

Heading. The end of a drift, gallery or tunnel.

Horse-whim. A device used for raising ore or water from mines, provided with radiating beams to which horses, oxen or camels may be yoked.

Intrados. The interior curve of an arch, as of a tunnel lining.

Invert. The curved floor of a tunnel.

Jumbo. Drilling platform used in tunnelling.

Jumper. A steel bar used in manual drilling.

kW. Abbreviation of kilowatt, or 1,000 watts, equivalent to 1·341 horsepower.

Lias. Oldest division of the Jurassic system.

Marl. Crumbling deposit consisting of clay and calcium carbonate.

Mesozoic. Belonging to the second geological period.

Micrometer. A screw with a graduated head used for measuring small distances.

Miocene period. Preceding the Pliocene.

Molybdenum. A brittle metallic element used in the alloying of steel for high-speed tools, construction members, etc.

Muck; mucker; to muck out. Broken rock or other material to be removed; the worker occupied with loading ore or debris; to do this work.

MW. Abbreviation of megawatt, or 1,000 kW.

Mylonite. A crumbling variety of quartz metamorphosed under great pressure.

Oolite. Limestone rock of the Jurassic system consisting of small round grains, resembling fish roe, cemented together.

Phyllite. A crumbling slatey rock metamorphosed by chemical and mechanical action under great pressure.

Pitman. Old term for connecting rod.

Portal. Entrance to a tunnel.

P.s.i. Pounds per square inch.

Pyrites. Common minerals of brass-yellow colour, 'fool's gold', containing iron, copper or tin.

Qanaat. A small capacity water-tunnel commonly used in the Middle East.

Rake; raker. A timber placed at an angle.

R.p.m. Revolutions per minute.

Schist; schistous. A metamorphic crystalline rock with a closely foliated structure, such as mica and hornblende schists. A schistous rock differs from gneiss by lacking feldspar.

Serpentine. A rock consisting of hydrous magnesium silicate, usually of a dull green colour.

Shaker. A workman who turns the drill steel while it is hammered into rock.

Shot-peen. Method of surface treating steel to increase its resistance to surface fatigue by bombarding the surface with high velocity steel shots.

Single-jack. Method of manual drilling with one man wielding the hammer and turning the steel.

Sinter, to sinter. Firing and fusing a mineral without actually melting it.

Spalling; to spall. To break off small flat pieces of rock, formerly by means of fire-setting. Rock under excessive tension may also spall, i.e. throw off thin surface slabs.

Spathic iron. A native ferrous carbonite, also called siderite, containing 48 per cent iron and usually traces of manganese. It is the best native ore for making steel tools by the direct method formerly used.

Spiles. Sharpened planks driven into the soft ground of headings as a protection against runs; also called forepoles.

Stope; to stope. Method and system involved in excavating an ore deposit; to extract ore underground. See *Drift.*

Stringer. In geology and mining, a narrow vein; in American railway building, a longitudinal construction member in a bridge or tunnel.

Taconite ore. A type of highly abrasive iron ore now extensively mined in America.

Voussoir. Any wedge-shaped piece of which an arch or vault is composed. The centre voussoir is the keystone.

BIBLIOGRAPHY

Abel, Deryck: *Channel Underground*, Pall Mall, London (1961).
Agricola, Georgius: *De Animantibus Subterraneis*.
  Ibid.: *De Re Metallica*, translated by H. C. Hoover and Lou H. Hoover, Dover, New York.
Andreae, C.: *Der Bau langer tiefliegender Gebirgstunnel*, Julius Springer, Berlin (1926).
Andree, J.: 'Bergbau in Vorzeit', in *Vorzeit*, by H. Hahne, Kabitzsch, Leipzig (1922).
Ardaillon, Edouard: *Les Mines du Laurion*, Paris (1897).
Aristotle: *Physics*, translated by P. Wicksteed and F. M. Camford, The Loeb Classical Library, Harvard.
Atlas Diesel & Sandvik Steel Co. Ltd.: *Rock Blasting Manual*, Stockholm (1954–62).
Boethius, B.: *Gruvornas, hyttornas och hamrarnas folk*, Tiden, Stockholm (1951).
Bromehead, C. E. N.: 'The Early History of Water Supply', *Geographical Journal*, 99 (1942).
Ibid.: 'The Evidence for Ancient Mining', *Geographical Journal*, 96 (1940).
Brückmann, F. E.: *Magnalia Dei in locus subterraneis* (1727).
Clark, G. and Piggot, S.: 'The Age of the British Flint Mines', *Antiquity*, 7 (1933).
Clark, J. G. D.: 'Water in Antiquity', *Antiquity*, 18 (1944).
Compressed Air Review (1920–60).
Delius, C. T.: *Anleitung zu der Baukunst* (1773).
Cancrinus, Franz Ludwig: *Erste Gründe der Berg- und Saltzwerkskunde* (1773–90).
Diodorus: The Loeb Classical Library, Harvard.

Dolezalek: *Der Eisenbahntunnel,* Urban & Schwartzenberg, Berlin, (1919).

Drinker, H. S.: *Tunneling,* John Wiley, New York (1878).

Ein Jarhundert Schweizer Bahnen, 1847–1947, Verlag Huber, Frauenfeld (1949).

Ellis, H.: *British Railway History,* Macmillan, New York (1955).

Engineering, 1871–1924, London.

Enzyklopädie des Eisenbahnwesens, Berlin (1921).

Frontinus: *De Aquis Urbis Romae (The Aqueducts of Rome),* translated by Charles Bennet, The Loeb Classical Library, Harvard.

Gurney, O.R.: *The Hittites,* Penguin Books, London (1952).

Granström, G. A.: *Ur Sala Gruvas Historia,* Västerås (1940).

Hammond, Rolt: *Tunnel Engineering,* Macmillan, New York (1959).

Herodotus: The Loeb Classical Library, Harvard.

IVA: *Bergsprängning,* Stockholm (1959).

Kossuth, F.: 'Mont Cenis Tunnel', *Engineering* (1871).

Lindroth, S.: *Gruvbrytning och Kopparhantering vid Stora Kopparberget,* I, Almqvist & Wiksell, Uppsala (1955).

Mathesius, Johan: *Sarepta oder Bergpostill,* Nürnberg (1562).

Ministero Dei Lavori: *Il Traforo Del Monte Bianco,* Rome (1959–1962).

Nash: *The Rio Tinto Mines,* London (1904).

Noble, C.: *The Brunels,* Cobden-Sanderson, London (1938).

Payne, R.: *The Canal Builders,* Macmillan, New York (1959).

Pestalozzi, S.: 'Die Bauarbeiten am Simplontunnel', *Schweizerische Bauzeitung,* 1958.

Pliny: *Natural History,* The Loeb Classical Library, Harvard.

Post & Inrikes Tidningar (1859).

Proceedings of the Institution of Civil Engineers, Vol. XXIII, London (1864).

Rehnberg, M. edit.: *Gruvminnen,* Nordiska Museet, Stockholm (1960).

Ibid.: *Rallarminnen,* Nordiska Museet, Stockholm (1949).

Richardson, H. W., and Mayo, R. S.: *Practical Tunnel Driving,* McGraw-Hill, New York (1941).

Rock Drill Data, Ingersoll-Rand Company, New York (1960).

Rössler, B.: *Hellpolierter Bergbauspiegel* (1700).

Sandars, H.: 'The Use of the Deer-horn Pick in the Mining Operations of the Ancients', *Archaeologia,* Vol. LXII (1911).

SBB Nachrichtenblatt, Berne (1955–6).

Schweizerische Bauzeitung (1890–1934).

Singer, C. *et al.*: *A History of Technology,* Oxford University Press, New York (1954–8).

Slater, H. and Barnett, C.: *The Channel Tunnel,* Allan Wingate, London (1958).

Strabo: *Geography,* translated by H. L. Jones, The Loeb Classical Library, Harvard.

Suetonius: *Vitae XII Caesarum, V. Claudius* (*Lives of the Twelve Caesars*), The Loeb Classical Library, Harvard.

Tacitus: *Annales,* The Loeb Classical Library, Harvard.

Tracy, J. C.: *Plane Surveying,* John Wiley, New York (1906).

Unesco Courier (1961).

Vattenfallsstyrelsen: *Statens Vattenfallsverk under fyra deceunier* (1948).

Vitruvius: *On Architecture,* edited from the Harleian manuscript 2767 and translated by F. Granger, Heinemann, London (1931).

Wolff, Hans.: *Hårdmetall för bergborr,* Bergslaget (1956).

Wylie, J. C.: *The Wastes of Civilization,* Faber, London (1959).

INDEX

Abbot's Cliff, tunnel at, 345
Abu Simbel, 2, 55 (*ill.*)
Agatharchides, 8–9, 26, 28
Agricola, Georgius, 7, 10, 42–51, 249, 251
Agrippa, Marcus, 66, 67
Aiguille du Midi, 386
Air compressors, 138, 140 (*ill.*), 141–2, 143 (*ill.*), 152, 155, 166 (*ill.*), 167, 181, 287; development of, 297–303 (*with ills.*)
Air locks, 234–7
Airolo, 164–6, 168 (*ill.*), 171, 173, 175 (*ill.*), 177 (*ill.*), 181
Alaric the Visigoth, 69
Albanus, Lake, 62
Alexander the Great, 39, 62
Allaria, Pietro, 383
Allegheny tunnel, 95, 115
Alps: Hannibal's crossing of, 29–30; first tunnel (Fréjus), 132–60; surveys, 252–7; tunnels (general), 14–18, 268, 286, 288, 310 (*see also* Arlberg, Lötschberg, Mt. Blanc, St. Gotthard *and* Simplon); tunnellers, 17 (*ill.*); underground power houses, 369
Althorp, Lord, 215
America, American: breakthroughs, 266; Broadway tunnel, 220; canals, 82–3; Channel tunnel scheme, 353; compressors, 298–299, 302–3; early tunnels, 82–3, 83 (*ill.*), 97 (*ill.*), 115, 156, 246; inventions, 287–8, 302, 310, 313;

mining methods, 275, 283; rock drills, 135, 145, 293–6; systems of tunnelling, 95, 97 (*ill.*), 113, 129–131, 360, 365–7, 390, 392, 394; underground power house, 368. (*See also* Great Lakes, Hoosac *and* Hudson River)
Angelini, Abbé, 341
Antwerp tunnel, 235
Appolonia, siege of, 4
Aqueducts: America, 95; Assyria, 52–3, 60; Egypt, 53–4; Greece, 60–62; Palestine, 57–9; Roman, 64–7, 134
Arabah mines, 25
Ararat mines, 24
Arlberg tunnel, 180–3, 187, 266
Armenia, 24, 25, 34, 59, 313
Aswan, 2, 54, 56
Athens, 35, 60
Atlas machines, 296, 324–6, 328, 360, 375–6, 389, 392
Australia: irrigation tunnels, 369
Austria: railway tunnels, 95, 107, 108 (*ill.*), 109; tunnelling system, 95 (*ill.*), 113, 119–24, 121–3 (*ills.*), 125 (*ill.*), 332
Avernus, Lake, 64

Bacon, Roger, 275–6
Baebelo tunnel, 27
Baker, Sir Benjamin, 235
Baltimore and Ohio Railroad, 97 (*ill.*), 130
Bardonnèche, 133–4, 136, 138, 139

(ill.), 140 (ill.), 142, 144, 253, 256
Barlow, P. W., 216, 219; shield, 216, 218, 219 (ill.), 220, 233
Bartlett, T., 135, 288
Beach, A. S., 220, 225, 246
Bech, A., 162
Belgium, Belgian: canals, 81 (ill.), 81–2; first Continental tunnel, 94; flint mines, 21–2, 22–3 (ills.); system of tunnelling, 115–18, 116–117 (ills.), 397 (ill.)
Berner Alpen Rly, 331
Bertola da Novate, 71
Bickford, William, 282
Bleechingly tunnel, 114
Borelli (engineer), 253
Borie, André, 384
Borsi (contractor), 174
Böschlin, Prof. F., 339
Boston–Hudson canal, 153
Box tunnel, 90–3, 92 (ill.)
Brandau, Karl, 185, 194
Brandt, Alfred, 181–3, 185, 194
Brazil: tunnel collapse, 107, 107 (ill.), 109
'Breaking out', 113
Bridel, M. G., 172
Bridgewater, Francis, Duke of, 75–6, 79, 84
Bridgewater Canal, 75–6
Brig, 186, 190, 330–1
Brindley, James, 75–7, 84
Brown, Nicholas, 77
Brunel, Isambard Kingdom, 90, 93, 134, 214 (ill.)
Brunel, Sir Marc Isambard, 90, 209–16, 219, 227; shield invented by, 209–16, 210 (ill.), 212 (ill.), 233
Brunlees, Sir James, 343
Bull, Sir William, 348
Burleigh, Charles, 155, 290–1, 295, 301, 302

Calais, 342, 344, 349, 358
Cambridge, George, Duke of, 346
Cameron, A. S., 292
Camillus, Marcus Furius, 5
Canals: American, 82–3; English, 73–80, 76 (ill.); European, 70–3, 80–2, 252; mitre lock gates, 72; pound-lock, 71

Canal tunnels, 14, 73–83; first tunnel, 73
Capello, Signor, 150, 253
Carlisle, Sir Anthony, 91
Carlo Alberto, King of Sardinia, 134
Cartagena, 27, 28
Caucasus: mines of, 24, 26, 34
Cavour, Count, 135, 136
Cemeteries, 3
Central London Rly., 241
Centre Core method, 54–5, 118, 119 (ill.)
Chamonix, 382, 384–5
Channel bridge: schemes for, 342, 348, 349
Channel ferry service, 351
Channel tunnel, 15, 268, 340–58; Committee report (1930), 349–351; dangers of, 339, 355–6; diagram of, 350; economic study (1960), 353–4; famous objectors to, 346; Low scheme tried, 345–6; present position, 351–8; Study Group, 353, 355
Channel Tunnel Co., 344, 345, 347, 349–50, 352–3; share prices, 353
Charleroi Canal, 81 (ill.), 82, 115
Charles I, King, 277
Charles IX, King of Sweden, 10
Chemnitz, 42, 297, 299, 313
'Cherry picker' method, 392–3
Chesapeake and Ohio Railroad, 98
Chesbrough, E. S., 220, 224
Chevalier, Michel, 343, 344
Chicago water tunnel, 220–3, 222 (ill.)
China: explosives, 275–6; pound-lock, 71 (n.)
Chorobate, Roman, 246
Churchill, Sir Winston, 357–8
Cincinnati tunnel, 246, 247 (ill.)
City and Southwark Subway, 237–241
Civil engineers, first, 85
Clausthal mines, 279, 281–2
Cleveland water tunnel, 223–6
Cocceius, 1
Cochrane, Lord, 234, 235
Colladon, Prof. D., 135, 142, 166–7, 173, 176, 301
Colombo, Prof. Giuseppe, 187
Computors (for tunnels), 380

Condotte d'Acqua company, 382 (*n.*), 384, 401
Conway machines, 392
Copais Lake drainage scheme, 61–2
Copper mining, 13, 24–6, 30, 33, 35, 42, 273, 274 (*ill.*), 310
Corinth, Isthmus of, 63
Coromant drills, 307, 312, 390
Couch, J. J., 289–91, 295
Courmayeur, 385–6, 409 (*ill.*), 410
Cristina tunnel, 124–9, 125–9 (*ills.*)
Croton aqueducts, 95
Ctesibius of Alexandria, 297
Cžernitz tunnel, 119, 119 (*ill.*)

De Gamond, Thomé, 341–4, 355
Delaware tunnel, 366
Digges, Thomas, 251
Diodorus, 27, 54
Dioptra, 247–8
Doane, Thomas, 155–7, 159, 290, 302
Dom Pedro tunnel, 107 (*ill.*), 107–9
Dover, 342, 344–5, 348, 351, 354–5, 358
Drainage schemes, ancient, 62–3
Dresden–Leipzig Rly, 94 (*ill.*), 118–119
'Drilling and shooting', 279, 280–2 (*ills.*), 296
Drilling contests (U.S.A.), 101
Drum digger shield, 243
Dubois–François machines, 302 (*ill.*)
Dynamite, 148, 164, 283–5, 304–5

Eastwear tunnel, 342
Edwards, A. F., 154, 287
Egypt: aqueducts, 53–4, 59; canal-building, 53–4; Labyrinth, 53–4; mining, 8–9, 10 (*ill.*), 24–6, 51, 248, 250, 251 (*map*), 271; quarrying, 54–7; temple organs, 297; tunnels to tombs, 2, 6
Ellora caves, 2
Erasmus, Desiderius, 42
Ericsson, John, 84
Erie Canal, 82, 153
Estaing, Edmund d', 406
Etruscans, 5, 248
Eupalinus of Megara, 61
Euphrates tunnel, 216

European Economic Community, 354
Explosives, 271–85. (*See also* Dynamite *and* Gunpowder)

Falu copper mine, 13, 42, 273, 274 (*ill.*)
Fanfani, Amintore, 408 (*ill.*), 410
Favre, Louis, 163(*ill.*), 164, 168, 171, 174, 176, 179, 197
Fazio, Giuseppe de, 398
Ferroux machines, 167–8, 181–3
Fertile Crescent, 13, 33, 35, 53, 60, 245
Filippo of Modena, 71
Fioravante of Bologna, 71
Fire-setting, 25, 28–30, 46–7, 50, 55, 271–3, 272 (*ill.*), 274 (*ill.*)
Fleuss, H. A., 229
Flint mines, 20–3, 21–3 (*ills.*)
Forepoling, 109–13, 111–12 (*ills.*)
Fosse Dike, 73
Fougerolle, (engineer), 357
Fourneaux, 136, 138, 256
Fowle, Joseph, 135, 290–1, 295
Fox, Sir Francis, 187, 348
Fox, James, 341
France: canals, 14, 72–3, 81–2; Channel tunnel schemes, 340–4, 350, 352; flint mines, 21–2; railway tunnels, 94; road tunnel, *see* Mont Blanc.
Frederick I, Emperor, 70
Frederick II, Emperor, 161
Freiberg, 42, 275, 279, 280, 288
Fréjus tunnel, 15, 17, 116, 133–52 (*with ills.*), 162, 164, 283, 287–8, 320, 383; drilling methods, 145–9, 301; opening of, 150–2, 151 (*ill.*), 180; portal installations, 138, 140 (*ill.*), 141; survey for, 252–3, 254–255 (*ills.*), 256–7, 260, 266; working conditions, 138–41, 147–50
Frindsbury tunnel, 79 (*ill.*)
Frisius, Gemma, 252
Frontinus, Julius, 65–9, 73
Fucinus Emissarium tunnel, 62–3

Gardner, G. A., 291
Gastern Valley, 331, 334–7
Gehrlich (engineer), 172
Gelpke, M. O., 162

Geneva, 383–4, 387
Geophysics, 269–70
Germany: compressor, 330; mining, 272 (*ill.*), 279, 281–2, 312; railway tunnels, 94 (*ill.*), 94–5; tungsten carbide developed, 305–6
Gervais, André, 403
Gerwig, R., 162, 172
Giorgio, Francesco di, 278
Gold mining, 6–9, 10 (*ill.*), 25–7, 35, 246, 250–1
Gooch, Sir Daniel, 232
Goppenstein, 331–3
Göschenen, 164–5, 174, 176
Goslar lead mines, 42
Göttingen, siege of, 278
Grakofel gold-mine, 251
Grand Trunk Canal, 76–7
Granholm, Axel, 320
Grattoni (engineer), 136, 150
Greathead, J. H., 218–20, 232–8, 241–2; shield invented by, 233–4, 240, 243
Great Lakes tunnels, 220–6, 232
Great St. Bernard, 367, 401
Great Western Rly, 90, 92, 226–32, 237
Greeks, ancient: conduits, 60–2; mining, 7–9, 24, 26, 33–9, 36 (*ill.*); syrinx, 297 (*n.*)
Greulich, C., 331
Grimes Graves, 21–2
Griz Nez, Cap, 342, 344, 355
Gumpoldskirch tunnel, 95, 95 (*ill.*), 120
Gunpowder: invention of, 275–6; electric firing of, 282–3; safety fuse for, 282; used for blasting, 148, 155, 278–83 (*with ills.*)
Gunter, Edmund, 251
Gustaf I, King of Sweden, 277

Hackworth, Timothy, 84
Hadrian, Emperor, 10, 41
Haglund, Wilhelm, 307
Hallstatt salt mines, 30–3, 36; tools from, 32 (*ill.*), 314–15
Hannibal, 27–9
Harecastle tunnel, 76–7
Haskins, De Witt, 235
Hauenstein tunnel, 95, 96 (*ill.*), 115

Hawkshaw, Sir John, 229–30, 233, 343–5, 348
Hawksworth, A. L., 310
Hawtree, Dr., 91
Hellwag (engineer), 172
Henry, John, 98–100
Hero of Alexandria, 247, 297
Herodotus, 54, 60–1
Hezekiah, King of Judah, 59, 245–6
Hill, Ebenezer, 303
Hiroshima, 359
Hittman, F., 331
Holland tunnel, 242
Holmes, Oliver Wendell, 152
Honduras compressor, 299
Hoosac tunnel, 15, 115, 152–60 (*with ills.*), 283, 286–8; contractors for, 154, 156–7, 159; lining, 159, 159 (*ill.*); methods used, 155–7, 291 (*ill.*); survey of, 257–60; tools, 290–1, 295, 300–1 (*ills.*), 301–2
Hoover, Herbert, 29
Horeau, M., 342
Huddersfield Canal Co., 78
Hudson River tunnels, 235–7, 242 (*ill.*)
Hulagu, General, 60
Hydro-electric schemes, *see* Power plants

India: rock temples, 2, 3 (*ill.*); water tunnels, 59
Ingersoll, Simon, 291. (*See also* Rock-drilling machines)
Iselle, 185–6, 188–90, 201
Italy: early railway tunnels, 95; medieval canals, 70–2; steel-making, 34; system of tunnelling, 124–9 (*with ills.*); tunnel schemes, 383–4; underground power station; 378 (*ill.*). (*See also* Mt. Blanc, Rome *and* Simplon)

Jackhammers, 295
Jacobs, Charles M., 236
Jericho, siege of, 4
Jerusalem: water tunnel, 59, 245
Jerwan aqueduct, 53
Jessops (canal-builders), 75
Jet piercing, 273, 275
Joachimsthal, 42, 49
Job, Book of, 25, 28

Johnson, Dr. James, 91
Julius Africanus, 275

Kander torrent, 331, 333-6, 339
Karst Rly, 107, 108 (*ill.*), 109
Kharga oasis, 59
Kiruna, 318, 322, 364
Königsdorf tunnel, 94 (*ill.*), 118
Kossuth, Francis, 133 (*n.*)

Ladder-drilling method, 397
Lambert (diver), 229-30
Languedoc Canal, 14, 72-3, 252
Lanino, G., 129
Lapland, 279, 312, 318, 329
Latrobe, Benjamin H., 97, 288
Lead mining, 35-6, 42
Leeds, Dewsbury and Manchester Rly, 93
Leone, Monte, 184-5, 189, 190, 194, 260
Lewis, John L., 314
Leyner, J. G., 294-5, 310-11
Lincoln tunnel, 242, 242 (*ill.*)
Linnaeus, Carolus, 13
Little St. Bernard Pass, 29-20
Liverpool-Manchester Rly, 87
Livy, 5, 28, 30
Locke, Joseph, 87-8, 343
Locker-Freuler, Edward, 194, 197
London: New River, 74 (*n.*); underground rlys, 237-44
London and N.-W. Rly, 93
London-Birmingham Rly, 89
Lonza Valley, 331-3
Lötschberg tunnel, 330-9, 360; breakthrough, 338; great achievement of, 339
Low, George, 293
Low, William, 343-5, 347
Lübeck canal, 70
Luft, Hans, 282
Luma factory, 306-7

McAdoo, William, 236
Manchester-Liverpool Canal, 76
Manchester-Sheffield Rly, 87-8
Mann, William, 300, 303
Marcus Graecus, 276
Marseilles, siege of, 4
Mathieu-Favier, Albert, 341

Mauri, Pietro, 396
Mauss, Heinrich, 134-5, 287
Measuring instruments: ancient, 246-8; medieval, 251; electronic 266-7
Médail, G. F., 133-4
Mediterranean: rock tombs, 2
Merat, 278
Mersey tunnel, 242
Merthyr Tydfil tramway, 84
Meschini, Giulio Cesare, 394(*n.*)
Metropolitan Rly. 237-8
Meyer, Jean, 185
Milan, 70-2, 161, 387
Miller, Sebastian, 275
Mining: Bronze Age, 24-33, 313; Iron Age, 34-41; early maps, 251; medieval, 41-51, 45 (*ill.*), 47-8 (*ills.*), 248-9, 250 (*ill.*), 313; modern methods, 313-15
Modane, 133-4, 138, 139 (*ill.*), 144
Moeris, Lake, 53-4
Mont Blanc motor-tunnel, 367, 381-410 (*with ills.*); accidents, 394, 396, 398, 401-2, 406; breakthrough, 406, 408; contractors, 384, 389, 393, 410; equipment used, 145, 389-94 (*with ills.*); finance, 384, 408; geological survey, 268, 387, 389; glaciers, 386, 398; measurements and other data, 384, 386-387, 404-5 (*ills.*), 408; miners, 381, 393, 401-2, 406, 408 (*ill.*), 410; rates of advance, 393-403, 406; situation of, 385 (*map*), 386, 388 (*map*), 409 (*ill.*): ventilation, 393, 410; work on French side, 387, 390, 391 (*ill.*), 392-4, 402-3, 406, 408; work on Italian side, 389-90, 392-402 (*with ills.*), 407 (*ill.*), 408
Mont Cenis tunnel, *see* Fréjus
Montecalvi trucks, 389
Montgolfier's water ram, 142
Mont Laurion mines, 35-9, 36-7 (*ills.*), 56
Morgenstern, Caspar, 279
Motor-tunnels, 367, 381; Channel schemes for, 352, 354
Mottray, Mr, 341
'Mucking', 312
Muir, E. E., 236

Mycenae, 58, 62
Myddleton Canal, 74 (*n.*)

Naples–Ostia canal, 63–4
Napoleon I, 15, 81, 161, 189, 340–1
Napoleon III, 342–3
Nasmyth, James, 288
Navarino, battle of, 213
Navarro, Pedro, 278, 279
Naviglio Grande, 70–1
Naviglio Interno, 72
'Navvies', 85–6
Nero, Emperor, 63–4
New York, 153, 209, 282, 292; code
    for tunnellers, 237; first rapid
    transit tunnel, 241; other tunnels,
    95, 220, 235–6
New Zealand, 115
Niagara Falls, 292 (*ill.*), 317
Nicholson, Thomas, 93
Nile, R., 26, 54, 55 (*ill.*)
Nineveh: sewer tunnel, 53 (*ill.*)
Nineveh Canal, 52–3, 57
Nobel, Alfred, 164, 283–4, 304
Noirieu tunnel, 81
North Africa: *qanaats*, 58
Norway: gunpowder, 279; tunnel-
    ling, 365
Nubia: gold-mines, 25–6;   rock
    temples, 2

Oberau tunnel, 119, 130
Oil prospecting, offshore, 356
Oppau: explosion at, 284–5
Osram factory, 305
Ostia, 63, 64
Outram, Benjamin, 75, 78
Oxford tunnel (U.S.A.), 130

Palestine, 57–8, 245
Papin, Denis, 298
Paris, 241, 343, 383, 387
Paris–Constantinople line, 181
Pausilippo tunnel, 1
Payerne, Prosper, 342
Pennines: canals through, 77, 78
    (*map*)
Persia (Iran): water conduits, 58–
    60, 246
Philbuick (engineer), 257
Phocylides, 7
Phoenicians, 27, 29, 245

Plenum process, 233–7
Pliny, 27–9, 41, 297
Po drainage scheme, 62
Polybius, 28
Pompidou, Georges, 410
Porjus power station, 317–29, 319–
    320 (*ills.*), 327 (*plan*), 364; condi-
    tions at, 321–4; excavation of
    cavern, 325–8; transport to, 320–
    321, 324; tunnels, 324–5, 328–9
Pound-lock, first European, 71
Power plants: early, 317; under-
    ground, 317–29, 319 (*ill.*), 367–79
Priestly's hydraulic pump, 298–9
Primrose Hill tunnel, 89

Qanaats, 13–14, 58 (*ill.*), 58–60, 134,
    246
Quarrying: ancient, 54–7

Raffles, Lady, 213
Railways: first British, 85–94; first
    public, 87; first tunnels for, 14–18,
    83–101, 106, 134, 216; Scandi-
    navian, 86
Rameses II, 2, 26
Rand, Addison C., 303
Rand mines, 295
Rathen, Baron von, 300
Red Sea Canal, 60
Rennie family, 75
Rhône, R., 184, 188, 200, 330
Richard I, King, 275
Richardson, Charles, 227
Rieti marshes, 62
Riquet, Pierre-Paul, 72–3
Riqueval tunnel, 81
Road-tunnels, *see* Motor-tunnels
Roanne–Andrezieux line, 87 (*n.*)
Rock-drilling machines, 286–312
    (*with ills.*); airleg, 295–6, 296 (*ill.*),
    389; American, 135, 145, 287–96
    (*with ills.*); Atlas, *see* Atlas mach-
    ines; boom-mounted, 367; Brand
    hydraulic, 181–3, 191, 205–6;
    British, 288, 291; Burleigh, 155,
    290–1, 291 (*ill.*), 295, 301 (*ill.*),
    302; downhole type, 390; Cavé,
    288; hammer drill, 293–6; Inger-
    soll, 205–6, 291–2, 295, 332, 390;
    jackleg, 360, 367; McKean, 227–8;
    Meyer, 332; St. Gotthard types,

167–8,168 (*ill.*); Schumann's, 288, 289 (*ill.*); Sommeiller's, 135, 138, 141–5, 143–6 (*ills.*), 167; Swedish, 296, 377 (*ill.*); tungsten carbide, *q.v.*

Rock temples, 2–3, 3 (*ill.*)

Rock tombs, 2

Rollier, Dr. L., 331

Romans: aqueducts, 64–7; canals in Britain, 73; drainage schemes, 62–3; engineering instruments, 246–8, 248 (*ill.*); horse harness, 64; mining, 9, 26, 28, 39–41 (*with ills.*); tunnels, 1, 4–5; water laws, 67–70

Rome, 62, 161, 383, 387; catacombs, 2; water supply, 64–70

Rosenmund, Max, 260, 265

Rössler, Balthasar, 279

Rotherhithe–Wapping tunnel, 87, 209, 211–17 (*with ills.*)

Route Blanche, 383–4

Rowe (engineer), 298

Ruggeri, Ercole, 394

Ruhr, 161

Russia: machine for soft ground, 208, 314

Ryd, Erik, 296, 306

Safety devices, modern, 362–3

Sahara, 59

St. Barbara, *Frontispiece*, 193, 381

St. Cloud tunnel, 116

St. Gotthard Pass: carriage road, 161–2; hospice, 161; railway schemes, 162

St. Gotthard tunnel, 15, 17, 115, 116, 118, 124, 150, 161–79 (*with ills.*), 180–2, 186–7, 190, 197, 206, 266, 284, 301, 302, 316; analysis data, 178; completion of, 174–6, 175 (*ill.*), 177 (*ill.*); costs, 162, 166, 172, 178; difficulties, 171–174; machinery for, 166 (*ill.*), 166–168; portal installations, 165–6; working methods, 169

Sala mine, 10

Salamis, battle of, 35

Saltpetre, 275–9

Saltwood tunnel, 114

Samos water tunnel, 60–1, 61 (*ill.*), 245

Sangatte, 345–7, 355

Sardinia, 134–6, 344, 383

Sartiaux (engineer), 348

Saunders, W. L., 293

Saussure, Horace Bénédict de, 382

Saxon mining, 10, 42–51, 248–9, 271–2

Scandinavia: Arctic rlys, 86; early mining, 6, 10; early use of gunpowder, 279; power houses, 102; tunnel costs, 408. (*See also* Sweden)

Scavarda, Virginio, 394 (*n.*)

Schuylkill tunnel, 82–3, 83 (*ill.*)

Schwartz, Berthold, 275

Sennacherib, King of Assyria, 52

Sergeant, H. C., 292, 293

Severn tunnel, 226–33, 227 (*map*)

Sforza, Duke Ludovico, 71

Shaw, C. H., 293–5

Shaw, Moses, 282

Siloam tunnel, 59, 59 (*ill.*), 245

Silver mines, 6, 7, 27–8, 35–6, 42, 251, 279

Simplon tunnel, 15–17, 103, 124, 129, 180, 184–207 (*with ills.*), 288, 316, 330, 331, 337–9, 356, 360; breakthrough, 199, 201, 202 (*ill.*); contracts and finance, 185–8, 198; lining of, 192 (*ill.*), 194, 202–3, 206 (*ill.*); railways connected with, 184–5, 188; steel frames for pressure zones, 196–7 (*with ills.*); survey of, 260–6; troubles, 195–203; tunnelling scheme, 190–4; ventilation, 393; welfare measures, 187, 189–90

Sinai mines, 24–5

Singer, Isaac, 288

Sismonda, Professor, 134

Snowy Mt. scheme, 369

Sobrero, Ascanio, 283

Solomon, King, 25

Sommeiller, Germain, 134–6, 137 (*ill.*), 138, 141–50, 152, 162, 164, 167, 181, 320

Sonar method, 356

South Eastern Rly, 345

Sowitz silver mountain, 251

Spain: blast forges, 297 298 (*ill.*); mining, 27–8, 40, 314

Sparker method, 356

Spiennes: mines, 22 (*with ill.*)

Spiez, 332
Stampf, Dr., 176
Standedge tunnels, 74, 77 (*map*), 77–9, 89, 93
Steam road locomotives, 84
Stephenson, George, 84, 87
Stephenson, Robert, 88, 132, 343
Stockalper (engineer), 174
Stornorrfors power plant, 366, 370 (*ill.*), 370–9, 376–7 (*ills.*)
Strabo, 28
Subways, early, 237–44
Suez Canal, 60, 352–3
Surveys: air, 268; geological, 268–9; tunnel, 245–70
Sweden: breakthroughs, 266; drainage tunnel, 366; drill steels, 306–7, 310–11; first mining map, 251; geodimeter, 267; mining, 10, 11–12 (*ills.*), 13, 42, 273, 274 (*ill.*), 275; power plants, 317–29, 319–320 (*ills.*), 327 (*ill.*), 361 (*ill.*), 368–79; rock shelters, 359; saltpetre search, 277; tunnelling methods, 359–66
Swinburne (engineer), 132
Switzerland: tunnel schemes, 15, 95, 96 (*ill.*), 180–3, 383. (*See also* Arlberg *and* Simplon)
Syria: saltpetre, 276; water tunnels, 58
Syrtis tunnel, 54

Täby tunnel, 366
Tarr brothers, 101
Telford, Thomas, 75, 77, 84
Tellurometers, 267
Terrenoir tunnel, 87 (*n.*)
Texas City: explosion, 285
Thames tunnels, 209–20 (*with ills.*), 232–3
Tin mining, 26–7, 33, 35
Totino, Count Dino, 383, 387
Tower Hill tunnel, 216, 218–20, 219 (*ill.*), 233
Trevithick, Richard, 84, 209, 288
Triangulation, 251–6, 254 (*ill.*), 261 (*ill.*)
Triebitz tunnel, 118
Tronquoy tunnel, 80 (*ill.*), 81, 118
Troy and Greenfield Rly Co., 153
Trypho of Alexandria, 4

Tungsten carbide, 304–9, 313, 361
Tunnelling hazards, 103–13, 104–108 (*ills.*), 362–3
Tunnelling methods, 102–31 (*with ills.*); American system, 97 (*ill.*), 113, 129–31; Austrian, 113, 119–121, 121–3 (*ills.*), 124–6, 125–6 (*ills.*), 130–1, 182; Belgian, 81 (*ill.*), 113, 115–18, 116–17 (*ills.*), 125, 131, 164–5, 170 (*ill.*), 174; English, 76 (*ill.*), 113–15, 158 (*ill.*); French, 80, 113, 118; German, 113, 118–19, 119 (*ill.*); Italian (Cristina), 113, 124–9, 128 (*ill.*); post-war (1945), 359–381; Subaqueous, 208–44; Swedish, 359–66
Tunnelling uses: for burial, 2; canals, 73–83 (*with ills.*); military, 3–5; mining, 5–13, 24–5, 48–9; quarrying, 54–7; railways, 14–18, 84–101; religious, 2, 3 (*ill.*); water supplies, 1, 13–14, 53–4, 57–65
Tunnels: British, 87–94; early American, 95–101, 97 (*ill.*); early Continental, 94–6 (*with ills.*); longest in world, 184. (*See also under tunnel names*)
Tunnel surveying, 245–70 (*with ills.*)
Turin, 134, 155, 283, 287
Turks: use of powder mines, 278
Tyrol: mining, 24, 30

Union Canal (U.S.A.), 82–3
U.S.A., *see* America

Varne Bank, 341–3, 355
Ventilation: Channel tunnel, 347, 357; Fréjus, 134–5, 149–50; Lötschberg, 337; Mt. Blanc, 393; Simplon, 189–91, 194, 263
Via Flaminia tunnel, 1
Victor Emmanuel Rly. 135
Victoria, Queen, 216, 340, 343, 346
Victoria rly line, 143–4
Vienna, siege of, 278
Vignoles, C. B., 88
Vinci, Leonardo da, 71–2
Vitruvius, 4, 67, 146, 278, 297

Wagner, Karl Johann, 187
Walker, T. H., 229–31, 233

Wapping tunnel, *see* Rotherhithe
Water conduits, ancient, 52–4, 57–
  70
'Water spout' compressors, 142, 143
  (*ill.*), 167, 181
Watford tunnel, 90
Watkin, Sir Edward, 345–6
Waugh, D. S., 294
Wedgwood, Josiah, 76, 77
Weigel, Martin, 279
Wellington, Duke of, 91, 215
Wetli (engineer), 162
Wharncliffe, Lord, 88
Whitworth family, 75

Wiborg castle, siege of, 278
Wolff, Hans H., 306–7
Wolseley, Sir Garnet, 346
Woodhead tunnels, 78 (*map*), 87–9
Woolwich tunnel, 233, 235
Worsley Canal, 75–6
Wylam colliery, 84

Young, C. E., 342

Zignoli, Prof. Vittorio, 383
Zollinger, Dr. A., 333–4
Zumbe, Carl, 281
Zürich, 161, 182, 260, 339

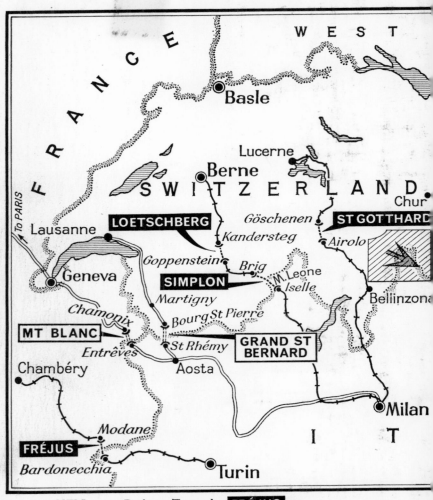

KEY: Railway Tunnels **FRÉJUS**
Road Tunnels *(Under construction)* **MT BLANC**

(Projected) **BRENNER**